AQA
GCSE Science
ADDITIONAL FOUNDATION

Editor: Nigel Heslop

Nigel Heslop, Graham Hill,
Toby Houghton, Steve Witney
and Christine Woodward

Hodder Murray
A MEMBER OF THE HODDER HEADLINE GROUP

The Publishers would like to thank the following for permission to reproduce copyright material:

p.1 *tl* Science Photo Library/Andrew Syred, *tc* Science Photo Library/Susumu Nishinaga, *tr* Science Photo Library/Dr Torsten Wittmann, *bl* Science Photo Library/Manfred Kage, Peter Arnold INC., *br* Science Photo Library/Steve Gschmeissner; **p.2** Science Photo Library/Omikron; **p.3** *t* Science Photo Library/Dr Gopal Murti, *b* Science Photo Library/Dr Jeremy Burgess; **p.13** *main photo* Corbis/Stefan Puchner/dpa, *inset* Science Photo Library/Eye of Science; **p.14** Science Photo Library/Biophoto Associates; **p.21** Alamy/Holt Studios; **p.22** *l* Alamy/Tom Mareachal, *tr* Corbis/Paul A Souders, *br* Corbis/Paul A. Souders; **p.23** Alamy/Phil Degginger; **p.24** Courtesy Wadsworth Control Systems; **p.35** *main photo* Science Photo Library/CC Studio, *t inset* Grace/zefa/Corbis, *b inset* Science Photo Library/Prof. K. Seddon & Dr. T. Evans, Queen's University, Belfast; **p.40** Getty/Hulton Archive; **p.45** Alamy/Phototake, inc.; **p.47** *tl* Anthony Blake Photo Library/Tony Robins, *tr* Getty/Gary Buss, *c* Lorna Ainger; **p.48** Lorna Ainger; **p.51** Alamy/WR Publishing; **p.53** PYMCA/Manuela Zanotti; **p.55** Corbis/Bettmann; **p.58** Science Photo Library/L. Willatt, East Anglian Regional Genetics Service; **p.59** Science Photo Library/Professor Miodrag Stojkovic; **p.61** *tl* Science Photo Library/Steve Gschmeissner, *tr* Science Photo Library/Susumu Nishinaga, *cl* Science Photo Library/Innerspace Imaging, *cr* Science Photo Library/Steve Gschmeissner, *bl* Science Photo Library/Steve Gschmeissner, *br* Science Photo Library/David McCarthy; **p.64** Science Photo Library/CNRI; **p.65** PureStockX; **p.72** *l* Science Photo Library/David Parker, *tr* Science & Society Picture Library/Science Museum, *br* Rex Features; **p.74** Corbis/Russell Boyce/Reuters; **p.78** University of Cambridge Cavendish Library; **p.79** Lorna Ainger; **p.80** Lorna Ainger; **p.81** *t* Alamy/Steve Atkins, *b* Alamy/Gunter Marx; **p.82** Rex Features/The Travel Library; **p.85** PureStock X; **p.87** PureStock X; **p.95** Corbis/Matthias Kulka; **p.96** *t* Alamy/Kevin Schafer/Peter Arnold Inc., *b* Science Photo Library/Sinclair Stammers; **p.97** Science Photo Library/Philippe Plailly/Eurelios; **p.98** *t* Science Photo Library/Kenneth Libbrecht, *bl* Corbis/Alan Goldsmith, *br* Corbis/David Samuel Robbins; **p.99** Science Photo Library/Charles D. Winters; **p.100** Corbis; **p.101** *c* Corbis/Owaki – Kulla, *b* Corbis/Nik Wheeler; **p.104** Hodder; **p.105** Corbis/Bruce Peebles; **p.106** *t* Corbis/Visuals Unlimited *b* Alamy/Frances Roberts; **p.107** *t* Still Pictures/Leonard Lessin, *b* Corbis/Paul McErlane/Reuters; **p.109** Wellcome Trust; **p.110** Alamy/Simmons Aerofilms Ltd; **p.115** Rex Features/Woman's Weekly; **p.117** Science Photo Library/Andrew Lambert; **p.118** Science Photo Library/Colin Cuthbert; **p.121** *tl* Alamy/David Hoffman, *tr* Corbis/Jon Hicks, *b* Corbis/photocuisine; **p.128** *t* PureStock X, *c* Nigel Heslop, *b* Lorna Ainger; **p.131** Purestock X; **p.133** *l* Robert Opie, *c* Alamy/Dennis MacDonald, *r* Rex Features/Dan Talson; **p.134** Nigel Heslop; **p.135** Nigel Heslop; **p.136** Science Photo Library/Emilio Segre Visual Archives/American Institute of Physics; **p.140** Science Photo Library/Alan Sirulnikoff; **p.142** Science Photo Library/Andrew Lambert; **p.145** *t* Science Photo Library/Gusto, *b* Science Photo Library/Andrew Lambert; **p.146** Science Photo Library/Martyn F. Chillmaid; **p.147** Nigel Heslop; **p.148** *t* Nigel Heslop, *b* Science Photo Library/James Holmes, Hays Chemicals; **p.152** *t* Rex Features/Andrew Drysdale, *b* Science Photo Library/Simon Lewis; **p.156** Science Photo Library/TRL Ltd.; **p.157** PureStock X; **p.158** Corbis/Seguin Franck/Sygma; **p.159** Getty/Tony R. Tolley/U.S. Air Force; **p.161** PureStock X; **p.165** *t* Getty/Bryn Lennon, *b* PureStock X; **p.169** Science Photo Library/Peter Bowater; **p.172** *t* Getty/Lester Lefkowitz, *b* Alamy/Sally & Richard Greenhill; **p.173** Rex Features/James Fraser; **p.175** *l* Alamy/Steve Bloom Images, *r* Rex Features; **p.177** *t* Action Plus, *c* Alamy/Tim Graham; **p.178** Empics/David Zalubowski/AP, *c* PureStock X, *b* Getty/Brian Bahr; **p.179** *t* Alamy/David Crausby, *b* Getty/Romilly Lockyer; **p.182** Corbis/Gulliver/Zefa; **p.186** Rex Features/Lewis Whyld; **p.188** Science Photo Library/Hank Morgan; **p.189** Science Photo Library/Andrew Lambert; **p.191** Science Photo Library/David Parker; **p.193** Corbis/Armando Arorizo/epa; **p.196** Alamy/Tim Gartside; **p.198** Lorna Ainger; **p.199** Science Photo Library/Andrew Lambert; **p.205** Alamy/Paul Bradforth; **p.207** Courtesy Peratech; **p. 210** *t* Science Photo Library/Andrew Lambert, *b* Science Photo Library/Adam Hart-Davis; **p.211** *t* Science Photo Library/Cordelia Molloy, *b* Alamy/Blue Shadows; **p.212** Science Photo Library/Sheila Terry; **p.213** Science Photo Library/Sheila Terry; **p.219** *l* Getty/Greg Mathieson/Time Life Pictures, *r* NASA; **p.225** Corbis/Massimo Listri; **p.226** Science Photo Library/Sheila Terry; **p.227** Science Photo Library/Emilio Segre Visual Archives/American Institute of Physics.

Every effort has been made to trace all copyright holders, but if any have been inadvertently overlooked the Publishers will be pleased to make the necessary arrangements at the first opportunity.

Although every effort has been made to ensure that website addresses are correct at time of going to press, Hodder Murray cannot be held responsible for the content of any website mentioned in this book. It is sometimes possible to find a relocated web page by typing in the address of the home page for a website in the URL window of your browser.

Risk Assessment
As a service to users, a risk assessment for this title has been carried out by CLEAPSS and is available on request to the publishers. However, the publishers accept no legal responsibility on any issue arising from this risk assessment: whilst every effort has been made to check the instructions of practical work in this book, it is still the duty and legal obligation of schools to carry out their own risk assessments.

Hodder Headline's policy is to use papers that are natural, renewable and recyclable products and made from wood grown in sustainable forests. The logging and manufacturing processes are expected to conform to the environmental regulations of the country of origin.

Orders: please contact Bookpoint Ltd, 130 Milton Park, Abingdon, Oxon OX14 4SB. Telephone: (44) 01235 827720. Fax: (44) 01235 400454. Lines are open 9.00–17.00, Monday to Saturday, with a 24-hour message answering service. Visit our website at www.hoddereducation.co.uk.

© Nigel Heslop, Graham Hill, Toby Houghton, Steve Witney and Christine Woodward 2006
First published in 2006 by
Hodder Murray, an imprint of Hodder Education,
a member of the Hodder Headline Group
338 Euston Road
London NW1 3BH

Impression number	10 9 8 7 6 5 4 3 2 1
Year	2011 2010 2009 2008 2007 2006

Cover photos Science Photo Library: salt crystals, Andrew Syred; lightning, Keith Kent; pollen grain, Andrew Syred
Illustrations by Barking Dog Art
Typeset in Times 11.5pt by Fakenham Photosetting Limited, Fakenham, Norfolk
Printed in Italy

A catalogue record for this title is available from the British Library

ISBN-10: 0 340 90710 X
ISBN-13: 978 0340 90710 8

Contents

iv   Introduction

1 Biology

1   Chapter 1   How do substances get into and out of cells?

13   Chapter 2   What are the energy inputs and energy losses in a food chain?

35   Chapter 3   Enzymes: How do they function and how can their properties be used industrially?

52   Chapter 4   How do our bodies control internal conditions and pass on characteristics?

72 Chemistry

72   Chapter 5   How do sub-atomic particles explain the structure and reactions of substances?

95   Chapter 6   How do the structures of substances influence their properties and uses?

115   Chapter 7   How do we control the rate of chemical reactions and measure energy transfer?

140   Chapter 8   How can we use ions in solutions?

156 Physics

156   Chapter 9   How can we describe and change the way things move?

186   Chapter 10   What is static electricity and how is it used?

196   Chapter 11   What affects the current in an electric circuit?

219   Chapter 12   What happens during radioactive decay, nuclear fission and nuclear fusion?

231   Data table

232   Periodic Table

233   Index

Introduction

AQA GCSE Science Additional Foundation Student's Book

Welcome to the AQA GCSE Science Additional Student's Book for the Foundation Tier. This book has been written to support you through your Additional Science GCSE with AQA. The book covers all the Biology, Chemistry and Physics material as well as the key 'How science works' elements of the new specification.

Each chapter begins with a list of **learning objectives**. Don't forget to refer back to these when checking whether you have understood the material covered in a particular chapter. **Questions** appear throughout each chapter, which will help to test your knowledge and understanding of the subject, as you go along. They will also enable you to develop key skills and understand how science works.

Activities are found throughout the book. These will take you longer to complete than the questions but will show you many of the real-life applications and implications of science. At the end of each chapter a **summary** evaluates the important points and key words. You will find the summaries useful in reviewing the work you have completed and in revising for your examinations. Don't forget to use the **index** to help you find the topic you are working on.

You will find **exam questions** at the end of each chapter, to help you prepare for your exams. These include similar questions to those in the structured questions for the exam.

You will take three written papers, one for Biology (chapters 1 to 4), one for Chemistry (chapters 5 to 8) and one for Physics (chapters 9 to 12).

This book is written for the **Foundation-tier** examination. It will push you so that you get the best possible result at GCSE. If you are planning to take the **Higher-tier** examination, you may wish to use the Higher Student's Book instead.

Good luck with your studies!

Nigel Heslop, Graham Hill, Toby Houghton, Steve Witney and Christine Woodward

Chapter 1
How do substances get into and out of cells?

At the end of this chapter you should:

✓ know the names and be able to explain the function of the different parts of animal and plant cells;

✓ be able to describe the differences between animal and plant cells;

✓ be able to identify a range of specialised cells;

✓ be able to relate the structure of a specialised cell to its function;

✓ be able to explain how substances move in and out of cells by diffusion;

✓ know how water moves in and out of cells by osmosis;

✓ understand how osmosis is affected by the concentrations of the solutions inside and outside a cell.

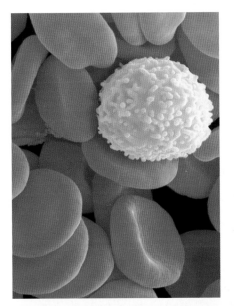

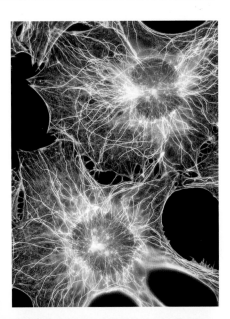
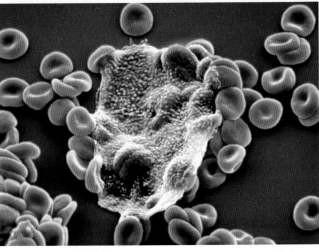
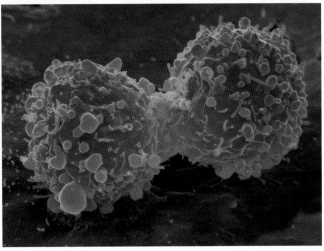

Figure 1.1 Cells are essential for life. They control all the processes in your body that keep you alive and are responsible for reproduction. The cells in the pictures are all very different. How does this allow them to do different jobs? Top: red and white blood cells; pollen cells; fibroblast making new connective tissue. Bottom: macrophage killing red blood cells; cancer cells.

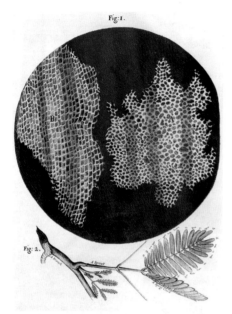

Figure 1.2 Robert Hooke's drawing of the cork cells he saw with his microscope

How do cells perform different functions?

All living things are made of cells. A scientist called Robert Hooke first noted this in 1665. Using a simple microscope, he discovered that the same tiny shape was repeated inside cork from a tree (Figure 1.2). He called these repeating shapes 'cells'.

Hooke could not see what was inside these cells. In 1831 better microscopes allowed Robert Brown to observe nuclei. He found nuclei inside all the cells he looked at from different parts of plants.

By 1840 two German biologists, Theodor Schwann and Matthias Schleiden, realised that animal and plant tissues both had cells with nuclei. Together they had the idea that all living things were made of cells. But when Schwann published his theory, he did not mention Schleiden's or anyone else's contributions.

Schwann was correct to suggest that cells are the unit that make up all living things. However, he also suggested that new cells formed out of nothing. This was proved to be wrong by Rudolph Virchow in 1858. Virchow proposed the theory that all cells come from other cells. How this happens is explained in Chapter 4.

❶ What are all living things made up from?

❷ Robert Hooke observed cells but did not identify anything inside them. Why couldn't he see anything inside cells?

❸ a) What did Robert Brown discover inside cells?
   b) Why do you think that this discovery was important? (*Hint*: Were all the cells he looked at the same?)

❹ Why do you think that Schwann did not mention any other scientists when he published his theory?

What are the functions of different parts of a cell?

Modern microscopes let us see a huge amount of detail about the structure of cells. Cells are made up of different parts that each carry out different functions. Table 1.1 lists the parts found in animal and plant cells.

Your body has more than 300 kinds of cell. Each type of cell is specialised to perform a particular function. Similar cells group together to form body tissue. For example, your skin is made up of layers of skin cells. New tissue forms when cells divide. The cells make exact copies of themselves. This includes making copies of all the cell parts you can see in Figures 1.3 and 1.4.

Most animal and plant cells have these parts	Most plant cells also have these parts
Cell membrane	Cell wall
Cytoplasm	Chloroplasts
Nucleus	A permanent vacuole
Mitochondria	
Ribosomes	

Table 1.1 The cell parts found in animal and plant cells

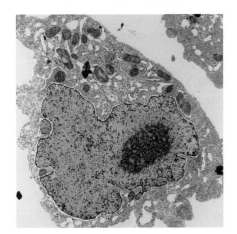
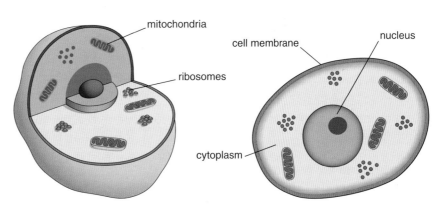

Figure 1.3 An animal cell shown as it is seen with a microscope (magnified × 4800) and as three- and two-dimensional diagrams

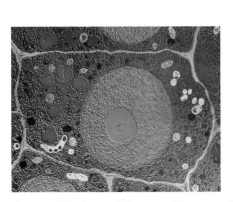
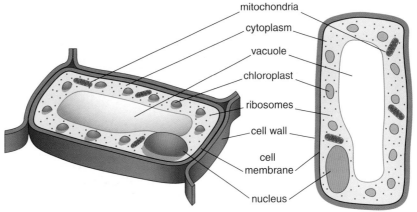

Figure 1.4 A plant cell shown as it is seen with a microscope (magnified × 2800) and as two- and three-dimensional diagrams. Note the cell wall, vacuole and chloroplasts that are not found in animal cells.

Each part of a cell carries out a different job. This allows the cell to contribute to the function of the tissue it is part of. Now we will look at the different parts of a cell and their functions.

Nucleus

The nucleus of a cell contains an individual's genes. Genes can:
- make copies of themselves to go in a new cell;
- control the production of **proteins**, such as enzymes.

Enzymes control the reactions that take place in the cell. These reactions include respiration, photosynthesis and protein synthesis. There is more information about enzymes and the reactions inside cells in Chapter 3.

Cytoplasm

The cytoplasm fills the cell membrane and is mostly water. It is where most of the cell's chemical reactions take place. The cytoplasm also stores raw materials, such as amino acids and glucose, needed for all these reactions.

Mitochondria

Your whole body needs energy to keep warm, grow and move around. This energy comes from your food.

Mitochondria release the energy from glucose molecules during respiration. Respiration is a series of chemical reactions. These chemical reactions take place on the surface of channels inside the mitochondria (Figure 1.5). These channels have a large surface area so that respiration can take place at a fast rate.

Ribosomes

Ribosomes are structures that control proteins being made. They join together amino acids into the long chains that become proteins.

> **Proteins** are long chains of amino acids that form the basis of most body structures, such as skin, muscle and hair. They also form chemicals in the body such as enzymes.
>
> **Mitochondria** are responsible for releasing energy from glucose by respiration.
>
> **Ribosomes** put amino acids into the correct order to make a specific protein.

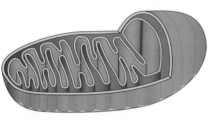

Figure 1.5 The channels inside a mitochondria are folded and so have a large surface area.

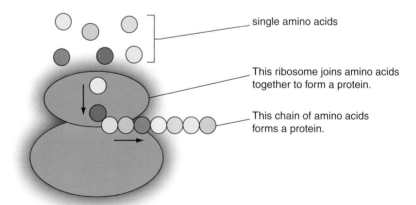

single amino acids

This ribosome joins amino acids together to form a protein.

This chain of amino acids forms a protein.

Figure 1.6 A ribosome forming a protein chain from amino acids in the cytoplasm

Cell membrane

The cell membrane surrounds the cytoplasm. Anything that has to get in or out of the cell has to pass through the cell membrane. For example, the glucose needed for respiration enters the cell through the cell membrane. Insulin produced in pancreas cells leaves the cell through the cell membrane.

Cell wall

Plant cells have a rigid cell wall around the cell membrane that strengthens the cell and keeps its shape. It is made from a chemical called cellulose. Without cell walls plants would not be able to stay upright.

Chloroplasts

Chloroplasts use light energy to make glucose and oxygen from carbon dioxide and water by photosynthesis.

Chloroplasts are structures that contain a chemical called chlorophyll. Chlorophyll absorbs light energy to make food for the plant by photosynthesis.

Permanent vacuole

The vacuole in a plant cell contains water and some dissolved chemicals. This mixture is called cell sap. The vacuole acts a bit like a reservoir for the cell.

❺ Copy and complete Table 1.2 to summarise the functions of the different cell parts.

❻ A cell could be compared to a factory with the different parts working together so that the cell can function. Copy and complete the sentences below using words from the box.

> cytoplasm   mitochondria   nucleus
> proteins   substances

In a cell the _____ releases energy like the generator in a factory. The ribsomes are similar to the production line because they make _____. The manager controls all the activities in a factory which is the job carried out by the _____ in a cell. The cell membrane controls the movement of _____ in and out of a cell, a bit like the security guards on a factory gate. Things are made on the factory floor, which could be compared to the _____ in a cell.

❼ Which part of a cell might someone compare to a brain? How good do you think this comparison is?

❽ People sometimes say they have a 'high metabolic rate' if they release energy from their food quickly. Use the information about the different cell parts to suggest why some people release energy from their food more quickly than others.

❾ Where in a plant would you expect to find cells with the most chloroplasts? Give a reason for your answer.

Cell part	Function	Found in ...
Nucleus	Controls the chemical reactions in the cell.	Animal and plant cells.
Cytoplasm		
Cell membrane		
Mitochondria		
Ribosomes		
Cell wall		
Chloroplasts		
Vacuole		

Table 1.2

1.2

How do dissolved substances move into and out of cells?

Chemical reactions such as respiration and photosynthesis take place inside cells. For the reactions to occur, substances need to get into the cell. Some new substances produced inside a cell need to leave the cell.

> **⑩** Make a list of substances that you think need to:
> a) get into a cell;
> b) leave a cell.
>
> **⑪** What do these substances need to pass through in order to enter or leave a cell?

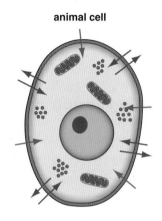
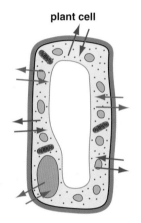

animal cell

plant cell

Key:
→ oxygen
→ water

• oxygen required for respiration

• oxygen required for respiration
• oxygen produced by photosynthesis

Figure 1.7 Diagrams showing the movement of oxygen and water in and out of animal and plant cells

Diffusion

> **Concentration** is the amount of one substance in a given volume of another.
>
> **Diffusion** is the movement of particles in a gas or any dissolved substance from a region of higher concentration to a region of lower concentration.

If you spray air freshener in one corner of a room it is not long before it can be smelt throughout the room. This happens because the particles that make up the air freshener move around. The particles quickly spread out. They move from a region where there is a higher **concentration** of particles to a region where there is a lower concentration. This process is called **diffusion** and it explains why gases spread out.

1
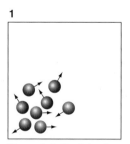

2
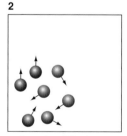

3
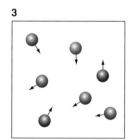

Figure 1.8 Particles in a gas spread out by diffusion.

Particles dissolved in a liquid will also diffuse. If you put a drop of ink in a glass of water you will see the ink gradually spread throughout the water. The ink particles are diffusing among the water particles. They are moving from a high concentration of 'ink' particles to a low concentration of 'ink' particles.

⓬ Copy and complete these sentences. Use words from the definition boxes to help you.

When a slice of lemon is left in a glass of cranberry juice it turns red. This happens because _____ from the juice move into the lemon. This movement is called _____. The _____ pass through tiny _____ in the _____ _____ and enter the cells in the lemon. The _____ move from a region of _____ concentration to a region of _____ concentration.

Oxygen dissolves in water and so oxygen particles can diffuse through water. This is how oxygen moves into cells. Oxygen is used up quickly in the mitochondria for respiration. There will usually be a lower concentration of oxygen inside the cell than in the liquid outside the cell. This means oxygen will always diffuse into the cell. The greater the difference in concentration, the faster is the rate of diffusion.

Oxygen, or anything else trying to get into a cell, has to get through the cell membrane. Oxygen can do this by passing through tiny gaps in the cell membrane. These gaps are too small to let larger particles through. So, the cell membrane is called a **partially permeable membrane**.

A **partially permeable membrane** is a membrane, such as a cell membrane, that has tiny gaps and will only allow some substances to pass through it.

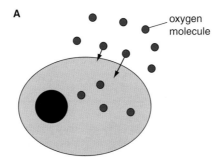

Figure 1.9 Diffusion of oxygen in cell B will take place faster than in cell A because there is a bigger difference between the concentration of oxygen inside and outside cell B.

Figure 1.10 Stabilised liquid oxygen is a dietary supplement.

⓭ 'Stabilised liquid oxygen' is a new product that claims to be able to increase your energy levels by raising the concentration of oxygen in the blood.
a) Would the rate of diffusion speed up or slow down if the concentration of oxygen in the blood increased?
b) Draw a diagram to explain your answer to part a).
c) What process that takes place in cells uses oxygen to release energy from glucose?
d) Many people do not agree that stabilised liquid oxygen actually works. Why might they think this? Remember, this product is a dietary supplement.

Osmosis

Osmosis is the diffusion of water through a partially permeable membrane from a region of higher water concentration to a region of lower water concentration.

The amount of water in your blood is controlled by your kidneys. If the concentration of water in your blood changes it affects the cells in your body because water can diffuse into and out of cells. The diffusion of water into or out of cells is called **osmosis**. This is shown very clearly by red blood cells (Figure 1.11).

Red blood cells are specialised cells with a large surface area and no nucleus. When they are in a solution with the correct concentration of water they have a 'bi-concave' shape. If the concentration of water around them is too low they shrivel up. If it is too high they swell up and can even burst. You can see a similar effect if you put one tomato in a glass of water and one in a glass of water with lots of salt dissolved in it.

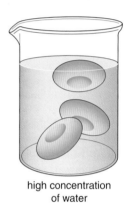

| correct concentration of water | low concentration of water | high concentration of water |

Figure 1.11 These diagrams show what happens to red blood cells in solutions with different concentrations of water.

⑭ The changes to the red blood cells in Figure 1.11 have happened because water may have moved into or out of the cells. Say what has happened to each cell.

⑮ What could happen to cells in your body if you get dehydrated when you are exercising?

⑯ Very occasionally marathon runners can drink too much water and become over-hydrated.
   a) What will happen to cells in the body if over-hydration causes a large increase in the amount of water in the blood?
   b) How does the body respond if there is too much water in the blood?

What can affect osmosis?

Remember to think about both the water molecules and any substances dissolved in the water. Look at Figure 1.12 and think about the number of water and sugar molecules on each side of the membrane.

In Figure 1.12 a) water moves from left to right. It moves from a region of higher water concentration to a region of lower water concentration. Water moves from a less concentrated (dilute) sugar solution to a more concentrated sugar solution through the partially permeable membrane.

In Figure 1.12 b) the water moves from right to left. The concentration of sugar is higher on the left than on the right. So, you can alter the movement of water by osmosis by adding more water or by adding more solute to the water.

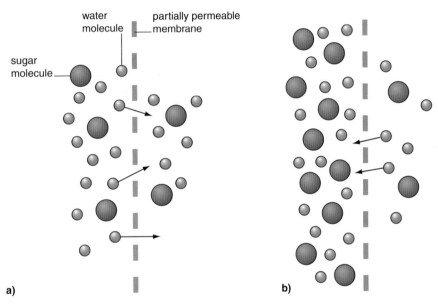

Figure 1.12 The diagrams show two partially permeable membranes. Both membranes have the same concentration of solution on the right hand side. However, water moves in opposite directions through each membrane.

⓱ Copy and complete Table 1.3 for each diagram (a, b and c) in Figure 1.13.

Diagram	The concentration of water on the left is (higher / lower)	The concentration of water on the right is (higher / lower)	Water will move to the (left / right)
a			
b			
c			

Table 1.3

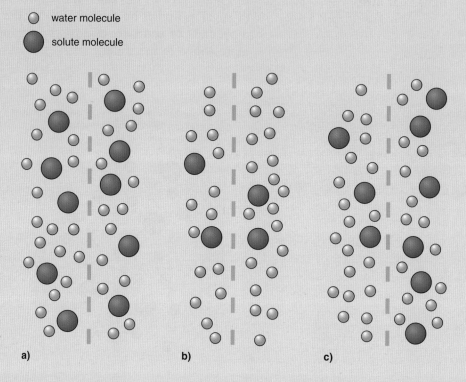

Figure 1.13 Each diagram shows a partially permeable membrane with a different solution on each side.

a) b) c)

⓲ There are three types of sports drinks:
- hypotonic drinks have a sugar concentration lower that your body fluid;
- isotonic drinks have the same concentration of sugar as your body fluid;
- hypertonic drinks have a higher sugar concentration than your body fluid.

a) Which type of sports drink would be best to drink if you wanted to re-hydrate your cells quickly?
b) Explain your answer to part a).
c) How would a hypertonic drink help you on a long bike ride?
d) What problems might a hypertonic drink cause you?

Activity – Changing the rate of osmosis

Two students carried out an investigation by following these instructions.
- Cut out five identical cylinders from a potato.
- Measure the mass of each cylinder.
- Collect five glucose solutions of different concentrations.
- Leave a potato cylinder in each solution for 24 hours.
- Take each cylinder out of the solution, dry it and measure its mass.

The results are shown in Table 1.4.

Glucose concentration in moles per litre	Starting mass of potato cylinder in grams	Mass of potato after 24 hours in grams	Change in mass in grams
0	7.76	9.38	1.62
0.2	8.01	8.04	
0.4	7.96	7.21	
0.6	7.92	7.78	
0.8	7.93	6.65	

Table 1.4 The results from the five potato cylinders left in different glucose solutions for 24 hours

1 Why is it important to dry the potato cylinders before the mass is measured?
2 Which of these factors do you think it was important to control to make the investigation a fair test?
- The starting time of the investigation
- The temperature of the glucose solution.
- The person who cut out the potato.
- The volume of glucose solution used for each cylinder.
3 Copy the table and work out the change in mass for each cylinder. To do this, subtract the starting mass from the mass after 24 hours (the first one is done for you). These changes will be positive for the potato cylinders that got heavier and negative for those that got lighter.
4 Now plot a graph for this data showing glucose concentration on the horizontal axis and change in mass on the vertical axis. Think carefully about how you set this out so that you can plot positive and negative values on the same graph.

5 One of the results appears to be anomalous. It does not fit in with the overall pattern. At which concentration did the anomalous result occur?
6 Copy and complete these sentences to write a conclusion for the results:
The potato cylinders in the _____ and _____ glucose solutions both increased in mass. This happened because the _____ of water in the solution was _____ than the concentration of water in the cells. This caused water to move through the _____ _____ membrane in to the cells. This is called _____. The potato cylinders in the 0.4, 0.6 and 0.8 M solutions all _____ in mass. This happened because water moved out of the _____. The water moved from a _____ concentration of water to a _____ concentration.
7 Use the graph to predict the concentration of glucose you would use that would cause no change in mass of the potato. Explain why.

Summary

✓ All living things are made up of cells.

✓ Most animal cells have a nucleus, a cytoplasm, a cell membrane, **mitochondria** and **ribosomes**.

✓ In addition to these parts, plant cells often have **chloroplasts** and a permanent vacuole.

✓ Each cell part has a specific function.

✓ The chemical reactions that take place inside a cell are controlled by enzymes.

✓ Enzymes are made from **proteins**, which are long chains of amino acids. Proteins also form the basis of most body structures such as skin, muscle and hair.

✓ Some cells are specialised to carry out a particular function.

✓ The structure of a specialised cell relates to its particular function.

✓ **Diffusion** is the spreading out of particles of a gas or a substance dissolved in a liquid.

✓ Particles move by diffusion from a region of higher **concentration** to a region where there is a lower concentration.

✓ Oxygen diffuses into cells through a **partially permeable membrane**.

✓ Water moves through a partially permeable membrane by **osmosis** from dilute solutions to more concentrated solutions.

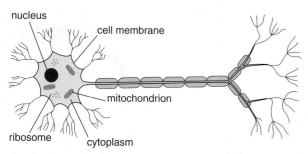

Figure 1.14 A nerve cell with some cell parts labelled

EXAMQUESTIONS

1 a) Name the labelled part of the cell that releases energy from glucose.   (*1 mark*)
   b) Name the part of the cell that synthesises enzymes.   (*1 mark*)
   c) A nerve cell is a specialised cell that carries electrical nerve impulses throughout the body.
      i) Describe one feature of a nerve cell that allows it to carry out this function. (*1 mark*)
      ii) Explain how this feature allows a nerve cell to carry out this function.   (*1 mark*)

2 a) Red blood cells are specialised to carry oxygen around the body. Explain how the structure of a red blood cell relates to its function.   (*2 marks*)
   b) Explain how oxygen enters a red blood cell.   (*3 marks*)
   c) When mountaineers climb high mountains the concentration of oxygen in the air decreases. Explain how this will affect the uptake of oxygen by their red blood cells.   (*2 marks*)

3 A chip shop owner claimed that if he soaked his potato chips in water before he fried them they were firmer than if he cut them up and fried them without soaking them.
   a) Explain how scientific ideas can be used to back up his claim. Use correct scientific words in your explanation.   (*4 marks*)
      Once when some uncooked chips were soaking a worker in the shop poured some salt into the water and left the chips soaking in salty water.
   b) Suggest how this may have affected the potato chips.   (*2 marks*)
      A student carried out an experiment to see if adding salt to the water that potato chips were soaking in affected the amount they changed in mass while soaking. She soaked one potato chip in pure water and one in a concentrated salt solution. She measured their masses before and after they had been soaked.
   c) i) State the dependent variable in this investigation.   (*1 mark*)
      ii) State the independent variable in the investigation.   (*1 mark*)
   d) Do you think that the results from this investigation would provide enough information to draw a firm conclusion about the effect of salt concentration on the change in mass of potato chips? Explain the reasons for your answer.   (*3 marks*)

Chapter 2
What are the energy inputs and energy losses in a food chain?

At the end of this chapter you should:

✓ understand the process of photosynthesis;
✓ know the factors that affect the rate of photosynthesis;
✓ know how plants use the products of photosynthesis;
✓ be able to apply knowledge of the factors affecting photosynthesis in a range of habitats and agricultural situations;
✓ understand why plants need minerals and the effects of a lack of them;

✓ understand the construction of pyramids of biomass;
✓ be able to apply biomass and energy principles to the efficiency of food production;
✓ be able to evaluate the conflicts and compromises between feeding the population and damaging the environment;
✓ understand the role of microorganisms in decomposition and recycling carbon and plant nutrients.

Figure 2.1 The start of the food chain. The rough pasture isn't just grass. Inset photograph shows the stomata of a leaf. Carbon dioxide diffuses into the leaf through the stomata for photosynthesis.

2.1

Photosynthesis

We can break down the summary equation for **photosynthesis** into three parts, as shown below:

> **Photosynthesis** is the process in which green plants use light energy to combine carbon dioxide and water into glucose molecules, using the enzymes in chloroplasts.

Raw materials	Conditions	Products
carbon dioxide + water $6CO_2 + 6H_2O$	light energy enzymes $\longrightarrow$ chlorophyll	glucose + oxygen $C_6H_{12}O_6 + 6O_2$

Figure 2.2

How is the light energy captured?

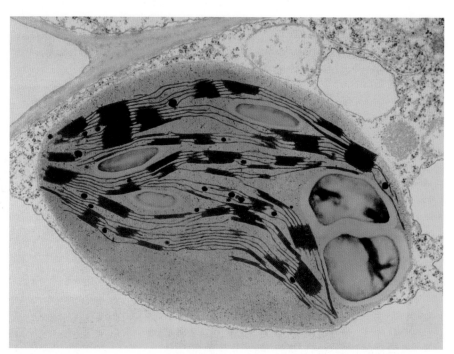

Figure 2.3 The structure of a chloroplast (magnification about 50 000)

You will remember that some plant cells have chloroplasts, which absorb light energy. A chloroplast contains chlorophyll, which makes the leaves appear green.

> Remember you should always write **light energy**, not light or Sun.

Enzymes in the chloroplasts use light energy from the Sun to catalyse reactions that produce glucose. Glucose is quickly changed to starch that can be stored in the leaf. Oxygen is released as a waste product of photosynthesis.

We can write the carbon dioxide concentration of the atmosphere as a percentage or as ppm (parts per million). Atmospheric carbon dioxide levels are increasing, but the figure we use now is 370 ppm (370 parts in a million of air).

How does carbon dioxide get into the leaf?

During the day, leaves photosynthesise and use carbon dioxide. Carbon dioxide diffuses into the leaf from the air.

Diffusion always takes place from an area of higher concentration to a lower concentration.

When a leaf is photosynthesising it is using up carbon dioxide inside the leaf. So, even though the concentration of carbon dioxide in the air is very small (on average only about 0.037%, or 370 ppm) it will always be higher than the concentration in the leaf. This difference in concentration means that carbon dioxide diffuses into the leaf.

❶ What materials are needed for photosynthesis?

❷ What is the energy input for photosynthesis?

❸ What are the products of photosynthesis?

❹ A variegated plant has many white leaves.
   a) What substance that is needed for photosynthesis is missing in the white parts of the leaves?
   b) Explain why this green and white leaved plant would not grow as rapidly as a normal plant with completely green leaves.

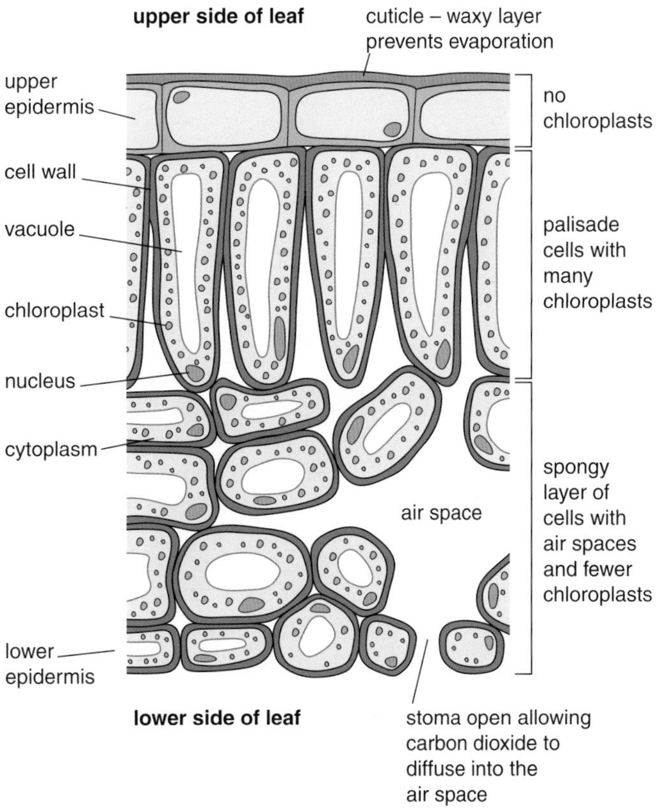

Figure 2.4 A section of a leaf showing the open stomata on the lower surface

How does water get to the leaf?

Roots take up water from the soil by osmosis. The water is then transported up the stem to the leaves. The leaves need water for photosynthesis and support. If there is not enough water the leaves wilt (become soft and floppy).

On hot and sunny days water is lost quickly from the leaves. If there is a shortage of water, the leaf pores (stomata) close to reduce water loss. This means photosynthesis stops.

2.2 What factors affect the rate of photosynthesis?

> A **rate** is the quantity produced or used in a given period of time, such as an hour.

The **rate** of photosynthesis is the speed at which the photosynthesis reaction takes place. It can be measured as the rate of formation of oxygen.

You can measure the rate of photosynthesis by finding the volume of oxygen produced per hour when an input value is changed. The possible different inputs are:
- concentration of carbon dioxide;
- light intensity (which can be increased from dim light to bright light);
- temperature.

We can use the simple apparatus shown in Figure 2.5 to measure the rate of photosynthesis. The volume of oxygen produced is measured in the top syringe.

> A **limiting factor** is one that controls the rate of the product formation. This is usually the factor that is present at the lowest value. For example, carbon dioxide forms only a small percentage of atmospheric gases and can be a limiting factor for photosynthesis when temperature is high.

Leaf cells respire 24 hours a day, producing carbon dioxide. However, carbon dioxide cannot leave the leaf at night, because the stomata are closed during this time. The pores are open only during daylight. This means that by daybreak there is a build-up of carbon dioxide in the leaf.

At the very start of the day, light levels are a **limiting factor** for photosynthesis. As the daylight gets brighter photosynthesis speeds up, using up the carbon dioxide built up in the leaf.

Activity – Investigating the effect of carbon dioxide concentration on the rate of photosynthesis

A group of students decided to investigate the rate of photosynthesis.

They chose to calculate the rate of photosynthesis by measuring the volume of oxygen produced in one hour using a plant called Canadian pondweed (see Figure 2.5).

The students knew that they should change only one input variable in their investigation. They decided to change carbon dioxide concentration.

The students used five different dilutions of sodium hydrogen carbonate solution, which provided carbon dioxide to the water plant.

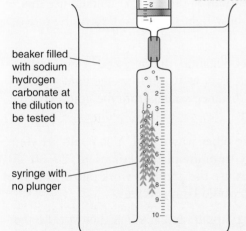

3 Set in constant light for 10 minutes to equilibrate.

4 To start the experiment, draw any gas up into the top syringe and record the volume.

5 Leave the apparatus in constant light for at least 2 hours.

6 Draw up any gas produced in the lower syringes. Record the volumes for each carbon dioxide concentration.

1 Connect the lower syringe to the empty upper syringe with a rubber connection.

beaker filled with sodium hydrogen carbonate at the dilution to be tested

syringe with no plunger

2 Put three sprigs of *Elodea* in the lower syringe with the cut end upwards; there should be no air in this syringe.

Figure 2.5 This simple apparatus can be used to measure the rate of photosynthesis when the input variable is carbon dioxide concentration.

To make their experiment a fair test, they chose three pieces of pondweed of similar length and with roughly the same number of leaves. They knew that the light intensity and temperature should be kept constant during the experiment.

1 What factors were the students controlling in this experiment?

2 This experiment was completed outside on a hot June day. Would you expect the temperature in the beaker to be the same after 2 hours? How do you think it might have changed?

3 The experiment was carried out from 9.30 to 11.30 a.m. Do you think the light intensity was the same throughout the experiment? What change would you expect?

4 Copy and complete Table 2.1 of the results that the students obtained. You need to calculate the volume of oxygen produced in one hour.

Use the following equation to complete the final column:

$$\frac{\text{volume of oxygen in cm}^3}{\text{time in h}}$$

5 Use the results from the table to draw a bar graph with volume of oxygen in cm³/h on the *y*-axis and concentration of sodium hydrogen carbonate solution (1 to 5) on the *x*-axis.

6 Suggest a suitable title for your graph, to describe how the output variable is linked with the input variable.

7 Describe the pattern shown by your graph.

Concentration of hydrogen carbonate solution	Volume of oxygen in cm³	Time in h	Volume of oxygen in cm³/h
1 strong	9.4	2	
2	8.2	2	
3 medium	6.8	2	
4	5.4	2	
5 very weak	4.4	2	

Table 2.1

Light intensity is the amount of light energy per unit area of a surface. Light intensity decreases rapidly as you increase the distance from the light source.

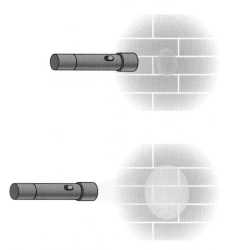

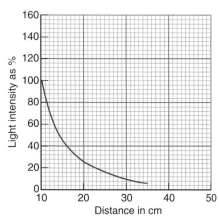

Figure 2.6 The light energy from the torch remains the same. As the torch gets further away the light spreads over a larger area, so the light energy per unit area is less.

How does light intensity affect the rate of photosynthesis?

Light intensity outdoors generally increases towards midday and then decreases towards evening, but can change quite quickly on a cloudy day. Light can have a significant effect on the rate of photosynthesis. If there are long periods of cloudy weather in summer a farmer's crop will grow more slowly.

Figure 2.6 shows a simple model to explain **light intensity**, or brightness.

If you switch on a torch and hold it close to a wall, you get a small circle of light. As you move the torch further away from the wall the circle of light gets larger and dimmer. The light energy given out by the torch is the same but the light energy falling on each square centimetre of wall (the light intensity) is less when the torch is further away.

Look at the graph of light intensity in Figure 2.7. You could use this graph for an experiment to find how light intensity affected the rate of photosynthesis.

Using the graph you could select distances that were 80%, 60% 40% and 20% of the original light intensity at 10 cm from the light source. However, when you read these distance values from the graph you'll find they are very close together.

You could also use the graph the other way round. You could set your lamp at different distances away from the plant, perhaps 10, 20, 30, 40 and 50 cm away. You could then use the graph to work out what sort of light intensities (in %) the plant would be receiving.

Remember that light is the energy input, and at values below 50% the plant isn't getting much energy to power photosynthesis.

Figure 2.7 How light intensity decreases as distance increases. For this graph the light intensity was taken as 100% at 10 cm distance.

⑤ Imagine you were carrying out an experiment to test the effect of light intensity on photosynthesis. You decide to use a normal filament bulb.
a) Normal light bulbs are very inefficient and give off heat as well as light. How will this affect your experiment when the lamp is very close to your apparatus?
b) Energy-efficient fluorescent bulbs give off less heat. Why would this type of bulb control the variables in your experiment?

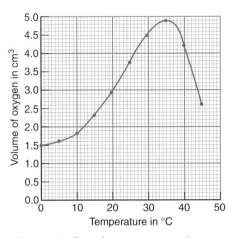

Figure 2.8 Effect of temperature on the rate of photosynthesis at a fixed light intensity and fixed carbon dioxide concentration

How does temperature affect the rate of photosynthesis?

Chloroplasts in the leaves contain enzymes that catalyse the chemical reactions that convert carbon dioxide into glucose and starch. These enzymes work fastest at warm temperatures. This is why glucose and starch are produced more slowly on a cold day.

However, if the temperature becomes too high, the enzymes are damaged and stop working properly. Above the optimum temperature (the peak in the graph in Figure 2.8) photosynthesis slows down because the enzymes are damaged.

We have seen that the rate of photosynthesis is a result of the interaction of carbon dioxide concentration, light intensity and temperature. Remember that any one of these can be a limiting factor. For example:
- low temperature could be the limiting factor on a bright winter day,
- low light intensity could be the limiting factor on a cloudy summer day,
- low levels of carbon dioxide could be the limiting factor on a hot sunny day.

❻ The sketch graph below shows the rate of oxygen produced on a bright winter day.

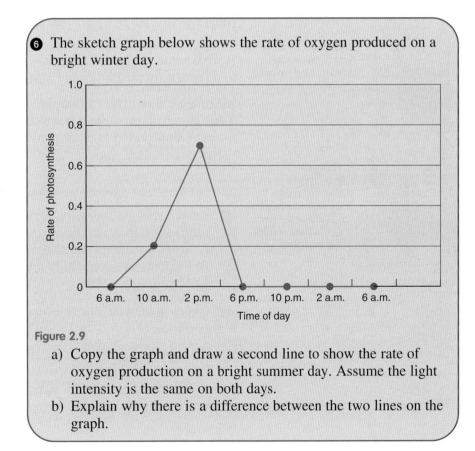

Figure 2.9

a) Copy the graph and draw a second line to show the rate of oxygen production on a bright summer day. Assume the light intensity is the same on both days.

b) Explain why there is a difference between the two lines on the graph.

CHAPTER 2 What are the energy inputs and energy losses in a food chain?

 ## How does the plant use glucose?

During photosynthesis, glucose is produced and then converted to starch in the leaf (Figure 2.10).

1 Dip
Take a leaf from a plant standing in sunlight and dip in boiling water for 10 seconds to denature enzymes and make the membrane permeable.

THEN TURN OFF BUNSEN because alcohol vapour is inflammable.

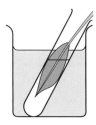

2 Decolorise
Put tube of alcohol into the water bath and allow to warm up. Add leaf and shake gently until alcohol becomes green.

3 Soften
Soften the leaf by rinsing in the hot water.

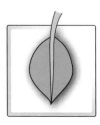

4 Flatten
Flatten the leaf underside up on a white tile and add a few drops of iodine. Where starch is present it will give a blue black colour.

Figure 2.11 Testing a leaf for starch

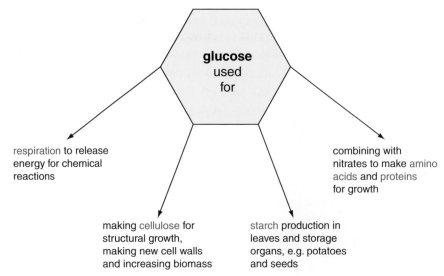

Figure 2.10 How the plant makes use of the glucose it produces

If we want to find out if a leaf has been photosynthesising all we need to do is test for starch (Figure 2.11).

Materials can only be carried through the plant dissolved in water. Since starch is insoluble it has to be converted into soluble sugar before it can be transported to other parts of the plant, such as stem tubers (potatoes), fruits (apples) or growing shoots.

❼ A plant was put into a black plastic bag and left for 24 hours. The leaves were then tested for starch.
  a) What was the plant short of during its time in the bag?
  b) Explain why you would not expect to find starch in these leaves even during the day.

❽ Where in the leaf cell are the enzymes that convert carbon dioxide to glucose?

❾ When you test a leaf for starch you dip it into boiling water to stop enzyme reactions.
  a) Which enzyme reactions might be stopped?
  b) What is washed out of the leaf that makes the alcohol become green?

⑩ A student tested a green and white leaf for starch using the iodine solution test.
  a) The parts which had been green became black after the test. What does this show?
  b) The areas that had been white stayed the brown colour of the iodine solution. What does this show?
  Explain your answers.

Figure 2.12 A shortage of magnesium in this plant has turned the leaves yellow.

All parts of the plant need a supply of glucose for respiration. For example, the growing shoots of the plant need the chemical energy released from glucose for making new cells.

Like us, plants need minerals to stay healthy. For example, farmers add nitrate fertiliser to the soil before planting their crops and you may 'feed' your houseplants with plant food containing minerals.

Nitrate minerals are needed to make amino acids in plants, which can be joined up to form proteins. If a plant is short of nitrates it means it cannot make new cells and so will grow slowly and stay small.

Magnesium is a mineral needed to produce chlorophyll molecules. If a plant cannot obtain enough magnesium from the soil it will not be able to make chlorophyll. As a result, the lower leaves of the plant will become yellow and not photosynthesise efficiently (Figure 2.12).

⑪ A student grew a tomato plant in sand. After a month he compared it with his friend's tomato plant that had been grown in potting compost. Both plants had been watered regularly. Figure 2.13 shows the plants side by side.
  a) Write down three differences you can see.
  b) Explain these differences.

Figure 2.13

2.4

What factors limit the rate of photosynthesis in the environment?

We have seen that under laboratory conditions light intensity, carbon dioxide concentration and temperature can all affect the rate of photosynthesis.

Activity – From laboratory to outdoors

Look at the photos showing photosynthesis in three different environments and then answer the questions.

A field crop on a hot, sunny day

Figure 2.14

❶ Will light intensity be a limiting factor?
❷ By 9 a.m. the rate of photosynthesis has reached a constant level and does not increase, even though the light intensity is still increasing. What factor could be limiting the rate of photosynthesis?
❸ At night, the stomata are closed and the plant continues to respire. This results in a build-up of carbon dioxide inside the leaf. What effect would you expect this to have on the rate of photosynthesis when it first gets light in the morning?

A forest in Iceland

People say that you can't get lost in a forest in Iceland because the birch trees only grow to about 1.5 m high. Iceland has periods of 24 hours' darkness in winter and 24 hours' light in summer, although the light intensity is not the same during the 24 hours.

Figure 2.15

❹ What factors limit the growth of the trees?
❺ Is carbon dioxide concentration likely to be a limiting factor? Explain your answer.

A pond

Figure 2.16

Geese use the pond and their waste has resulted in extra nitrates (plant food) in the water. As a result there is a dense weed growth.

❻ What do you think will happen to the carbon dioxide concentration in the water overnight? Explain your answer.
❼ During mid-morning, streams of tiny bubbles can be seen rising to the surface. What gas do you think these bubbles contain, and where does it come from?
❽ What do you think happens to the carbon dioxide content of the water during the day? Explain your answer.

Can understanding photosynthesis be used to increase greenhouse crop production?

Figure 2.17 A large commercial greenhouse

In parts of England and Holland, large areas of land are used for growing crops in greenhouses so that fruit and vegetables can be sold in supermarkets throughout the year.

For maximum profit, greenhouse crops must have a high yield and be good quality. Farmers need to grow crops quickly so they mature in the minimum possible time.

We have already seen that carbon dioxide can be a limiting factor for photosynthesis. Many experiments have been carried out to find the optimum light intensities and carbon dioxide concentrations that will increase the rate of photosynthesis for crop plants.

Activity – Greenhouse crop production

In winter, gardeners close their greenhouses to protect their plants against the cold. Due to the lack of ventilation, the levels of carbon dioxide during the day can drop to 200 ppm.

The vertical red line on the graph in Figure 2.18 shows the normal concentration of CO_2 found in the greenhouse when the doors are open (370 ppm of carbon dioxide). The rate of photosynthesis at 370 ppm carbon dioxide is shown as 100%.

Use the graph in Figure 2.18 to answer the questions.

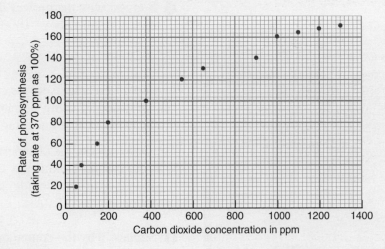

Figure 2.18

❶ a) What is the rate of photosynthesis when carbon dioxide levels drop to 200 ppm?
b) What effect will this have on the growth rate of the plants?

Increased carbon dioxide concentration results in larger leaves, which increases the size and quality of lettuces. Colorado State University found that increasing carbon dioxide levels to 550 ppm meant that they could fit only 16 instead of 22 lettuces into a box.

2 Use your knowledge of photosynthesis to explain why the lettuces were bigger.

3 Look again at the graph on page 23.
   a) What is the rate of photosynthesis at 550 ppm carbon dioxide?
   b) Work out the difference between the rate of photosynthesis at 550 ppm and the rate at 370 ppm.

If the carbon dioxide concentration is raised to 1000 ppm, salad crops such as tomatoes, peppers and cucumbers flower earlier, producing more flowers and more fruits.

4 a) What happens to the shape of the curve on the graph when carbon dioxide rises above 1000 ppm?
   b) Does increasing the carbon dioxide concentration above 1000 ppm have an effect on the rate of photosynthesis?
   c) Would you expect increasing the carbon dioxide concentration above 1000 ppm to have an effect on the growth rate of the plants?

5 Suggest why the grower does not usually increase the concentration above 1000 ppm.

In modern greenhouses, the carbon dioxide concentration in the air can be raised by using a heater that burns oil. However, the heater produces water that encourages mould to grow.

The best, but not the cheapest, way of increasing carbon dioxide is to use carbon dioxide gas cylinders. A computer is used to regulate the carbon dioxide gas concentration within the greenhouse.

6 Suggest why the computer is programmed to activate a valve that increases the carbon dioxide concentration as the light intensity increases.

Figure 2.19 Conditions in the greenhouse are monitored by sensors and controlled by a computer.

2.6 Pyramids of biomass

Plants (primary producers) are at the start of the food chain. A bigger plant will be heavier, or in scientific terms will have a greater plant **biomass**.

Plants are eaten by herbivores (primary consumers). Herbivores can be eaten by carnivores. Both herbivores and carnivores use the energy from the things they eat for growth and other life processes.

To draw a **pyramid of biomass** you need to:
- estimate the numbers of each organism in a certain area;
- find the dry mass of an average sized organism;
- calculate the biomass of each species (number × average mass);
- group different organisms into **trophic** (feeding) **levels** and calculate the biomass for each level;
- create a pyramid on graph paper where the area of each rectangle is proportional to the biomass you calculated.

If you were to construct a pyramid of biomass to scale you would find that as you go up the pyramid, the biomass at each feeding level becomes smaller. For example, there is a large plant producer biomass, possibly a tree. At the second feeding level there are herbivores which may be very small insects or caterpillars in large numbers. The secondary consumers are carnivorous insects or birds that are larger but there are not many of them.

So the patterns you see are that:
i)   the biomass decreases at higher feeding levels and;
ii) the size of the organisms increases but the numbers as you go up the pyramid decrease.

It is difficult to construct a pyramid of biomass from organisms you catch in the wild.

Finding the dry mass of an animal means killing it. You would have great difficulty in finding dry mass if your herbivore were a cow! To get around this, we can use data which has already been worked out.

A pyramid shows the biomass of what is growing at that moment. A tree, for instance, may have accumulated its biomass over 30 years, in contrast to green algae that grow quickly, reproduce and die within a few weeks.

There are seasonal variations. Some plants grow quickly in spring, seed and then die by mid-summer. These plants would obviously not be available all year round.

Biomass is the mass of living material at each stage in the food chain. Biomass is measured as dry mass. You can find the dry mass of something by removing all the water from it and then weighing it.

Pyramid of biomass is a diagram that shows the mass of all living material in each level of a food chain.

The mass at each level decreases as you go up the pyramid, so the size of the bars gets smaller.

Trophic level is a feeding level in a food chain, such as primary producer (plant).

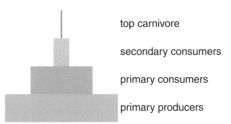

top carnivore

secondary consumers

primary consumers

primary producers

Figure 2.20 A pyramid of biomass. The largest biomass at the base represents the plant producer level.

CHAPTER 2 What are the energy inputs and energy losses in a food chain?

A **pyramid of energy** is a diagram that shows the transfer of energy at each level of a food chain.

Efficiency of energy transfer is the percentage of the energy that is passed on to the next organism in the chain and is not lost.

Pyramids of energy

A **pyramid of energy** shows the reduction of energy available in organisms as you move up the food chain. Biomass decreases at each trophic level, so there is also less energy available at each level.

It is easier to examine energy loss in a food chain for animals.

At each link of a food chain energy is released from food by respiration and used for:
- chemical reactions in the cytoplasm;
- nerve impulse conduction;
- muscle contraction, for movement;
- muscle contraction for keeping the body temperature constant, and above that of the environment;
- keeping warm – energy is lost as heat when it is cold.

Chemical energy is also lost from the food chain in faeces and urine.

The food chain in Figure 2.21 shows how little of the original energy input from the Sun reaches the secondary consumer, the fox.

The percentage of energy transferred in a food chain is different for every ecosystem. We can show the **efficiency of energy transfer** from one trophic level to the next by using a pyramid of energy.

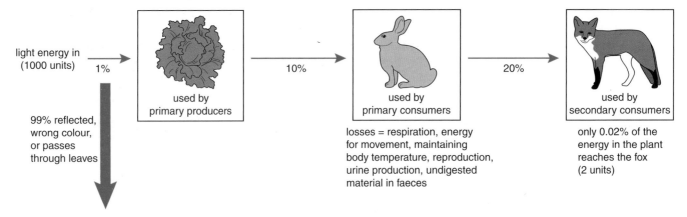

Figure 2.21 A simple food chain

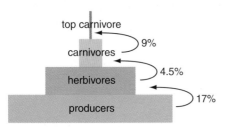

Figure 2.22 A pyramid of energy shows the efficiency of energy transfer from one trophic level to the next.

Can the biomass and energy principles be applied to food production?

Food production must be properly managed if a population is to be fed. We have already seen that energy is lost at each link in a food chain. By reducing the number of links in the chain, we can reduce the amount of energy lost and increase the efficiency of food production.

We can see from Figure 2.22 that secondary consumers (carnivores) receive less of the original energy input in a food chain than primary consumers (herbivores).

By looking at the energy conversion for a cow (Figure 2.23) you can see just how little energy (in the grass) is converted to increased biomass (muscle tissue).

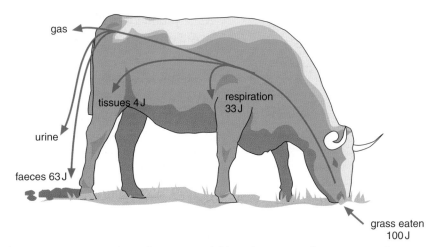

Figure 2.23 For every 100 J of energy available in the grass, only 4 J gets into the cow's tissues.

This raises some interesting questions.
- Would less energy be lost in producing animals with a shorter 'age to slaughter' such as rabbits and ostrich? Do you think people would be willing to start eating rabbit and ostrich meat instead of beef?
- We could restrict the movement of beef cattle and keep them in an insulated barn to maintain warm temperatures. This would reduce the amount of energy lost by the cattle.
- Would it be more energy efficient for humans to eat more at the herbivore level, such as beans, rather than red meat?
- Should we use biotechnology to produce more foods such as the mycoprotein, Quorn™?

The costs of food production and distribution

There are conflicts between the demands of the shopper for a good quality product at the lowest possible price and the needs of the producer to increase productivity and reduce costs.

Crops sold in supermarkets are intensively produced using fertilisers, pesticides and irrigation. This means that crops are produced quickly but also more expensively.

Where greenhouses are used there will be extra costs for the input of heat, light and carbon dioxide.

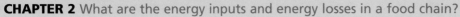

CHAPTER 2 What are the energy inputs and energy losses in a food chain?

Biodiversity is the number of different types of plants and animals living and feeding in the ecosystem. These will include pollinators and biological control species that are beneficial to crops.

Herbicides are chemicals that are used to kill weeds so the weeds do not compete with the crop for water, light or nutrients.

Insecticides are used to kill insect pest species that eat and damage the crop plants, but insecticides can also kill beneficial insects, such as bees.

Exotic or out of season crops that are grown abroad have to be flown or shipped to the UK and so have more 'food miles' and therefore more cost.

Transporting food uses up non-renewable fuels.

Meat production costs include costs of rearing, feed material, housing, waste disposal, distribution transport to market, veterinary bills and labour.

After the outbreaks of foot and mouth disease in the UK, the public became much more aware of the serious effects of transporting livestock long distances.

In the 1980s, intensive rearing of livestock involved using animal carcasses as a protein supplement in food. Carcass meat of cattle infected with BSE (also known as 'mad cow disease') was fed to healthy cows, spreading the disease further.

At the moment, bird flu is a big worry for poultry farmers and consumers. Poultry imports from certain countries to the UK are banned for fear of infecting the UK's bird population.

Agricultural production methods can reduce biodiversity. For example, use of fertilisers, herbicides and insecticides.

Activity – Are shoppers becoming more aware?

In a small group, take a large piece of paper (A3). Using a pencil and ruler, measure and mark the paper into four sections as shown below.

Write down the good points and bad points of managing food production.

For example, you might say that the use of an insecticide reduced the holes in cabbage leaves caused by caterpillars. Someone else might argue that they are worried about any remaining insecticide on the food they eat.

You might like to include other topics such as:
- selling only seasonal or local produce;
- genetically modified (GM) crops;
- organic farming;
- free-range chicken or pigs;
- land set-aside;
- problems faced by families on very low income; and
- any issues relevant to your local area.

You could do a web search for 'sustainable farming' to help you with this activity. You might find the following website useful: www.sustainweb.org.

Food production	
Good points	Concerns

Food distribution	
Good points	Concerns

2.7 What happens to the waste material produced by plants and animals?

> Bacteria and fungi are examples of **microorganisms**. A microscope is needed to see bacteria because they are very small.

> **12** Dead leaves have cellulose cell walls. Name the types of enzymes that are needed to break open the cellulose cell walls.
>
> **13** Name the nutrient that is taken up by plants and combined with sugars to make amino acids, which can then be joined together to make proteins.
>
> **14** Name the mineral ion which is taken up from soil and used to make chlorophyll.

What happens to dead leaves, plants and animals and piles of faeces and other natural debris? What causes them to decay?

Dead leaves, other dead organic matter and animal waste are broken down, or decomposed, by bacteria and fungi. If you turn over a damp leaf on the ground, in autumn, you might see fine threads like cotton-wool on the underside. These are the feeding structures of the fungi, which are chemically breaking down, or digesting, the dead leaf cells.

Microorganisms break down waste materials into simpler, soluble materials that can be used as nutrients by plants. In a stable ecosystem, some nutrients released by the decay process are used for bacterial or fungal growth. Some nutrients are taken up by the trees to be used again to make more leaves – in this way the nutrients are cycled.

The cellulose of plant cell walls is very difficult to break down, so the enzyme cellulase, secreted by fungi, starts the decay process by opening up the cell walls.

The digestion reactions of fungi happen more quickly when there is warmth and oxygen. These are the conditions you will find in a garden compost bin.

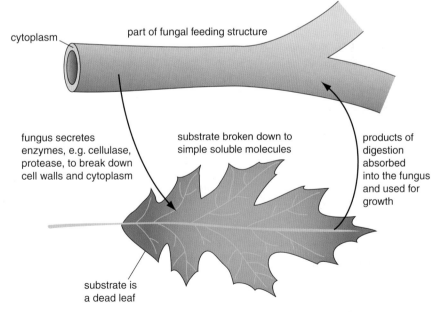

cytoplasm

part of fungal feeding structure

fungus secretes enzymes, e.g. cellulase, protease, to break down cell walls and cytoplasm

substrate broken down to simple soluble molecules

products of digestion absorbed into the fungus and used for growth

substrate is a dead leaf

Figure 2.24 Fungi carry out extracellular digestion to break down dead leaves.

2.8 How do carbon atoms move around in the carbon cycle?

The **carbon cycle** is a description of how carbon atoms circulate through carbon compounds in living organisms, to carbon dioxide in the air, and back again.

Microorganisms involved in the process of decay are called **decomposers**.

We already know that carbon dioxide is a raw material needed for photosynthesis. Now we will look at a possible journey taken by a carbon atom of a carbon dioxide molecule as it moves through the **carbon cycle** (Figure 2.25).

During photosynthesis a plant combines carbon dioxide with hydrogen from water to form glucose.

The glucose formed by photosynthesis is used to make structural and storage materials in the plant. Carbon atoms from the carbon dioxide are used to make oils, starch, cellulose and proteins in the plant.

If the plant is eaten by a herbivore, the carbon atoms become part of the fat, glycogen or proteins in the animal. If the herbivore is eaten, the fat, glycogen and proteins may pass to the next animal in the food chain, a carnivore. This chain (plant to herbivore to carnivore) can be thought of as the 'light chain' because it starts with the process of light energy capture.

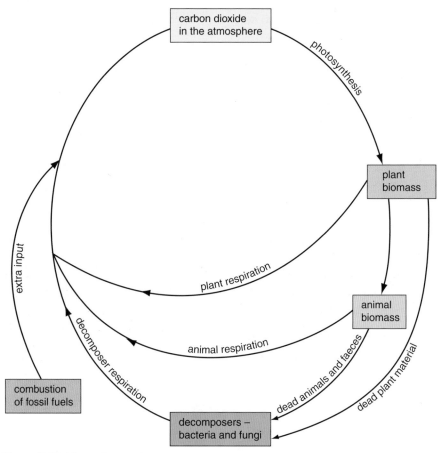

Figure 2.25 The carbon cycle

When a plant or animal dies, **decomposers** begin to break down the dead remains. The materials pass to the decomposers (bacteria and fungi) in the soil or leaf litter. This can be called the 'dark chain' and is very important for cycling nutrients and energy flow.

Figure 2.24 shows how bacteria and fungi secrete enzymes onto the dead organic matter to break it down (digest it). Some of the soluble products of digestion are taken up by the bacteria and fungi for their growth or respiration. The remainder stay in the soil and can be taken up by plants and used for growth.

As plants, animals and decomposers respire, they return carbon atoms to the atmosphere in the form of carbon dioxide.

There can be an extra input of carbon dioxide into the atmosphere through the burning of fossil fuels such as methane, diesel, petrol, coal, oil and gas and by the burning of wood.

You have looked at the cycling of the carbon atoms and at how nutrients are released and cycled by microorganisms. In the carbon cycle diagram the arrows go around in a circle, showing the route of the carbon. However, energy flow through an ecosystem is in a straight line. Energy enters the ecosystem, is converted and used and some passes out of the ecosystem – it cannot be cycled.

Answers to these question can be found in Figure 2.25.

15 In the carbon cycle, what is the only process that removes carbon dioxide from the atmosphere?

16 What three groups of living organisms are shown respiring in the carbon cycle diagram?

17 What is the additional source of carbon dioxide that is increasing atmospheric carbon dioxide?

18 Copy and complete the paragraph right about the cycling of a carbon atom, using the words in the box to fill in the blanks.

> break down   carbon dioxide   cellulose
> diffuses   glucose   osmosis   respiration
> starch   sugar

Carbon dioxide _____ into the leaf. Photosynthesis takes place and the carbon from the carbon dioxide is converted to _____. This can be changed to _____ as a storage material or used to make _____, which is a structural material used for cell walls. The plant can be eaten by a rabbit and the bacterial enzymes in the large intestine _____ _____ the carbon compounds into _____, which can be used for _____, and carbon dioxide is returned to the atmosphere.

19 Two organisms known as decomposers are _____ and _____.

20 Decomposers break down dead organic matter into small soluble molecules. Give two different uses for these molecules.

CHAPTER 2 What are the energy inputs and energy losses in a food chain?

Summary

✓ **Photosynthesis** is the process in green plants that converts light energy into chemical potential energy.

✓ The raw materials for photosynthesis are carbon dioxide and water.

✓ The products of photosynthesis are oxygen and glucose.

✓ The rate of photosynthesis is reduced if:
  – carbon dioxide is in short supply;
  – light intensity is low;
  – temperatures are low.

✓ The rate of photosynthesis can be measured by finding the volume of oxygen produced per hour.

✓ A **limiting factor** is one that is in short supply and controls the rate of the process.

✓ If carbon dioxide is in short supply or if the **light intensity** is low, the rate of photosynthesis will be reduced.

✓ To maximise photosynthesis and greenhouse crop production the following are controlled:
  – light intensity;
  – carbon dioxide concentration;
  – temperature.

✓ A **pyramid of biomass** shows the mass of organisms at each **trophic** (feeding) **level**. It measures the material present at the time.

✓ In a pyramid of biomass there are generally large numbers of small organisms at the base. The size of the organisms increases and the number of organisms decreases as you go up at each feeding level.

✓ In a **pyramid of energy** there is less energy in each successive level.

✓ Energy transferred between each level is reduced because energy is used for:

  – movement;
  – keeping the body temperature above that of the environment (in mammals and birds).

✓ **Efficiency of energy transfer** is the amount (percentage) of energy that is transferred from one feeding level to the next feeding level.

✓ Food production would be more energy efficient if humans fed as herbivores.

✓ 'Food miles' are the number of miles that a food is transported from its place of production to its final selling place.

✓ Farmland is an ecosystem that is carefully managed to maximise productivity. More and more farmers are starting to farm organically, or in a way that is less damaging to the environment. They do this by reducing the use of chemicals and managing habitats to prevent loss of animal and plant species.

✓ **Microorganisms** are so small that you can only see them with a microscope, for example bacteria. Bacteria and fungi (**decomposers**) play an essential role in decomposing dead plants and animals and in recycling mineral ions back into plants.

✓ Bacteria and fungi break down dead organic matter by extracellular digestion.

✓ Nutrients cycle within and are reused in an ecosystem – there is a fixed supply of nutrients which pass round and round the ecosystem.

✓ Energy flows through an ecosystem – the light energy input is available every day.

✓ The **carbon cycle** describes how carbon atoms circulate through carbon compounds in living organisms to carbon dioxide in the air and back again.

❶ A glasshouse owner wishes to grow many crops of lettuce so that he can harvest the crops all year round.

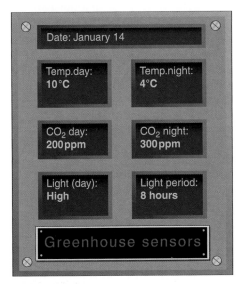

Figure 2.26

a) The normal atmospheric level of carbon dioxide is 370 ppm.
   i) Describe how the carbon dioxide levels would change during the day.   (*1 mark*)
   ii) Why would this happen?   (*2 marks*)
b) Look at the control panel and decide which two factors you would change to increase the growth rate of the lettuces.   (*2 marks*)
c) The grower considers fixing up electric lighting. Explain why he thinks this might increase growth rate.   (*1 mark*)
d) The glasshouse owner notices the leaves of the lettuces are rather yellow and decides to apply fertiliser.
   i) What mineral shortage do you think is affecting the lettuces?   (*1 mark*)
   ii) Why would a shortage of this mineral slow the growth?   (*1 mark*)
   iii) The fertiliser contains nitrates. What will the plants use the nitrates for?   (*1 mark*)

❷ Look at the carbon cycle in Figure 2.27.

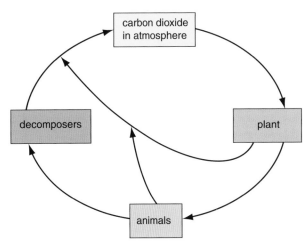

Figure 2.27 Carbon cycle

a) i) Name the only type of organism shown which removes carbon dioxide from the atmosphere.   (*1 mark*)
   ii) For what process is the carbon dioxide used?   (*1 mark*)
b) Name:
   i) a structural material; and
   ii) a storage product in a plant, which contain carbon.   (*2 marks*)
c) If a cow eats grass it assimilates the carbon atoms into compounds in its body. Name:
   i) a structural material; and
   ii) a storage product in a cow, which contain carbon.   (*2 marks*)
d) The manure (cow pat) of the cow contains the remains of the grass. What is the general name given to organisms that help in the chemical breakdown of the manure?   (*1 mark*)

❸ A student turns over a dead leaf and finds fine cotton-like threads on the underside. Complete the labels on Figure 2.28 to explain what is happening.

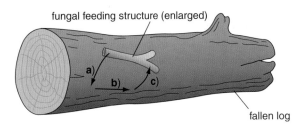

Figure 2.28

a) Enzymes are secreted by the fungus to _____ the cellulose cell walls. (*1 mark*)

b) These enzymes will include _____ to break down the cell walls, and _____ to break down the protein of the cytoplasm. (*2 marks*)

c) The products made by the enzyme reactions will include _____ and _____, which are absorbed by the fungus and used for growth. (*3 marks*)

❹ The mangrove swamps in the Gulf of Mexico support several feeding levels.
- The main producer in this ecosystem is the seagrass, which grows like an underwater meadow, and is eaten by small herbivorous fish.
- Single-celled algae make up a smaller biomass, but they are the main food of the zooplankton (microscopic animals).
- The zooplankton provide the food source for the invertebrates, such as shrimp, and for small carnivorous fish.
- Puffer fish eat mainly the invertebrates and, together with the larger fish, they make up the next feeding level.
- The top carnivore is the snapper fish.

a) How many feeding levels are there in this pyramid of biomass? (*1 mark*)

b) Use the names in the box to label the pyramid of biomass. (*4 marks*)

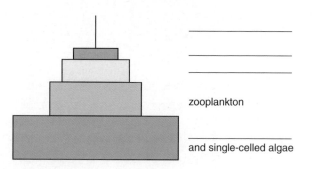

| puffer fish | seagrass | shrimps |
| snapper fish | | |

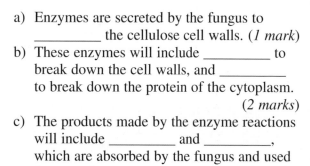

zooplankton

_____ and single-celled algae

Figure 2.29

c) What happens to the biomass as you go up each level? (*1 mark*)

d) What changes would you expect in the size of the animal as you go up from one feeding level to the next? (*1 mark*)

e) What would you expect to find in larger numbers: snapper fish or puffer fish? (*1 mark*)

f) Suggest another animal that might be catching and eating fish. (*1 mark*)

Chapter 3
Enzymes: how do they function and how can their properties be used industrially?

At the end of this chapter you should:

- ✓ know that enzymes are proteins which act as biological catalysts that increase the rate of reactions in living organisms;
- ✓ understand that protein molecules and enzymes are made of chains of amino acids coiled together;
- ✓ be able to explain why the shape of an enzyme is important for its function;
- ✓ be able to explain that heat affects enzyme function;
- ✓ know that enzymes have an optimum temperature and optimum pH;
- ✓ know that enzymes catalyse the reactions in processes such as respiration, photosynthesis and protein synthesis;
- ✓ be able to summarise aerobic respiration and explain how energy is released by a chemical reaction inside mitochondria;

- ✓ explain how amino acids and proteins are made (synthesised) in reactions catalysed by enzymes;
- ✓ be able to describe the digestive enzymes that catalyse the breakdown of different foods, and where this happens;
- ✓ be able to describe how enzymes produced by microorganisms are used in detergents to remove food stains;
- ✓ be able to describe applications of enzymes used in industry including pre-digested baby food and products containing sugar or fructose syrup; and
- ✓ be able to evaluate the advantages and disadvantages of using enzymes in the home and in industry.

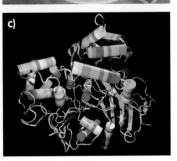

Figure 3.1 a) Why is biological washing powder called biological when it's full of chemicals? **b)** All detergents contain hydrocarbon molecules that help remove dirt and grease. **c)** Biological detergents work really well on food stains because they contain enzymes, like the one shown here, that digest the food just like the enzymes in your digestive system.

What are enzymes and what are some of their functions?

> **Enzymes** are the biological molecules that catalyse reactions in living organisms.

Enzymes are called biological catalysts because they control most of the reactions that take place in living organisms. Enzymes catalyse important reactions such as respiration and photosynthesis.

At low temperatures, such as the temperature of the human body, the chemical reactions inside cells would take place very slowly without enzymes. Enzymes make the reactions faster at these low temperatures.

All catalysts change the rate of chemical reactions but are not themselves changed by the reaction. The enzyme is not used up so it can catalyse the same reaction many times.

Enzymes differ from chemical catalysts because enzymes are protein molecules. Therefore, they have some properties of both catalysts and proteins. As catalysts, enzymes change the rate of reactions. Because they are proteins, they have a complex three-dimensional structure. This allows specific molecules to fit into the enzyme.

Uses of enzymes

Enzymes are used in many processes in the food and biotechnology industries to reduce reaction temperatures. This means less energy is used to heat the reaction container and so saves money. Enzymes also increase the reaction rate so that large amounts of product can be produced quickly.

Cracking the name code

The ending *–ase* tell you that the substance is an enzyme. The first part of the name tells you what it breaks down, for example protease is the enzyme that breaks down protein, while cellulase breaks down cellulose.

---

❶ What is the benefit to living organisms of enzymes controlling reactions inside living cells?

❷ Give three reasons why enzymes are used in industrial applications.

❸ Give two similarities and two differences between enzymes and catalysts, using the information above.

How do enzymes work?

Each type of enzyme works for only one particular reaction. When your body digests food, different enzymes work on different food types:
- protease enzymes speed up digestion of protein to form amino acids;
- the enzyme amylase breaks down starch to give the products glucose and fructose.

> A **substrate** is the substance broken down by an enzyme.

This shows that each enzyme will interact with only one **substrate**.

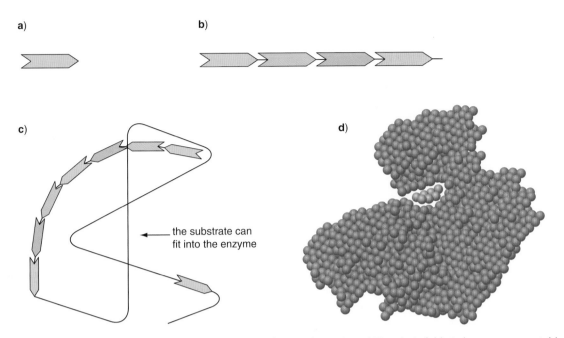

Figure 3.2 a) A single amino acid. **b)** A long chain of amino acids joined together. **c)** The chain folds to become more stable. **d)** The complete three-dimensional enzyme with its substrate.

the substrate can fit into the enzyme

Why does an enzyme only work on one substance?

To answer this you need to think about the three-dimensional structure of the enzyme. Remember that enzymes are protein molecules.

- **Amino acids** are the building blocks of proteins. They are joined end to end to form a long chain (like a row of beads). All enzymes have this same basic structure, but they have a different order of amino acids to form different protein molecules.
- The chain of amino acids (a very long molecule) is stabilised when it is folded into a three-dimensional shape and cross-bonds form between the amino acids (rather as a girl might twist up her hair and secure it with slides).
- Each tightly folded enzyme molecule is like a ball but with ridges and grooves that give it a unique shape. Only one substrate can fit into the grooves.
- The idea that the substrate must fit the enzyme is called the **'lock and key' model** for enzyme structure. Enzymes 'unlock' a particular molecule so that a chemical reaction can take place. The word unlock here means to break a chemical bond.

> **Amino acids** are molecules that can be combined in long chains to form proteins.
>
> A **model** is a simplified picture that scientists make to fit observed data to a theory.
>
> The **'lock and key model'** suggests that each enzyme has a special shape, which means that only one substrate can fit into each enzyme.

What conditions affect enzymes?

Enzyme reactions are slow at low temperatures (10 °C) but the rates of enzyme reactions increase as the temperature rises. To understand why, you need to apply your understanding of what is happening to the molecules.

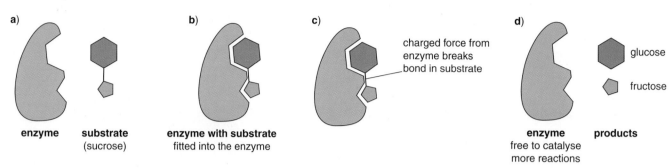

Figure 3.3 This sequence of diagrams shows how an enzyme breaks down a substrate. Here, the substrate is sucrose and the products are glucose and fructose.

Optimum means the best. For an enzyme the optimum temperature is the temperature at which the enzyme functions best. In the same way, the optimum pH is the pH at which the enzyme works best.

The **activation energy** is the energy that must be provided to the reactants to start a chemical reaction.

When temperature destroys the three-dimensional shape of a protein molecule or enzyme, it is **denatured**. This means that the enzyme can no longer work.

- The enzyme and substrate molecules must collide with enough energy for the substrate to fit into the enzyme structure. This is called the **activation energy**. This is a bit like putting a missing piece into a jigsaw puzzle – you can place a missing piece over a gap, but it needs a little push (energy) to fit it in.
- An increase in temperature makes the particles move faster and increases their kinetic energy. As a result the enzyme molecules and substrate molecules collide more often and with more energy. The enzyme can catalyse more reactions so the reaction rate is increased.

But this is where enzymes differ from catalysts: enzymes function best at an optimum temperature. An increase in temperature above the optimum changes the shape of the protein molecule. We say that the enzyme has been **denatured**.

You can see the effect of change in protein structure when you cook an egg white. These changes in protein structure are irreversible. When the enzyme molecule shape has been changed the substrate no longer fits into the enzyme and it no longer works as a catalyst.

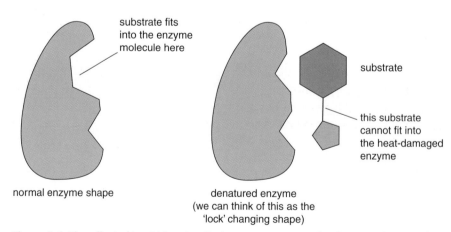

Figure 3.4 The effect of heat (denaturation) on an enzyme molecule. Heat changes the bonds and changes the three-dimensional shape.

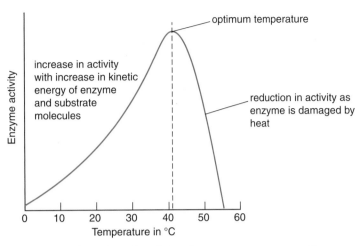

Figure 3.5 Sketch graph to show the effect of heat on an enzyme reaction

④ Why are enzyme reactions slow at low temperatures?

⑤ Why is more product made from a reaction at 30 °C than at 5 °C?

⑥ A student was carrying out an experiment using the enzyme protease on egg white protein solution, which was cloudy white to start with. Copy and complete his results table below.

Volume egg white solution in cm³	Volume protease in cm³	Temperature in °C	Colour at end of test	Conclusion
5.0	2.0	25	Clear	Egg white protein digested
5.0	2.0	30	Clear	
5.0	2.0	35	Clear	
5.0	2.0	40	Slightly cloudy	
5.0	2.0	45	Cloudy white	
5.0	2.0	50	Cloudy white	

Table 3.1

⑦ What word describes the temperature at which an enzyme functions most efficiently?

⑧ Why can protease break down protein but not starch?

⑨ The mouth is slightly alkaline (pH 8), but the stomach is acidic (pH 2). Why do you think salivary amylase stops working when the food enters the stomach?

Activity – Who was Emil Fischer?

Emil Fischer was born in Germany in 1852. He went to the University of Bonn in 1871 to study chemistry. In 1902 Fischer won a Nobel prize. This was the first prize awarded for organic chemistry. Emil was famous for careful teaching and for making links between science and industry. Six of the students that he taught also won Nobel prizes.

Emil Fischer first suggested the 'lock and key' model in 1894. The amazing thing about Fischer's model was that he suggested this before scientists had discovered that enzymes were protein molecules.

The lock and key model is used today to develop computer simulations that investigate possible new drugs. The programs design and test thousands of different molecules with different shapes to see how they could 'fix' onto receptors on the surface of target cells in the same way that substrates fit into enzymes.

Figure 3.6 Emil Fischer

❶ Write and illustrate a newspaper report about Fischer's great award. Find out about him by searching for his name on the internet. Don't forget to say how long after his discoveries he was rewarded with the Nobel prize.

❷ Find the answers to the following questions.
  a) In Emil Fischer's model, what does the lock represent?
  b) How long after the 'lock and key' model was suggested was the nature of enzymes worked out, and how long before a three- dimensional model of a protein was first made?

❸ Draw a diagram to show the 'lock and key model' as a lock and key, and a more modern diagram showing an enzyme and substrate.

 3.3

What reactions do enzymes control inside cells?

Different enzymes catalyse each of the many chemical reactions in cells such as photosynthesis and respiration. Only two reactions are discussed here: building proteins and respiration.

Building proteins for growth

So far we have talked about enzymes breaking down molecules, but enzymes can also join small amino acid molecules together to make larger protein molecules. Growing cells need to make proteins to build

> **Protein synthesis** is the building of protein molecules from a chain of amino acid molecules, using enzymes to catalyse the reaction.
>
> **Aerobic respiration** occurs when oxygen reacts with glucose and releases energy. Carbon dioxide and water are the products of the reaction.

new structures inside the cell or more organelles such as mitochondria. Enzymes catalyse the reactions inside the cell that make proteins. This is called **protein synthesis.**

Different enzymes control which proteins can be built. Different cells do different jobs and so there are thousands of different proteins needed.

Respiration to release energy

Making larger molecules from smaller molecules needs energy. All cells in living organisms release energy from food by respiring. **Aerobic respiration** is a reaction in cells that uses glucose and oxygen to release energy. Aerobic respiration occurs as a series of reactions, each controlled by an enzyme.

The reactions in aerobic respiration are summarised by the equation:

$$\text{glucose} + \text{oxygen} \rightarrow \text{carbon dioxide} + \text{water} (+ \text{energy})$$

First, glucose is broken down in the cytoplasm to form smaller molecules that can enter the mitochondrion. In the mitochondrion a series of reactions takes place, each releasing a little energy.

So why is respiration a series of reactions and not a single reaction? If you oxidise glucose by setting fire to it you end up with the same overall reaction as respiration and the same products, but a great deal of energy is released rapidly causing heating – we call this combustion. This type of reaction within cells would damage (denature) the proteins.

Instead, in respiration the energy is released bit by bit at each reaction in small units that have enough energy for other reactions in the cell. You could think of it as taking all your money as large value notes when you go on holiday. In fact, it's best if you have smaller value notes and coins for buying drinks and chocolates.

What do cells do with these small units of energy?

Remember that energy is needed for all the chemical reactions in the cytoplasm:
- All living cells need energy to join amino acids together to form large protein molecules.
- Plants need energy to add nitrates to the sugars produced by photosynthesis to form amino acids.
- Plants also build up glucose molecules into cellulose to make new cell walls.

Energy released by respiration is also used by warm-blooded animals to maintain their body temperature, and for muscle fibre contractions so that the animal or bird can move.

Photosynthesis is a series of chemical reactions that could not take place without plant enzymes. Enzymes in chloroplasts catalyse the reaction that converts carbon dioxide and water to glucose. Nearly all food webs are based upon photosynthesis, so most life on Earth depends on the enzymes that catalyse photosynthesis.

⑩ Name two large molecules made in plant cells by joining together smaller molecules.

⑪ In which part of the cell is most of the energy in respiration released?

⑫ Give three uses that animals make of the energy released in respiration.

⑬ Combustion is just one reaction, but respiration takes place as a series of small reactions. What points are the same about these reactions, and how do they differ?

 ## Are enzymes used outside cells in the body?

Digestive enzymes are produced by specialised cells in **glands,** such as the salivary gland or the pancreas, or by cells in the lining of the stomach and intestine. These enzymes pass out of the cells and into the intestine.

> A **gland** is an organ that produces and releases or secretes a substance used by other cells.

Digestive enzymes catalyse the breakdown of food as it passes down the intestine from the mouth. The digestive system can be thought of as a tube through the body carrying food.

The purpose of digestion is to break down large insoluble molecules into small molecules.

> **Amylase** is the digestive enzyme that breaks down starch into glucose and fructose.

For example, **amylase** breaks down starch to give glucose and fructose. Smaller molecules are needed because they are soluble and can pass (diffuse) through cell membranes from the small intestine into the blood plasma for transport to body cells. These smaller molecules, like glucose and amino acids, are also in a form that cells can use.

Enzyme	Site of production	Site of action	pH	Substrate	Products
Salivary amylase	Salivary glands	Mouth	8	Starch	Sugars
Pancreatic amylase	Pancreas	Small intestine	8	Starch	Sugars
Protease	Cells in stomach wall	Stomach	2 (hydrochloric acid produced by the stomach acidifies food)	Protein	Polypeptides and amino acids
Protease	Pancreas	Small intestine	8 (bile from the liver neutralises the acid food leaving the stomach)	Protein	Polypeptides and amino acids
Protease	Small intestine wall	Small intestine	8	Peptides	Amino acids
Lipase	Pancreas and cells in small intestine wall	Small intestine	8	Lipids	Fatty acids and glycerol

Table 3.2 Enzymes of the digestive system

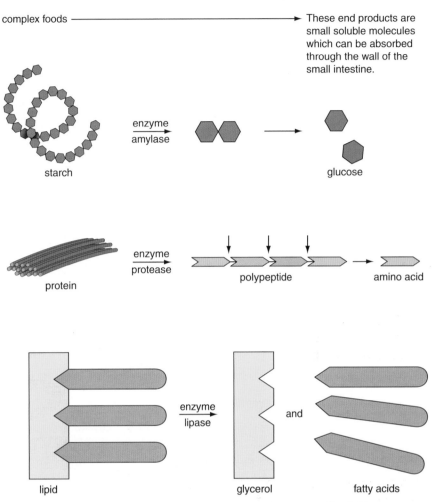

Figure 3.7 The breakdown of the complex food molecules into small, soluble, usable molecules

Protease is the digestive enzyme that breaks down proteins into amino acids.

Lipase is the digestive enzyme that breaks down lipids (fats and oils) into fatty acids and glycerol.

Bile is a substance produced by the liver and released during digestion into the small intestine to provide alkaline conditions. Bile also reduces the size of the fatty droplets, making them easier to digest.

Cells in the stomach lining produce **protease** enzymes that break down protein, so protein digestion begins in the stomach. Different proteases are produced by the pancreas and secreted into the small intestine, where proteins continue to be broken down into amino acids. The stomach protease and the pancreatic protease function at different pH levels, as you can see in Table 3.2.

In the small intestine, **lipase** breaks down fats and lipids into fatty acids and glycerol.

Other substances are released that help digestive enzymes function.
- Hydrochloric acid is released into the stomach to provide the low pH required by protease enzymes.
- **Bile** produced in the liver is added to the small intestine to increase the pH again. The enzymes that work in the small intestine need a nearly neutral pH. Bile is stored in the gall bladder and added to the small intestine from a small duct (tube).
- Bile also breaks up the fat droplets to give a greater surface area so that the lipase can work more efficiently.

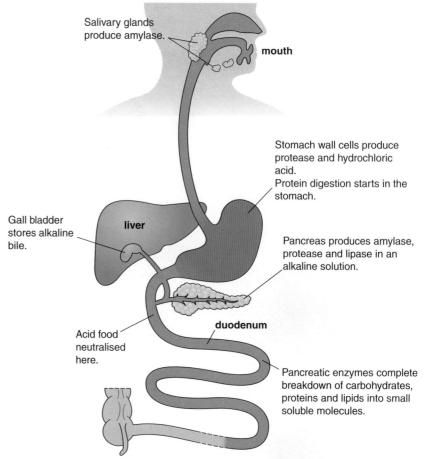

Figure 3.8 Digestive enzymes control reactions that take place in the digestive system.

⓮ a) What is the optimum pH for the enzyme amylase?
  b) The food leaving the mouth is slightly alkaline. How is the pH lowered when the food enters the stomach?
  c) The food leaving the stomach is strongly acidic. How is the pH raised when the food enters the small intestine?

  d) What is the optimum pH for all the pancreatic enzymes?
  e) What is the optimum pH for stomach protease?

⓯ During digestion large molecules are broken down into small molecules. Why is this necessary?

⓰ Copy and complete Table 3.3.

Enzyme	Large complex molecules	Small soluble end products of digestion
Amylase	Starch	a) _____
Protease	b) _____	Amino acids
c) _____	Lipids (fats and oils)	d) _____ and glycerol

Table 3.3

a) Name the two places where amylase is produced.
b) Name the two parts of the digestive system where protein digestion takes place.
c) Describe where fats and oils are digested.

a) Where is bile produced?
b) Where is bile stored?
c) What is the function of bile?

Figure 3.9 An industrial fermenter for producing enzymes

A fermenter is a large steel vessel used for biochemical reactions. Sensors monitor the conditions inside. The sensors send information to a computer. The computer opens or closes valves to keep the temperature, pH, nutrient and oxygen levels at the optimum value.

3.5 Industrial production and use of enzymes

The list of industrial applications for enzymes is amazing and includes food, wine and beer production, making fructose sweeteners for soft drinks, laundry detergents, producing the 'stone-washed' jeans effect and manufacturing pharmaceuticals. The food industry uses many different enzymes produced from microorganisms.

Like all living organisms, bacteria and fungi produce and secrete enzymes. The enzymes pass out of their cells into the environment to digest dead plants and animals. The products of the enzyme action are small soluble molecules which the organism can take into its cytoplasm to use for growth.

Microorganisms are collected from different locations around the world and the enzymes they produce are tested. Biotechnologists look for enzymes that could be used for particular industrial processes, for example to develop a new food.

As bacteria and fungi normally live in cool environments, their enzymes usually function at low temperatures. However, if an industrial process needs an enzyme that works at high temperature or extremes of pH, then enzymes have to be found from microorganisms living in those environmental conditions, for example bacteria from hot springs.

Enzymes that act on the right substrates but at the wrong temperature may need to be modified by gene transfer.

To produce the enzymes, the microorganisms are cultured in a fermentation process. At the end of the batch process, the fermenter is emptied and the enzymes are collected from the solution in which the bacteria have grown.

Carbohydrase enzymes break down complex carbohydrate molecules such as starch into simple sugars.

Isomerase is an enzyme that converts glucose into fructose.

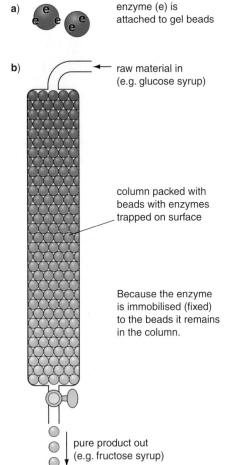

a) enzyme (e) is attached to gel beads

b) raw material in (e.g. glucose syrup)

column packed with beads with enzymes trapped on surface

Because the enzyme is immobilised (fixed) to the beads it remains in the column.

pure product out (e.g. fructose syrup)

Figure 3.10 In a continuous flow column the substrate (glucose) reacts as it flows slowly over beads that have the enzyme attached to their surface. The product can be collected from the bottom of the column.

Enzymes in the food industry

One of the first uses of enzymes in the food industry was the production of sweet syrups by breaking down starch. This can be done by boiling starch with acid, but using the enzyme method gives a pure and reliable product, with no by-products. Another advantage is that energy costs are lower as the enzyme process can be carried out at a lower temperature.

Glucose syrup is widely used as an ingredient and food additive. Most glucose syrup is produced from maize waste products (corn) using enzymes. Using a common and cheap (waste) material as the raw material for glucose syrup saves a great deal of money.

Many **carbohydrase** enzymes are used in sequence to produce a variety of syrups of different sweetness. For example:
- maize starch is treated with one form of amylase to convert it to a thick starch paste;
- this paste is then reacted with different amylase enzymes to form sugars such as maltose or glucose. The reaction can be stopped here; or
- the final stage is the conversion of glucose syrup to fructose syrup using the enzyme **isomerase**.

In the early 1970s a continuous-flow system was developed to produce fructose syrup. Glucose solution is added to the top of a reaction column and fructose solution comes out the bottom. The continuous process can run for about 6 months non-stop.

As enzymes are proteins, their structure eventually breaks down and the enzyme needs replacing. The old enzymes are biodegradable so do not result in toxic waste.

Fructose syrup is much sweeter than sucrose or glucose syrup so it can be used in smaller quantities as a sweetener. This saves food manufacturers money. In the 1970s fructose syrup began to be used in slimming foods to give sweetness with fewer calories.

Although there are economic advantages of using enzymes in industrial processes, there are also some disadvantages:
- development and production of new enzymes is costly;
- each enzyme works on only one substrate so they have only one use;
- they only work at exactly the right temperature and pH;
- enzymes are proteins and so can cause allergic reactions; they must be enclosed in capsules to minimise the risk of skin contact or inhalation; and
- some people may object to genetically modified (GM) enzymes being used to produce food.

Other food products made from enzymes

Figure 3.11 What is the connection between these two?

Figure 3.12 An enzyme product loved by many people

You would not expect anything in common between babies and bodybuilders, but there is. Some baby food is pre-digested using proteases. Pre-digested means that the baby can use the amino acids without having to digest the food by itself.

Protein supplements taken by bodybuilders are also pre-digested. This means the amino acids can be quickly taken up for building and repairing muscles if they are consumed straight after training.

Soft-centred chocolates start with the centre as a hard sugar paste so that it can be easily handled for chocolate coating. Invertase enzyme is added and converts the sucrose to glucose and fructose syrup within 1–2 days. In other words, by the time the chocolates reach the shop the hard centre has become soft.

19 List the economic advantages of using enzymes in the food industry.

20 a) In a continuous-flow column, what is the advantage of having the enzymes immobilised on beads?
   b) In a batch process, the raw materials and the enzymes are reacted together in a reactor vessel until an economic concentration of products has been formed. The remaining raw materials and the enzymes are then separated from the products.
   What are the advantages of 'continuous-flow' rather than 'batch' processes?

21 Complete Table 3.4 showing the use of enzymes in common food production:

Food product	Enzyme used in manufacture	Substrate	Product	Advantage of the product
Baby food	Protease		Amino acid	Readily available amino acids for baby growth
Slimming products	Invertase	Glucose syrup		Sweetens without adding calories
Soft drinks	Carbohydrase	(Maize) starch		
Baby food		Fats	Fatty acids	No digestion needed

Table 3.4

CHAPTER 3 Enzymes: how do they function and how can their properties be used industrially?

Laundry detergents

Washing used to be carried out at high temperatures with a great deal of agitation to break down dirt. Electricity costs are high for high-temperature washes. Modern detergents use enzymes that function efficiently at low temperatures, reducing fuel costs.

Food or biological stains on clothes can include fats and oils from fried items, butter or oily dressings, proteins such as eggs, grass or blood, and starches from sauces made with flour.

Biological washing powders have the following enzymes added:
- lipase to break down fats;
- proteases to digest proteins;
- carbohydrases to remove starch stains.

Similar enzymes are used in dishwasher detergents to remove the food remains on the plates.

Figure 3.13 What stains might be on the toddler's T-shirt? How could these be removed in a cool wash?

Activity – Stone-washed jeans

Denim fabric is made by weaving. The cross threads are unbleached cotton and the warp (vertical threads) are dyed with indigo. Indigo takes strong bleach (high pH and high temperature) to remove it chemically.

Stone-washed jeans were originally produced with stones. An enormous machine would shake 150 kg of pumice stone with 150 pairs of jeans for up to 6 hours. The stones damaged the cellulose fibres and released the indigo dye. This process also damaged the seams of the jeans, the machines and the operators because of the pumice dust in the air. It also took a lot of water to rinse off all the grit particles from the jeans.

The new method of producing stone-washed jeans uses an enzyme called DeniMax. This produces the stone-wash effect faster without damaging the fabric and uses a smaller quantity of water.

The new enzyme process removes the need for pumice stones yet the final look is the same and the jeans last longer.

❶ List four problems with the old stone-wash system.

A new enzyme has been developed which is specific to indigo and which works at lower temperatures so that it can also be used on stretch-denim (higher temperatures used for other enzymes damage the Lycra®). Using the enzyme reduces the colour and produces an aged effect.

❷ What is meant by saying the enzyme is 'specific to indigo'?
❸ What are the environmental advantages of the enzyme process used in the manufacturing of jeans?

Figure 3.14 Modern 'stone-washed' jeans

Laundry detergents and the environment

Although using 'biological detergents' improves stain removal and reduces costs, so much washing detergent is used in factories, the hotel and catering industry and in the home that any possible damage to the environment must be minimised.

Biological detergents are biodegradable, because enzymes are proteins and break down naturally in the environment. They also have other environmental advantages in energy efficiency (low-temperature washes) and water efficiency (less water is needed to wash away the spare powder and dirt).

㉒ What are the environmental advantages of using enzymes in detergents?

㉓ The instructions on the box state that biological wash powders are not effective when used at temperatures above 40 °C.
a) Explain why this is so.
b) If you had dropped fruit and cream down the front of your best silk shirt, what is the advantage of using biological washing powder?

㉔ Figure 3.13 shows a typical toddler's T-shirt. Explain how biological washing powder will solve the problem for each stain, for example the egg, butter and tomato.

What do the homemaker, laundry and hotel industry want from a detergent?	What are the environmental requirements of a detergent?
• A good clean wash. • Low temperatures to reduce the cost of heating the water • Less water used as many houses and businesses now have water meters • Less agitation to reduce wear on fabrics • All stains removed • Fabrics to feel soft after washing • Shorter washing time	• No foam in water treatment works • Reduced amount of energy used, to reduce air pollution and greenhouse gas emissions from electricity generation • Reduced amount of water used, to avoid water shortages particularly in the south of England • Biodegradable materials

Table 3.5 The requirements for a good washing powder

Summary

✓ **Enzymes** are biological catalysts that enable reactions to take place more quickly and at a lower temperature.

✓ An enzyme breaks down a **substrate** to form products, for example protease breaks down proteins into amino acids.

✓ Proteins can be built up by joining **amino acids** together in a long chain.

✓ Enzymes are proteins with a particular three-dimensional structure. At high temperatures enzymes are **denatured**. Denatured means that their shape is changed so that they no longer work as catalysts.

✓ The temperature at which an enzyme works best is called the optimum temperature.

✓ **Activation energy** is the energy that must be provided to start a chemical reaction.

✓ Enzymes inside living cells catalyse respiration, photosynthesis and **protein synthesis** reactions.

✓ **Aerobic respiration** reactions release energy from glucose. This energy is needed for movement, building new molecules and maintaining body temperature.

CHAPTER 3 Enzymes: how do they function and how can their properties be used industrially?

✓ Some enzymes are secreted from cells and function outside the cell, for example in the digestive system.

✓ Digestive enzymes are secreted by specialised cells in **glands,** such as the salivary gland or the pancreas, or by cells in the lining of the stomach and intestine.

✓ **Amylase** is the digestive enzyme that breaks down starch into glucose and fructose, **lipase** breaks down lipids (fats and oils) into fatty acids and glycerol, and **protease** breaks down proteins into amino acids.

✓ **Bile** is a substance produced by the liver and released during digestion into the small intestine to provide alkaline conditions. Bile also reduces the size of the fatty droplets, making them easier to digest.

✓ Microorganisms that secrete enzymes outside their cells are used in industry for enzyme production.

✓ Enzymes are used in industry because they save time, money and environmental pollution.

✓ In the food industry **carbohydrase** enzymes are used to produce sugar syrup from starch and **iosmerase** is used to make fructose syrup used in slimming products. Other enzymes are used to make pre-digested baby foods.

✓ Enzymes are used in domestic detergents to improve stain removal by digesting protein and fat in foods.

EXAM QUESTIONS

❶ Pectin in fruit holds the cellulose fibres in the cell wall together. To get juice from fruit you need to break down the cell walls so the juice can be released. This can be done more easily with enzymes. The enzyme pectinase breaks down the cell walls and releases the juice.

A student did a laboratory experiment to extract apple juice from the apple pulp.

1 She grated the apple and weighed it out into five beakers so that each had 50.0 g pulp.

2 The beakers of apple pulp were placed in water baths for 30 minutes to warm the pulp.

3 2 cm³ of the enzyme pectinase was added to each beaker, stirred and then left it for another 15 minutes to break down the pectin.

4 The apple pulp was strained over a fine mesh into a measuring cylinder to collect the juice. The results are shown in Table 3.6.

Water bath temperature in °C	Volume of juice collected in cm³
10	12
25	25
35	50
45	78
60	45
70	12
85	12

Table 3.6

a) Plot the results on a graph. (Temperature should be on the horizontal axis and volume on the vertical axis.)   *(3 marks)*

b) At what temperature did this enzyme give the highest volume of juice?   *(1 mark)*

c) Describe and explain the pattern shown by the results.   *(3 marks)*

d) Do you think there are enough results to make an accurate prediction of the volume of juice you would expect at 50 °C?   *(1 mark)*

e) If you did the experiment again, what temperatures would you choose to find out exactly how temperature affects the enzyme pectinase?   *(2 marks)*

❷ A boy eats a sandwich made of white bread, butter and meat. Copy and complete this table to show what happens as it passes through his digestive system. The first line has been completed as an example. (*8 marks*)

Region of intestine	pH	Enzyme	Breaks down	Products
Mouth	7–8	Amylase	Starch/bread	Sugar
Stomach	a)	b)	Meat protein	c)
Small intestine	8	Amylase	d)	e)
		f)	Butter fat	Fatty acids
		g)	Proteins	h)

Table 3.7

❸ Coloured leather settees and chairs are in demand. They are produced from animal hides that have been treated with the industrial enzyme Greasex™. This breaks down and removes the natural fats on the hide. The advantage is that strong detergents and large volumes of water do not have to be used. The hides are softer, and waterproofing and colour treatments take evenly on the hide.

Figure 3.15

a) What are the products of the breakdown of the fats? (*2 marks*)
b) Give two reasons why using Greasex is environmentally friendly. (*2 marks*)
c) What other advantage is there to the appearance of the furniture? (*1 mark*)
d) What enzyme in the body digests fats? (*1 mark*)
e) Where is this fat-digesting enzyme produced? (*1 mark*)
f) Another substance helps this enzyme to function well in the body. What is this substance? How does it help? (*3 marks*)

❹ This sketch graph shows the effect of heat on an enzyme reaction.

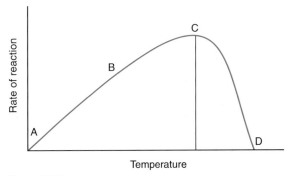

Figure 3.16

a) Give the letter or letters on the graph which show:
   i) the optimum temperature; (*1 mark*)
   ii) the part of the graph where there are increasing numbers of collisions of the substance with the enzyme; (*1 mark*)
   iii) the part of the graph where the enzyme is being destroyed by the higher temperatures. (*1 mark*)
b) If this was a human enzyme, what temperature would you expect at C? (*1 mark*)
c) What word describes the enzyme at D? (*1 mark*)

Chapter 4
How do our bodies control internal conditions and pass on characteristics?

At the end of this chapter you should:

✓ understand how the water and ion content of the body are controlled;
✓ know that ADH secreted by the pituitary gland controls the water content of urine;
✓ be able to explain how body temperature is maintained;
✓ know that the pancreas controls blood glucose concentration through the production of insulin;
✓ be able to explain how diabetes affects the body and how it can be treated;
✓ know how carbon dioxide and urea are removed from the body;

✓ understand the importance of DNA in living organisms;
✓ understand that mitosis and meiosis are different types of cell division and understand the role these two processes play in the living organisms;
✓ be able to describe how sex is determined;
✓ be able to explain how simple characteristics and some diseases are inherited;
✓ be able to complete genetic diagrams to illustrate inheritance;
✓ be able to make judgements about the applications of embryo screening.

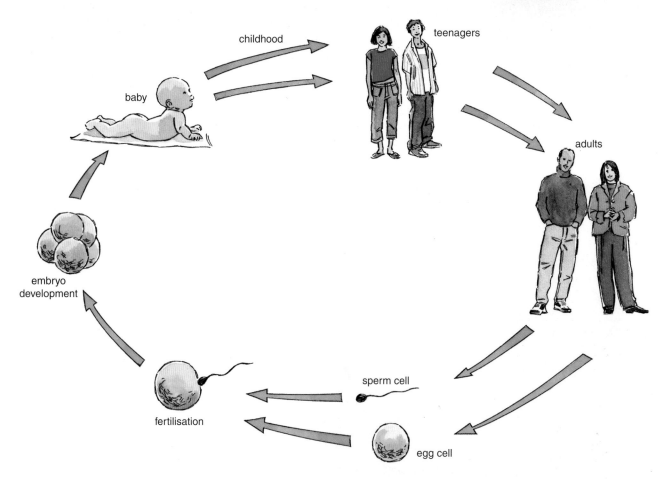

Figure 4.1 The human life cycle. At every stage the body monitors and controls the changes that are taking place. All the information that allows you to do this is inherited from your parents and can be passed on to your children. How can all this develop from just one cell?

4.1 How does your body control its internal conditions?

> **Homeostasis** is the maintenance of steady conditions within the body, including water content, blood glucose concentration and body temperature.

Your body has to control conditions in the cells, blood and body tissue. Remember from Core Science that your body temperature is controlled at its normal temperature of 37 °C. This is because the enzymes in the body work best at this temperature. Other internal conditions that are controlled include the water and ion content of the body, and blood sugar levels. The mechanisms in the body that regulate its internal conditions are together called **homeostasis**.

Controlling the water and ion content of the body

When you get too hot you sweat. The water in the sweat evaporates from your skin, cooling you down. You have to take in more water in food or drink to replace the water lost, since too much or too little water in our cells means that they stop working properly. Body tissues such as muscle can stop working, and cells can be permanently damaged.

Sweat doesn't only contain water. Essential ions, such as sodium and potassium, are dissolved in your sweat. So ions lost in sweat also have to be replaced when we eat and drink. The wrong concentration of ions dissolved in the blood interferes with water uptake by the cells. You will remember the effects of different concentrations on cells from the osmosis section in Chapter 1. A low concentration of ions (too much water) in the blood means too much water moves into cells. This can cause body cells to swell up or even burst. A high concentration of ions in the blood causes water to move out of cells causing them to shrivel.

Figure 4.2 The girl is sweating to control her body temperature, which leads to water loss from the body. What else is lost from her body in sweat?

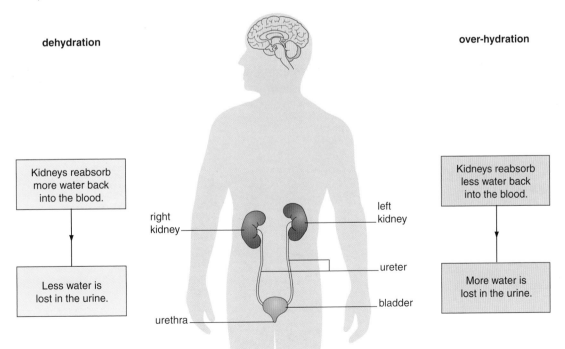

Figure 4.3 The kidneys control the level of water in the blood. The kidneys can adjust the amount of water in the urine.

Controlling the water content of the blood is the job of the kidney. When a person becomes dehydrated the kidneys respond by absorbing more water back into the blood. This means that less water is lost in urine. When a person becomes over-hydrated the kidney reabsorbs less water into the blood. This results in more water going into urine and then being lost from the bladder when the person goes to the toilet.

❶ Look at Figure 4.2 on page 53. The girl in the picture is losing water by sweating. How else may she lose water from her body?

❷ What else does she lose from her body in her sweat?

❸ How should she replace the water lost from her body?

❹ Imagine that the girl has only just started to dance.
 a) How would her kidneys respond to save water?
 b) What effect would this have on her urine?

Controlling body temperature

The **thermoregulatory centre** in the brain monitors and controls body temperature.

Humans usually maintain a body temperature of between 36.5 and 37.5 °C. If body temperature drops below 30 °C sleepiness can set in, followed by unconsciousness. This can lead to death if the condition is not treated. Fortunately the body has a very effective way of monitoring and controlling its temperature.

Body temperature is monitored and controlled by a part of the brain called the **thermoregulatory centre**. The centre receives nerve impulses from two sets of temperature receptors. Temperature receptors in the brain sense the temperature of blood flowing through the brain. The thermoregulatory centre also receives impulses from temperature receptors in the skin. If the temperature is too high or too low, the centre responds by sending impulses out to other parts of the body. These parts of the body make changes to adjust the temperature. All of these responses are automatic or reflex responses. Figure 4.4 summarises this system.

❺ Copy and complete these sentences.
 The temperature of the body is monitored by the _____ centre. This receives impulses from receptors in the _____ and skin. If the body gets too hot the skin releases _____, which cools the body.

❻ Sweating helps to cool down the body. The hotter it is, the more you sweat.
 a) What problem can sweating cause the body?
 b) What should you do to avoid this problem?

❼ On a hot day your skin often becomes red very quickly. Explain why this happens.

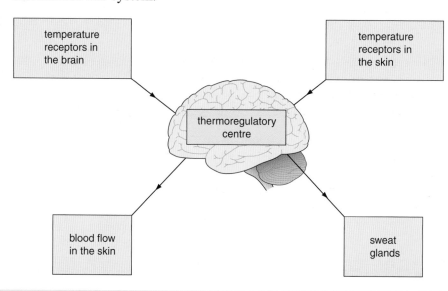

Figure 4.4 The thermoregulatory centre monitors and controls body temperature by co-ordinating a response to impulses received from receptors.

Controlling blood sugar levels

> The **pancreas** is an organ that produces the hormone insulin.
>
> **Insulin** is a hormone that causes glucose to be moved from the blood into liver and muscle cells.
>
> People who suffer from **diabetes** do not produce enough insulin in their pancreas.

Blood sugar levels are monitored and controlled by an organ called the **pancreas**. Too much glucose in the blood can damage blood vessels and cells. The pancreas detects high glucose levels and produces a hormone called **insulin**. Insulin causes glucose to move from the blood into cells. The production of insulin allows glucose to be stored in the liver and muscles. It is essential that the pancreas produces the right amount of insulin to control the level of glucose in the blood.

Diabetes is a disease that occurs when the pancreas does not produce enough insulin. This means that the amount of glucose in the blood rises. If the amount of glucose in the blood gets too high it can lead to unconsciousness or even death. Before 1922, nothing was known about insulin and the effect it had on the body. Most diabetics died at a young age.

Fortunately, diabetes can now be treated because sufferers can inject insulin to reduce their blood glucose levels. Diabetics can also control their illness by being very careful about what foods they eat.

Activity – Discovering insulin

A doctor called Fredrick Banting had studied diabetes. He thought that the condition was linked to the pancreas but he didn't know how. With an assistant called Charles Best, he carried out a set of experiments on dogs. Best first tied up the tube connecting the dog's pancreas to its blood system. This caused the dog's blood glucose level to increase.

He then removed the dog's pancreas. He also removed the pancreas from another dog, ground this with salt water, and injected this mixture into the first dog. Best observed that the first dog's blood glucose levels dropped. However, the levels soon rose and the dog died the following day. He concluded that the pancreas produces a substance that controls blood glucose level. He called this substance insulin.

Banting went on to show that insulin obtained from healthy dogs could be used to treat diabetic dogs, if the treatment was regular. He won the Nobel Prize for his work.

Figure 4.5 Fredrick Banting and Charles Best with one of the dogs they used in their experiment

❶ Copy and complete this flow diagram summarising the work of Banting and Best.

The tube connecting the dog's _____ to its blood was tied up.

↓

The dog's blood _____ level increased.

↓

The dog's _____ was removed.

↓

The pancreas from another dog was removed and ground up with _____ water.

↓

The mixture was _____ into the first dog.

↓

The first dog's blood glucose level _____ temporarily but then _____ again.

❷ Some people said that Banting was lucky to make this finding because he only used two dogs in his first piece of research. What might be the problem only using two dogs in the experiment?

❸ State two improvements that Banting could have made to his experiment to collect more reliable results.

❹ Do you think it is right to use animals for research to find new medical treatments? Explain your opinion.

Once people realised that insulin could be used as a treatment for diabetes more research was quickly carried out. It was found that insulin could be extracted from the pancreases of cows and pigs and used successfully to treat diabetics. Many thousands of lives were saved. However, a huge amount of insulin was needed. Nowadays insulin is manufactured using genetically modified bacteria. This removes the need to use the pancreases from slaughtered animals.

❺ Some people objected to using insulin from an animal's pancreas, even if the animal wasn't killed for its pancreas. What reasons do you think they had for this viewpoint?

❻ Produce an information sheet for people who have just been diagnosed with diabetes. You should include a summary of the disease and information about the different ways of treating the disease.
A search for diabetes at www.bbc.co.uk/ is an excellent starting point. You may find that www.diabetes.org.uk is also useful.

4.2 How does your body get rid of waste products?

Your body produces waste products. Two of these are:
- carbon dioxide produced by respiration;
- urea produced in the liver.

These waste products must be continually removed from the blood, as they can damage cells in large amounts.

How is carbon dioxide removed from the body?

Respiration takes place in cells. It is summarised by the equation:

glucose + oxygen → carbon dioxide + water + energy

The carbon dioxide produced moves from the cell into the blood by diffusion (see Chapter 1). When the blood flows through the lungs, carbon dioxide diffuses out of the blood and into the air in the lungs. Once the carbon dioxide is in the air in the lungs it is breathed out of the body.

How are other types of waste removed from the body?

Proteins are broken down by enzymes into smaller molecules called amino acids. These amino acids are used by the body to make other useful proteins. You often have more amino acids in your blood than your body can use. The liver converts these excess amino acids into a chemical called urea. Urea can harm the body so it must be removed. Figure 4.6 shows how this happens.

8 Name two waste products that have to be removed from the body.

9 Why do you produce more carbon dioxide when you go for a run?

10 How does the body get rid of this carbon dioxide?

11 Copy and complete these sentences.

Protein in your food is digested into amino acids by _____. These amino acids are then used by the body to produce other _____. Any excess amino acids are broken down into _____ by the _____. The _____ is removed from the blood in the kidneys and used to form _____ with water and salts.

12 Urine can be tested for the presence of amino acids. What possible medical problems do you think somebody may have if amino acids are detected in their urine?

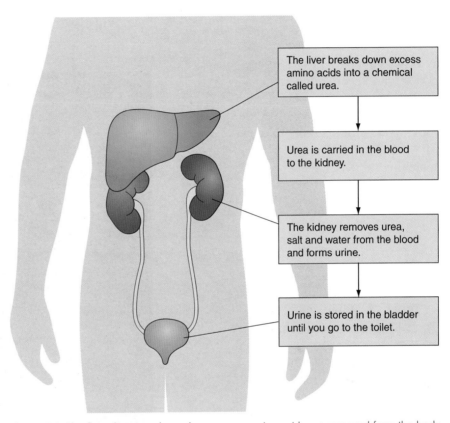

The liver breaks down excess amino acids into a chemical called urea.

Urea is carried in the blood to the kidney.

The kidney removes urea, salt and water from the blood and forms urine.

Urine is stored in the bladder until you go to the toilet.

Figure 4.6 The flow diagram shows how excess amino acids are removed from the body.

As you can see in Figure 4.6, the liver and the kidney work together to remove amino acids from the body.
- The liver breaks down excess amino acids.
- This produces urea, which dissolves in the blood.
- The blood transports urea to the kidney.
- The kidney removes the urea.
- Urea, water and some salts form urine in the kidney.
- Urine is stored in the bladder until you go to the toilet.

4.3 Why is cell division so important?

Chromosomes are found in the nucleus of a cell. When cells divide they form new cells with copies of these chromosomes. Without cell division, people would not grow, reproduce or be able to repair damaged body tissue.

Chromosomes are molecules of DNA found in cells. A single chromosome is made up of a single strand of DNA.

DNA (deoxyribonucleic acid) is a long-chain molecule, made up from a series of bases.

A **gene** is a length of DNA that codes for a specific protein.

DNA fingerprinting involves looking at the non-coding pieces of a sample of DNA and matching the DNA sequence to the unique pattern of a person's DNA.

⑬ Copy and complete these sentences

Chromosomes are found in the _____ of cells. In a normal human body cell there are _____ chromosomes and they are usually arranged in _____. Chromosomes are chains of a chemical called _____.
Everybody's chromosomes are different unless they have an identical twin. This means that your chromosomes can be used to identify you by using a technique called

_____ _____.

⑭ Why do there have to be so many genes in a human cell?

What are chromosomes and genes?

Humans have 46 chromosomes inside the nucleus of a normal cell. The chromosomes are normally found in pairs, so humans have 23 chromosome pairs. **Chromosomes** are each made up of a long molecule of **DNA** (deoxyribonucleic acid). A single chromosome is made up from a molecule of DNA about 5 cm long. This is amazing when you consider that chromosomes can only be seen under very powerful microscopes (Figure 4.7). Each DNA molecule is very thin and has to be coiled up very tightly to form a chromosome (Figure 4.8).

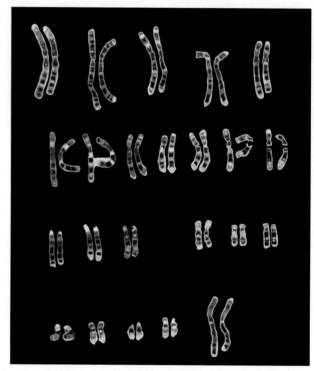

Figure 4.7 The chromosomes from one human cell

A **gene** is a small section of a DNA molecule. There are between 20 000 and 25 000 genes in each human nucleus.

All humans have the same types of gene, so what makes us unique? Some areas of DNA, called non-coding sequences, don't contain any genes. These areas are different for each person in the world, unless you have an identical twin. This means that a person can be identified from the non-coding DNA obtained from a swab of their cells. This technique is called **DNA fingerprinting**. It can be used to link people to a crime scene. For example, if skin cells are found at a crime scene, then the DNA inside them can be removed and identified. If the non-coding DNA matches the DNA collected from a suspect, then it places the suspect at the scene.

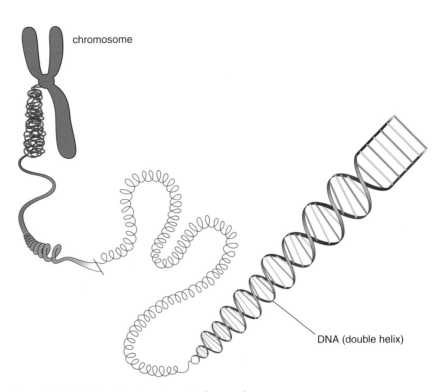

chromosome

DNA (double helix)

Figure 4.8 A DNA molecule coils up to form a chromosome.

> A cell divides by **mitosis** to produce two genetically identical cells with a full set of chromosomes.

> **Stem cells** are a special kind of cell found only in human embryos and adult bone marrow. Stem cells can **differentiate** into the many specialised cell types of the body.

Figure 4.9 Embryonic stem cells, like those shown here, can **differentiate** into completely different types of cell. Do these cells have any specialised features?

What happens to chromosomes when cells divide?

A cell can make a genetically identical copy of itself. This allows living things to grow and also to replace cells that die. Cell division is also used to repair damaged body tissue. When a cut heals, new skin cells are formed by skin cells dividing. When a cell divides in this way the two new cells are both genetically identical to the original cell. This type of cell division is called **mitosis**. This can happen because chromosomes have the amazing ability to make identical copies of themselves (Figure 4.10).

Stem cells and specialised cells

Figure 4.9 shows some human **stem cells**. They look like normal cells, so why are they so important? Stem cells can carry out one function that other cells cannot. When stem cells divide they can make specialised cells.

Specialised cells have features that make them different from other cells, for example nerve cells are different from muscle cells. Stem cells are undifferentiated, which means that they have no specialised features to carry out a specific function. Stem cells can develop into other types of cells such as liver, brain or heart muscle cells. It is still not understood how they do this.

There are two groups of stem cells: embryonic stem cells and adult stem cells. Embryonic stem cells are found in the embryo soon after an egg cell has been fertilised. Embryonic stem cells differentiate into all

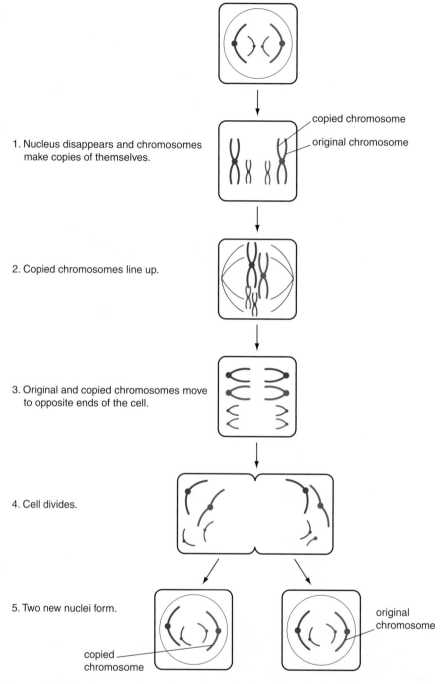

1. Nucleus disappears and chromosomes make copies of themselves.

copied chromosome

original chromosome

2. Copied chromosomes line up.

3. Original and copied chromosomes move to opposite ends of the cell.

4. Cell divides.

5. Two new nuclei form.

original chromosome

copied chromosome

Figure 4.10 The diagram shows the main stages in mitosis for a cell with just two pairs of chromosomes. The original and the copied chromosomes are labelled so you can see that the new cell is an exact copy of the original cell.

⑮ What does the body use the cells produced by mitosis for?

⑯ Write a list of the main stages that take place during mitosis.

the different specialised cells in an embryo. The specialised cells in the embryo divide and eventually form a fetus and then a baby. Adult stem cells are found inside bone marrow.

In animals most cell differentiation happens in the early stages of embryo development. However, many plant cells retain the ability to produce different differentiated cells throughout their life. A plant can grow leaves and flowers from the tip of a shoot.

Activity – Stem cells and medical research

'Stem cell promise lures patients'

'Stem cells treat blood disorder'

'Stem cell heart cure to be tested'

'MS sufferer in stem cell gamble'

'Winston warns of stem cell "hype"'

These are just a few recent headlines about research on human stem cells. This topic has probably attracted more attention from the media than any other medical research – and there hasn't even been any real breakthrough yet.

To understand the range of opinions for and against, it is crucial to know exactly what happens when stem cells divide and the medical benefits these cells could bring.

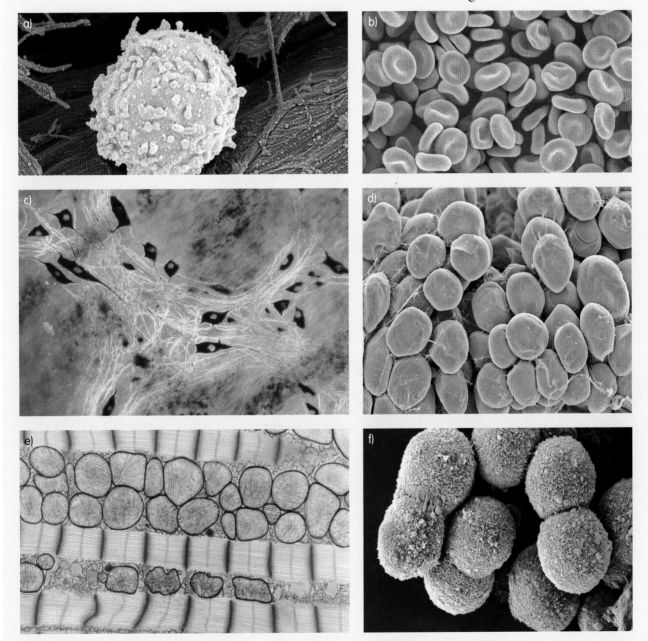

Figure 4.11 Some of the specialised cells that can develop from stem cells. **a)** white blood cell; **b)** red blood cells; **c)** nerve cells; **d)** fat cells; **e)** heart muscle cells; **f)** liver cells

1 Write down one sentence to summarise what stem cells do.

2 Figure 4.11 shows some of the specialised cells that stem cells produce. Each one has a specific structure that allows it to carry out its function. Carry out research to find out the function of each of these specialised cells. Explain how each cell's structure enables it to carry out its function.

Stem cells can be collected and kept alive outside the body. Researchers use these stem cells to try to produce specialised cells in the laboratory. These new specialised cells could be transplanted to replace cells that have been damaged, either by a disease or by an accident.

Scientists have not yet been able to create specialised cells. However, they believe that one day it may be possible to grow entire organs using this process.

To create stem cells for research scientists make a new embryo. They take an unfertilised egg cell from a donor and insert the patient's DNA into its nucleus (Figure 4.12). The cell then divides in a laboratory until a clump of cells is formed – a tiny embryo. Like all embryos it contains embryonic stem cells, which are removed. The embryonic stem cells are grown separately to try to produce the specialised cells required.

Stem cells produced like this may one day be used to treat diseases such as Parkinson's disease. Patients with Parkinson's disease have nerve cells that are damaged. As more and more nerve cells become damaged, the patient suffers from paralysis. If nerve cells could be created from stem cells, they could replace those that are damaged in the Parkinson's patient.

Opinions on stem cell research are mixed. Some people support stem cell research as they feel it may give patients with previously incurable

body cell / nucleus

1. A nucleus is removed from a body cell of the patient.

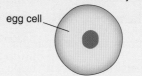
egg cell

2. An egg cell is removed from another adult female.

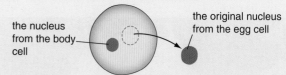
the nucleus from the body cell / the original nucleus from the egg cell

3. The nucleus is removed from the egg cell and replaced with the nucleus from the first adult body cell.

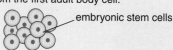
embryonic stem cells

4. The egg cell starts to develop into embryonic stem cells.

Figure 4.12 The procedure used to produce 'tailor-made' stem cells.

diseases a better quality of life. Other people say that researchers should not be allowed to experiment on embryos since these balls of cells could develop into a complete human being.

3 In small groups discuss reasons that people may have to support or oppose embryonic stem cell research. Write these down as a list of reasons for and a list against the research.

4 Now put the reasons in each list into order based upon which ones present the strongest arguments for and against stem cell research.

5 Finally, write a paragraph expressing your views about this issue. Support your views with reasons.

4.4 How are characteristics passed on from one generation to the next?

When a sperm cell fertilises an egg cell the genetic information from the mother and father is brought together. Fertilisation produces a single cell, called a zygote, which contains a full set of chromosomes. Unlike all other body cells, **gametes** (sperm or egg cells) have only one set of chromosomes.

When the two gametes come together, the full set of 23 pairs is produced. At fertilisation, all the characteristics that are controlled by your genes were determined. For example, your eye colour and hair colour were determined. After fertilisation, this single cell divides again and again by mitosis and develops into an embryo.

> **Gametes** are sex cells. These include sperm cells, egg cells and pollen cells.

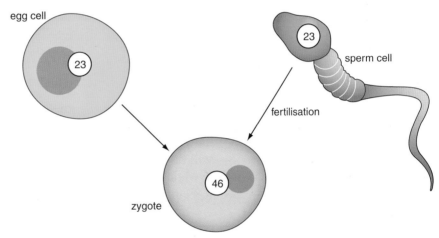

Figure 4.13 During fertilisation the sperm and the egg cell bring together 23 chromosomes from each parent to form the first cell that goes on to produce a new human being. After fertilisation, this cell has the full number of chromosomes – 46.

How is the sex of a person determined?

One of the most obvious differences between children in a family is their sex – whether they are a boy or a girl. A person's sex is determined at fertilisation because it is controlled by the genes found on a particular pair of chromosomes. All the differences between males and females are actually controlled by just one chromosome.

You can see in Figure 4.14 that both chromosomes in the last pair of 23 are the same in females, but different in males. These chromosomes are called the **sex chromosomes.** They are the 23rd pair in each cell.

> **17** Describe what happens during fertilisation.
>
> **18** How can one cell turn into an embryo of a few hundred cells, and then into a baby?

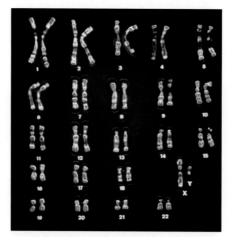 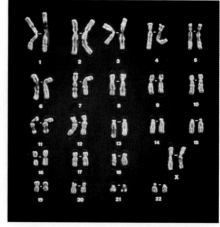

Figure 4.14 A full chromosome set from a man and a woman. Look at the last pair of chromosomes in each set.

In females both of the sex chromosomes are X chromosomes. Males have one X and one Y sex chromosome. Every egg cell that a woman produces carries an X chromosome. Half the sperm cells that a man produces carry an X and half carry a Y chromosome.

Remember that each gamete gets one randomly selected chromosome from each pair. So if an X carrying sperm cell fertilises an egg then a baby girl will be born. If a Y carrying sperm cell fertilises an egg a boy will be born.
- Males have XY sex chromosomes.
- Females have XX sex chromosomes.

The 23rd pair of chromosomes in each cell are the **sex chromosomes** and they determine a person's sex. XX = female. XY = male.

A **genetic diagram** shows all the possible combinations of chromosomes or genes that could be passed on during fertilisation.

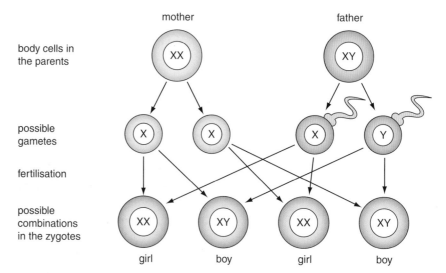

Figure 4.15 This genetic diagram shows how sex chromosomes are inherited.

The **genetic diagram** in Figure 4.15 shows how sex chromosomes are passed on from parents to their children.

Figure 4.16 Each child in this family inherited half their chromosomes from their mother and half from their father. The differences between them exist because each gamete carries a randomly selected choice of chromosomes from each pair.

Why aren't children in the same family the same?

Even identical twins have some differences. Some differences are partly due to the different environments in which the individuals live and grow.

Children in a family never have the same genes unless they are identical twins. This is because each sperm cell their father produces and each egg cell their mother produces contains only one chromosome from each pair in a normal body cell.

The one chromosome from each parent's chromosome pair is random (just like a sperm cell could have either an X chromosome or a Y chromosome). When gametes fuse in sexual reproduction, there is a very large number of possible combinations of chromosome pairs.

This variation does not happen in asexual reproduction. When bacteria divide, the two new bacteria cells are identical. They both contain the same genes as the parent cell. When a strawberry plant produces runners, each new strawberry plant has only one parent, so all the plants contain the same genes as the parent plant.

⑲ Copy and complete these sentences.

During _____ a sperm cell and an egg cell fuse together. Each of these sex cells or _____ contains _____ chromosomes. One of these chromosomes will be a sex chromosome. Sperm cells can have an _____ or a Y sex chromosome and egg cells only contain an _____ sex chromosome. If the egg cell is fertilised by a sperm cell carrying an X chromosome the baby will be a _____. If the sperm cell carries a Y chromosome the baby will be a _____.

⑳ There are now two methods available to parents which enable them to select the sex of their baby. The first is called the 'sperm cell selection method' and the second is known as the 'embryo selection method'. Both of these methods are based on being able to detect the X and Y chromosomes in cells.
a) Explain how you think each of these methods works.
b) Give one reason for and one reason against giving people the chance to select the sex of their baby.

㉑ Give two reasons why children with the same parents can look different.

㉒ Explain why when parts of a plant break off and grow into a new plant, all the new plants produced look identical.

How are some characteristics controlled by a single gene?

You may remember that a monk called Gregor Mendel did not agree with the explanation of inherited features. The original 'blending theory' was that all your characteristics were simply a mixture of your parents' characteristics. Mendel worked in the monastery gardens. He noticed that pea plants had either red or white flowers. When they were bred together the new plant still produced red or white flowers, but never pink or a mixture of red and white flowers.

Mendel thought that there must be a single factor for inheriting either 'red' or 'white' flowers. This could be inherited separately from other characteristics, such as stem length.

To test this idea he carried out many repeated experiments and collected reliable evidence that gave similar results every time. This evidence supported his idea that individual characteristics, such as flower colour, were inherited separately, and not simply a mixture of the parents' characteristics. However, his discovery was not initially accepted.

Years after Mendel died, other scientists carried out similar experiments that led to the same conclusions. Mendel's reports were also translated into English, which meant that they were read by more scientists.

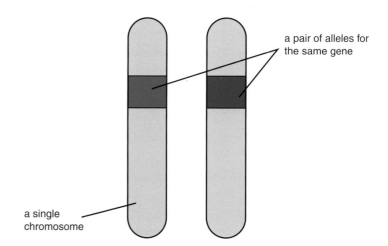

a pair of alleles for the same gene

a single chromosome

Figure 4.17 The red and the green section on the chromosomes represents a pair of alleles for the same gene.

Alleles are alternative forms of a single gene.

A **dominant** allele will lead to a dominant characteristic when only one dominant allele is present.

A **recessive** allele will lead to a recessive characteristic only when no dominant allele is present. This usually means that it is present on both chromosomes in a pair.

We now know that many characteristics are controlled by two possible forms of a single gene. The flower colour in Mendel's pea plants was controlled by a single gene. Each gene has two possible forms called **alleles**. One is known as the **dominant** allele and the other the **recessive** allele. In pea plants the dominant allele produces a protein that turns white flowers red. The recessive allele cannot produce this protein. If one or both of the genes in the pair is the dominant allele the plant will have red flowers. When there is no dominant allele (i.e. the plant has both recessive alleles), the flowers will be white because there is no protein produced to turn them red. You often use a capital letter (e.g. R) to represent the dominant allele and a lower case letter (e.g. r) to represent the recessive allele.

> ㉓ What was the main difference between Mendel's explanation of inheritance and 'the blending theory'?
>
> ㉔ What pair of alleles will a white flowering pea plant have?

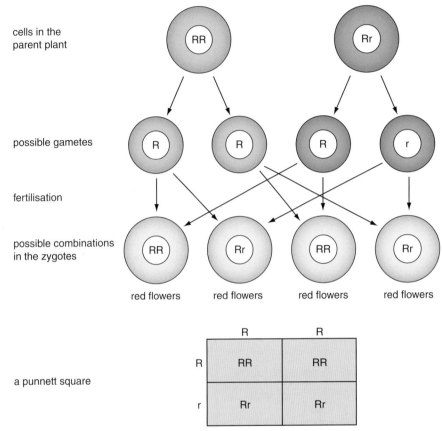

cells in the parent plant

possible gametes

fertilisation

possible combinations in the zygotes

a punnett square

Figure 4.18 These two genetic diagrams both explain the same thing about Mendel's pea plants. Each shows all the possible combinations of alleles that could be passed on for a single gene.

How are some diseases inherited?

Some diseases are caused by a defective gene. These can be passed to children from their parents. These diseases are called inherited diseases.

Huntington's disease is an inherited disease that affects the nervous system. Sufferers have movements they can't control and dementia (mental decline). Symptoms do not usually start to develop until people are in their 30s or 40s. Huntington's disease is caused by a dominant allele. A person will develop the disease if they inherit one dominant allele for this condition.

Cystic fibrosis is also an inherited disease. It affects cell membranes in the lungs and a build-up of thick mucus can cause breathing problems. Cystic fibrosis is caused by a recessive allele. This means that a person needs to inherit two recessive alleles and no dominant alleles for this condition.

㉕ Humans may produce two types of ear wax: a wet sticky type, or a dry hard type. The wet type is caused by a dominant allele, and the dry type is caused by a recessive allele.
   a) Write down the pairs of alleles that somebody with wet, sticky ear wax may have.
   b) Explain why it is impossible to say what alleles a person who produces wet ear wax will have.
   c) Rob and Jo are married. Rob has wet ear wax and Jo has dry ear wax. They have a child who produces wet ear wax.
   What pair of alleles for ear wax will their child have?

Huntington's disease

If you use an H to represent the dominant allele and an h for the recessive allele, the possible pairs of alleles are:
- HH – this is a lethal combination. A fetus with this genotype would not develop.
- Hh – this pair will cause the disease.
- hh – this pair will not cause the disease.

Huntington's disease is an inherited disease that affects the nervous system. It is caused by a dominant allele.

Cystic fibrosis is a disease that affects membranes of cells that line the lungs, gut and reproductive tract. It is caused by a recessive allele and therefore has symptomless carriers.

A **carrier** has one allele for an inherited disease caused by a recessive allele but does not have the disease. Two carriers can have children who inherit the disease.

㉖ A father had Huntington's disease and was Hh but his wife did not have the disease. She was hh.
   a) If they had a baby, explain how it may inherit Huntington's disease.
   b) If you were in this couple's situation would you try to have children? Give reasons for your answers.

Cystic fibrosis

Cystic fibrosis is caused by a recessive allele. This means that a person can have the allele for this disease without actually suffering from the disease. In this case they would have one dominant and one recessive allele. A person with this pair of alleles is called a symptomless **carrier**. Figure 4.19 shows a family tree that has the cystic fibrosis allele in it. The cystic fibrosis gene is shown by cf.

```
                    James              Mary
                    CFcf               CFCF
                      |                  |
        _____|_____
       |              |        |        |                    |
    Georgia          Tim      Jess     Luke               Lizzie
    CFCF             CFcf     CFCF      CFcf               CFcf
       |_____|                  |_____|
             |                              |              |
    _____            Claire          Stewart
   |                      |           cfcf             CFcf
  John                  Lucy
  CFcf                  CFcf
   |_____|
             |
            Tom
            cfcf
```

Figure 4.19 In this family the cystic fibrosis allele, cf, has passed through the generations.

> **27** Name three people in the family tree who were cystic fibrosis carriers.
>
> **28** Name one person who suffered from the disease.
>
> **29** Explain why Jess is completely unaffected by the disease.
>
> **30** If Claire has children with somebody who is a carrier of cystic fibrosis, is it likely that the children will have cystic fibrosis? Explain your answer.

Embryo screening

Embryo screening can be used to identify some inherited diseases, such as Huntington's and cystic fibrosis. Embryo screening is used only as part of IVF (*in vitro* fertilisation), and only offered to parents with a family history of inherited disorders.

This list summarises the process of embryo screening during IVF:
- Egg cells are taken from the woman's ovaries.
- The egg cells are fertilised with sperm cells from the man.
- The fertilised egg cells divide in a laboratory to form clumps of cells called embryos.
- The embryos are tested for inherited diseases.
- Only embryos that are free from any inherited diseases are implanted into the mother's womb.
- Any embryos carrying faulty genes are discarded.

Embryo screening is controlled by the Human Fertilisation and Embryology Authority (HFEA).

31 It costs about £2000 to carry out IVF with embryo screening. This is twice as much as it costs without screening. With this in mind, do you think that the use of embryo screening should be extended to include all births conceived by IVF? Give reasons for your answer.

32 Can you suggest any other reasons why some people object to embryo screening, apart from financial reasons?

Summary

✓ The body controls its temperature, blood sugar, water and ion content to avoid cells becoming damaged.

✓ These processes that maintain the internal conditions are known as **homeostasis**.

✓ Body temperature is monitored and controlled by the **thermoregulatory centre** in the brain.

✓ Blood glucose concentration is monitored and controlled by the **pancreas**. The pancreas produces **insulin** to move glucose from the blood into cells.

✓ **Diabetes** is a disease where the pancreas does not produce enough insulin. It is treated by controlling a person's diet and injecting with insulin.

✓ Urea and carbon dioxide are waste products of chemical reactions in the body.

✓ Carbon dioxide is removed from the body by the lungs and urea is removed by the kidneys.

✓ **Chromosomes** are molecules of **DNA** and are normally found in pairs.

✓ **Genes** are lengths of DNA responsible for making a specific protein.

✓ Each person has a unique pattern of non-coding DNA. **DNA fingerprinting** involves matching this pattern to a sample of DNA to identify the person from which the sample came.

✓ Body cells divide by **mitosis** to produce genetically identical cells used for growth and for replacement of older cells.

✓ **Gametes** join at fertilisation to form a single body cell with a full set of chromosomes that divides by mitosis to form a new individual.

✓ **Stem cells** can divide to produce a range of different types of cells.

✓ Asexual reproduction by mitosis produces genetically identical offspring.

✓ Sexual reproduction leads to genetic variation because an individual inherits one allele in each pair from each parent.

✓ A person's sex is controlled by the **sex chromosomes**: XX is female and XY is male.

✓ **Alleles** are alternative forms of a gene for a specific characteristic.

✓ Some characteristics are controlled by a single pair of alleles which may be **dominant** or **recessive**. **Genetic diagrams** show the possible combinations of dominant and recessive genes.

✓ Some disorders, such as **Huntington's disease** and **cystic fibrosis**, are inherited. Huntington's disease is controlled by a dominant gene. Cystic fibrosis is controlled by a recessive gene so there can be **carriers**.

✓ Pre-implantation embryo screening can be used to test for a faulty allele that causes inherited disorders.

EXAMQUESTIONS

❶ a) Which part of the body monitors and controls body temperature? *(1 mark)*
   b) Describe, in as much detail as you can, how the body responds to an increase in body temperature. *(2 marks)*
   c) On a cold day people often appear to have very pale skin. Explain the scientific reason behind this observation. *(2 marks)*

❷ a) Which organ in the body does not function properly in somebody who suffers from diabetes? *(1 mark)*
   b) Explain how diabetes affects the body. *(3 marks)*
   c) Describe two ways in which diabetes may be treated. *(2 marks)*

❸ When a bodybuilder trains his muscles get bigger because more muscle cells are produced.
   a) What is the name of the process that produces the new muscle cells? *(1 mark)*
   b) What has to happen to each chromosome in a muscle cell before a new cell can be produced? *(1 mark)*
   c) Why do gametes have only 23 chromosomes inside their nucleus? *(2 marks)*

❹ Fur length in rabbits is controlled by a single gene which has two alleles, L and l. A pair of rabbits bred together. The mother had long fur and the father had short fur. All their babies had long fur.
   a) Give the alleles for fur length present in the body cells of:
   i) the mother;
   ii) the father. *(1 mark)*
   b) Explain what causes some of the baby rabbits to be male and some female. *(3 marks)*

❺ Medical researchers hope that human stem cells could be transplanted into patients to make new cells in patients with diseased or damaged body tissue. This could lead to treatments for diseases such as Alzheimer's and Parkinson's, or for spinal cord injuries.

Most human stem cells used in research came from embryos created but not used at *in-vitro* fertilisation clinics. The cells are taken from embryos a few days old and the embryo is destroyed. The cells are then grown in the lab. At the moment no-one is quite sure how to make the stem cells form particular types of tissue – such as nerve rather than brain.

Because the cells come from embryos, the research is controversial. To some people, an embryo is a human and has a right to life. Those who support the use of stem cells from embryos say that a four-day-old embryo has not yet developed to a stage where a human life has begun.

Stem cells are also found in adult bone marrow and in a baby's umbilical cord blood. Some people say that embryonic stem cells are not the only hope of a treatment for, say, Parkinson's disease. Unfortunately, those stem cells may be limited in the cell types they can develop into. Embryonic stem cells can grow into 200 different types of specialised cell.
   a) Explain why researchers think stem cells collected from embryos could lead to medical treatments. *(1 mark)*
   b) Use the information in the passage to suggest why people may be concerned about the source of stem cells used in medical research. *(1 mark)*
   c) A patient who is paralysed says that whatever the ethical concerns, they think the research should continue so that a cure can be found. Explain the difficulties researchers have to overcome for this therapy to become available to patients in the future. *(2 marks)*

Chapter 5
How do sub-atomic particles explain the structure and reactions of substances?

At the end of this chapter you should:

✓ know the relative masses and relative charges of protons, neutrons and electrons;

✓ understand the terms atomic number and mass number;

✓ know that isotopes have the same atomic number, but different mass numbers;

✓ know that elements are arranged in the modern Periodic Table in order of their atomic number;

✓ be able to calculate relative formula masses and the percentages of elements in compounds;

✓ understand how bonds are formed between atoms either by transferring or by sharing electrons in the outer shells of atoms;

✓ understand how positive and negative ions are formed when electrons are transferred and that these ions are held together by ionic bonds;

✓ understand how molecules are formed when electrons are shared between atoms and how the atoms are held together by covalent bonds;

✓ be able to represent the electronic structures of the atoms and ions of the first 20 elements in the Periodic Table;

✓ be able to represent the covalent bonds in simple molecules.

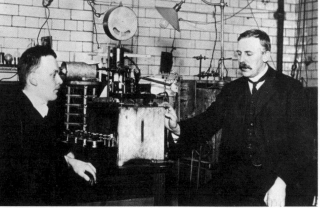

Figure 5.1 The work of scientists with sub-atomic particles has completely changed since J. J. Thomson first discovered electrons in 1897 (top right) and Rutherford and Geiger (bottom right) found evidence for protons. Today, scientists working with particles smaller than atoms use hi-tech equipment like this particle detector at CERN in Geneva (above, left). This equipment can accelerate particles almost to the speed of light.

5.1 What's inside atoms?

A hundred years ago, scientists thought that atoms were hard, unbreakable particles like tiny snooker balls. Then experiments showed that atoms contained three smaller particles – electrons, protons and neutrons. These are sometimes called sub-atomic particles because they are smaller than atoms. But how were they discovered, and how did this change our ideas about atoms?

Activity – Thomson's big surprise!

In 1897, J. J. Thomson was trying to find out how gases conduct electricity. When he connected 15 000 volts across a tube containing air, rays were produced. These rays travelled in straight lines from the negative to the positive terminal (Figure 5.2). Thomson studied a narrow beam of the rays and got a surprise. The rays were tiny, negative particles about 2000 times lighter than hydrogen atoms. Thomson called these tiny negative particles electrons.

❶ Why was Thomson surprised by his discovery of electrons? (Hint: In 1897, scientists thought that atoms could not be broken apart.)

❷ a) Look at Figure 5.2. Which way did the rays move when the plates were charged?
b) Why did the rays move when the plates were charged?

❸ Why did Thomson conclude that particles in the beam were negatively charged?

❹ Thomson obtained rays of electrons even when the tube contained other gases and the terminals were made of different metals. What could he conclude from this?

❺ Our TV screens today work like the one used by Thomson. Why do you think the material on the screen fluoresces when the beam of electrons hits it?

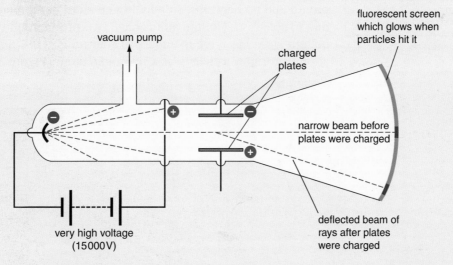

Figure 5.2 The effect of charged plates on a beam of electrons

Electrons, protons and neutrons

After Thomson's experiments, scientists concluded that all atoms contain electrons. As atoms are neutral, they must also contain positive charge to cancel the negative charge on their electrons.

CHAPTER 5 How do sub-atomic particles explain the structure and reactions of substances?

Figure 5.3 If the nucleus of a hydrogen atom was the size of a marble at the centre of Westminster Abbey, the atom's electron would be outside the walls of the Abbey.

Ernest Rutherford and his colleagues found a way of probing inside atoms, using alpha particles from radioactive substances. Chapter 12 describes how these experiments led to a better understanding of the structure of atoms.

Through Rutherford's work we know that:
- atoms have a small positive nucleus surrounded by a large empty space in which there are electrons;
- the positive charge of the nucleus is due to positive particles which Rutherford called protons;
- protons are about 2000 times heavier than electrons;
- atoms have equal numbers of protons and electrons;
- the positive charges on the protons just cancel the negative charges on the electrons so that atoms have no overall charge;
- the smallest atoms are those of hydrogen with one proton and one electron. The next smallest atoms are those of helium with two protons and two electrons, then lithium atoms with three protons and three electrons, and so on.

Although Rutherford's experiments explained a lot about the structure of atoms, one big problem remained. Hydrogen atoms contain one proton and helium atoms contain two protons. This means that the mass of helium atoms should be twice the mass of hydrogen atoms. But the mass of helium atoms relative to hydrogen atoms is four and not two.

In 1932, James Chadwick discovered why there was extra mass in helium atoms. The nuclei of atoms contain uncharged particles as well as protons. Chadwick called these uncharged particles neutrons.

Neutrons have the same mass as protons. Hydrogen atoms have one proton and no neutrons, so a hydrogen atom has a relative mass of one unit (Table 5.1). Helium atoms have two protons and two neutrons, so a helium atom has a relative mass of four units. This makes a helium atom four times as heavy as a hydrogen atom (Figure 5.4).

	Hydrogen atom	Helium atom
Number of protons	1	2
Number of neutrons	0	2
Relative mass	1	4

Table 5.1 The relative masses of hydrogen and helium atoms

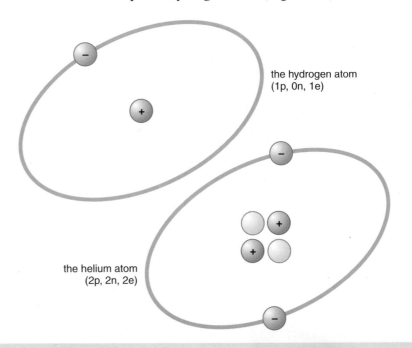

the hydrogen atom (1p, 0n, 1e)

the helium atom (2p, 2n, 2e)

Figure 5.4 Protons, neutrons and electrons in a hydrogen atom and a helium atom

We now know that all atoms are made up from protons, neutrons and electrons. The relative masses, relative charges and positions within atoms of these sub-atomic particles are summarised in Table 5.2.

Particle	Relative mass	Relative charge	Position within atoms
Proton	1	+1	Nucleus
Neutron	1	0	Nucleus
Electron	$\frac{1}{2000}$	−1	In space outside the nucleus

Table 5.2 The relative masses, charges and positions within atoms of protons, neutrons and electrons

Atoms and ions

We can now work out how an atom forms ions by losing or gaining electrons. A helium atom (He) has two protons each with one positive charge, two neutrons and two electrons each with one negative charge. If the helium atom loses one electron, it leaves an ion (charged particle) with two positive charges but only one negative charge. The ion has an overall charge of one positive charge. So, we can write the symbol He^+ for this particle.

If two electrons are removed from a helium atom, the remaining particle has two positive charges and no negative charges. This can be represented by the symbol He^{2+} (Figure 5.5).

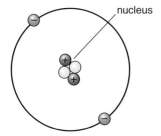

a helium atom, He (2p, 2n, 2e)

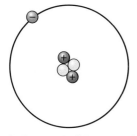

a helium ion, He^+ (2p, 2n, 1e)

a helium ion, He^{2+} (2p, 2n)

Figure 5.5 Protons, neutrons and electrons in a helium atom and helium ions

❶ Lithium atoms have three protons.
   a) How many electrons are there in one lithium atom?
   b) How many protons and electrons are there in one lithium ion, Li^+?

❷ Oxygen atoms have eight protons. How many protons and how many electrons are there in:
   a) one O atom;   b) one O^{2-} ion;   c) one O_2 molecule?

Atomic number and mass number

The **atomic number** is the number of protons in an atom.

The **mass number** is the total number of protons plus neutrons in an atom.

Atoms of different elements have different numbers of protons. Hydrogen atoms are the only atoms with one proton. Helium atoms are the only atoms with two protons. Lithium atoms are the only atoms with three protons, and so on. The number of protons in an atom tells you which element it is. Scientists call this the **atomic number**. So, hydrogen has an atomic number of 1, helium has an atomic number of 2, lithium has an atomic number of 3, and so on.

Notice that hydrogen, the first element in the Periodic Table, has atoms with one proton. Helium, the second element in the Periodic Table, has atoms with two protons. Lithium, the third element in the Periodic Table, has atoms with three protons, and so on. So, the position of an element in the Periodic Table tells us how many protons it has and also its atomic number.

The number of protons in an atom can tell you which element it is, but it cannot tell you its mass. The mass of an atom depends on the number of protons plus the number of neutrons. This number is called the **mass number** of the atom.

Hydrogen atoms (with one proton and no neutrons) have a mass number of 1. Helium atoms (two protons and two neutrons) have a mass number of 4 and sodium atoms (11 protons and 12 neutrons) have a mass number of 23.

We can write the symbol $^{23}_{11}Na$ (Figure 5.6) to show the mass number and the atomic number of a sodium atom. The mass number is written at the top left of the symbol and the atomic number at the bottom left of the symbol.

mass number = 23

Na

atomic number = 11

Figure 5.6 The mass number and atomic number shown with the symbol for sodium

❸ Look at Figure 5.6.
a) How many protons, neutrons and electrons are there in:
  i) one Na atom;
  ii) one Na^+ ion?
b) What do 27, 13, 3+ and Al mean when we write $^{27}_{13}Al^{3+}$?

5.2 Comparing the masses of atoms

Atoms are incredibly small. Atoms of chlorine are about one hundred millionth (1/100 000 000) of a centimetre in diameter. So, if you put 100 million of them in a straight line, they would still measure only one centimetre. Figure 5.7 will also help you to understand how small atoms are.

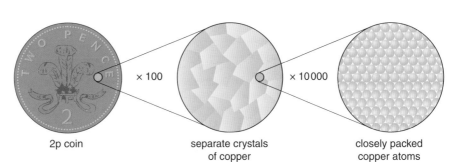

Figure 5.7 If a 2p coin is magnified one hundred times using an ordinary microscope, it is possible to see separate crystals of copper. If these crystals are magnified 10 000 times, it is possible to measure individual copper atoms. Altogether, the coin has been magnified first 100 times, then 10 000 times, which equals one million times in total (100 $\times$ 10 000).

Atoms are so small that it is impossible to weigh single atoms on a balance. However, scientists can compare the masses of different atoms relative to one another. They use an instrument called a mass spectrometer. Streams of atoms are deflected (bent) using a magnetic field. The heavier an atom, the less it is deflected. So, by comparing the deflections of different atoms, it is possible to compare their masses. This gives a list of their relative masses. The relative masses of different atoms are called **relative atomic masses**.

> **Relative atomic masses** tell us the relative masses of the atoms of different elements.
>
> One **mole** of an element is its relative atomic mass in grams.

As you might expect, the relative atomic mass of hydrogen is 1.0, the relative atomic mass of helium is 4.0 and the relative atomic mass of carbon is 12.0.

The symbol for relative atomic mass is A_r. We can write $A_r(H) = 1.0$, $A_r(He) = 4.0$ and $A_r(C) = 12.0$ or simply H = 1.0, He = 4.0 and C = 12.0.

The relative atomic mass of an element in grams is sometimes called one **mole**.

So, 1 g of hydrogen   = 1 mole

 12 g of carbon   = 1 mole

 24 g of carbon   = 2 moles and

 240 g of carbon   = 20 moles.

Notice that: number of moles $= \dfrac{\text{mass}}{\text{relative atomic mass}}$.

Isotopes and atomic mass

The mass of an atom depends on the number of protons and neutrons in its nucleus. The relative mass of both a proton and a neutron is 1.0, so relative atomic masses should be whole numbers.

Some elements have relative atomic masses that are nowhere near whole numbers. For example, the relative atomic mass of chlorine is 35.5 and that of neon is 20.2. The reason for this became clear when the first mass spectrometer was used in 1919.

> **Isotopes** are atoms of an element with the same atomic number, but different mass numbers.

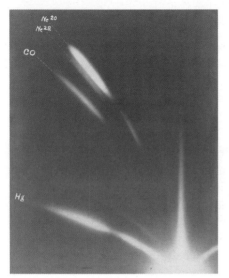

Figure 5.8 This photo shows evidence for the two isotopes in neon: neon-20 and neon-22.

Isotopes have the same:
- number of protons;
- number of electrons;
- atomic number;
- chemical properties.

Isotopes have different:
- numbers of neutrons;
- mass numbers;
- physical properties.

Table 5.3

When atoms of elements such as chlorine or neon passed through a mass spectrometer, the stream of atoms separated into two or more paths. This suggested that one element could have atoms with different masses. These atoms of the same element with different masses are called **isotopes**.

All the isotopes of one element have the same number of protons. They therefore have the same atomic number and the same number of electrons. This gives them the same chemical properties because chemical properties depend upon the number of electrons in an atom.

But isotopes have different numbers of neutrons, and this gives them different mass numbers (Table 5.3). For example, neon has two isotopes (Figures 5.8 and 5.9). Each isotope has 10 protons and therefore an atomic number of 10. But one of these isotopes has 10 neutrons and the other has 12 neutrons. Their mass numbers are therefore 20 and 22. They are sometimes called neon-20 and neon-22.

These two isotopes of neon have the same chemical properties because they have the same number of electrons. But they have different physical properties because they have different masses. So, $^{20}_{10}$Ne and $^{22}_{10}$Ne have different densities, different melting points and different boiling points.

	neon-20	neon-22
	$^{20}_{10}$Ne	$^{22}_{10}$Ne
number of protons	10	10
number of electrons	10	10
atomic number	10	10
number of neutrons	10	12
mass number	20	22

Figure 5.9 The two isotopes of neon

At one time, the standard for comparing atomic masses was hydrogen. Because elements can have isotopes with different masses, it is necessary to choose one particular isotope as the standard. Today, the isotope carbon-12 is chosen as the standard and given a relative mass of exactly 12.

The relative masses of other atoms are then obtained by comparison with carbon-12. On this scale, the relative atomic mass of hydrogen is still 1.0 and that of helium is 4.0. A few relative atomic masses are listed in Table 5.4.

Element	Symbol	Relative atomic mass
Carbon	C	12.0
Hydrogen	H	1.0
Helium	He	4.0
Oxygen	O	16.0
Magnesium	Mg	24.0
Sulfur	S	32.1
Iron	Fe	55.8
Copper	Cu	63.5
Gold	Au	197.0

Table 5.4 The relative atomic masses of a few elements

4 a) Use the relative atomic masses in Table 5.4 and the equation:

$$\text{number of moles} = \frac{\text{mass}}{\text{relative atomic mass}}$$

to find the number of moles in:
i)   9.0 g of carbon;   iii) 1.6 g of oxygen;
ii) 240 g of magnesium;   iv) 254 g of copper.

b) Use the relative atomic masses in Table 5.4 and the equation:

$$\text{mass} = \text{number of moles} \times \text{relative atomic mass}$$

to find the mass of
i)   0.1 moles of gold;   iii) 50 moles of sulfur;
ii) 3 moles of iron;   iv) 0.5 moles of helium.

5 a) Copy and complete the following sentence.

The relative atomic mass of carbon-12 is _____ times greater than the relative atomic mass of helium-4, because carbon-12 atoms contain _____ protons, _____ neutrons and _____ electrons, whereas helium-4 atoms contain _____ protons, _____ neutrons and _____ electrons.

b) The photo in Figure 5.10 shows an aluminium colander (mass 108 g), a copper bracelet (mass 12.7 g), some iron nails (mass 27.9 g) and some barbecue charcoal (carbon, mass 150 g). How many moles of each element do these objects contain?

(*Hint*: use the following relative atomic masses to help you: Al = 27.0, Cu = 63.5, Fe = 55.8, C = 12.0.)

6 Look at Table 5.4.
a) How many times heavier are carbon atoms than hydrogen atoms?
b) How many times heavier are magnesium atoms than carbon atoms?
c) Which element has atoms almost four times as heavy as oxygen atoms?

Figure 5.10

CHAPTER 5 How do sub-atomic particles explain the structure and reactions of substances?

5.3 Using relative atomic masses to find out about compounds

Comparing the masses of molecules

Relative formula mass is the mass of a compound, worked out by adding up the relative atomic masses of all the atoms in a molecule of the compound.

In the last section, we used relative atomic masses to compare the masses of different atoms. Relative atomic masses can also be used to compare the masses of molecules in different compounds. The relative masses of compounds are called **relative formula masses**. The relative formula mass of a compound is the sum of the relative atomic masses of all the atoms in its formula.

For example, the relative formula mass of water (H_2O):

$= 2 \times$ relative atomic mass of hydrogen + relative atomic mass of oxygen
$= (2 \times 1.0)$ $+ 16.0$
$= 18.0$

The symbol for relative formula mass is M_r, so we can write $M_r(H_2O) = 18.0$.

The relative formula mass of red iron oxide (Fe_2O_3):

$= 2 \times$ relative atomic mass of iron + $3 \times$ relative atomic mass of oxygen
$= (2 \times 55.8)$ $+ (3 \times 16.0)$
$= 159.6 \Rightarrow M_r(Fe_2O_3) = 159.6$

The relative formula mass of a compound in grams is known as one mole of that substance. So,

1 mole of water is 18.0 g and

0.1 mole of water = $0.1 \times 18.0 = 1.8$ g

1 mole of red iron oxide = 159.6 g

∴ 5 moles of red iron oxide = $5 \times 159.6 = 798.0$ g

❼ What is the relative formula mass of:
a) black copper oxide, CuO;
b) carbon dioxide, CO_2;
c) sulfuric acid, H_2SO_4?

❽ Calculate the mass of:
a) 3 moles of carbon dioxide;
b) 0.6 moles of carbon dioxide;
c) 5 moles of sulfuric acid;
d) 0.2 moles of sulfuric acid.

Finding the percentage composition of compounds

Relative atomic masses can be used to calculate the percentage of different elements in a compound.
- First you work out the relative amounts of each element in the relative formula mass of the compound. For example, carbon dioxide contains 12.0 g of carbon and 2×16.0 g (32.0 g) of oxygen in 44.0 g of carbon dioxide.
- Then you work out the fractions of each element in the relative formula mass of the compound. For example, carbon dioxide is $\frac{12}{44}$ parts carbon and $\frac{32}{44}$ parts oxygen.
- Finally, you change the fractions to percentages. So, carbon dioxide is

$\frac{12}{44} \times 100 = 27.3\%$ carbon and $\frac{32}{44} \times 100 = 72.7\%$ oxygen

Figure 5.11 The chemical formula for table sugar is $C_{12}H_{22}O_{11}$. The relative formula mass of sugar, $(C_{12}H_{22}O_{11})$
$= 12 \times A_r(C) + 22 \times A_r(H) + 11 \times A_r(O)$
$= (12 \times 12.0) + (22 \times 1.0) + (11 \times 16.0)$
$= 144 + 22 + 176$
$= 342$

9 Look at Figure 5.12 and its caption.
a) What elements are present in lead chromate besides lead?
b) Calculate the relative formula mass of lead chromate (PbCrO$_4$). (Pb = 207, Cr = 52, O = 16)
c) In a sample of 323 g of lead chromate, how many grams of lead are there?
d) What is the percentage of lead in lead chromate?

Figure 5.12 The yellow substance in 'no parking' double lines is lead chromate, PbCrO$_4$.

Figure 5.13 This sulfur is being stored after mining. The sulfur can be reacted with oxygen and water to make sulfuric acid.

Using relative atomic masses and relative formula masses in industry

In industry, it is important to know how much product can be obtained from a given amount of starting material. Industrial chemists work this out using relative atomic and relative formula masses.

For example, during the manufacture of sulfuric acid, if all the sulfur (S) is converted to sulfuric acid (H$_2$SO$_4$), 1 mole of S can form 1 mole of H$_2$SO$_4$.

So, 32.1 g of S can form $(2 \times 1.0) + 32.1 + (4 \times 16.0)$ g H$_2$SO$_4$.

$$32.1\,g\ S \rightarrow 98.1\,g\ H_2SO_4$$

$$1.0\,g\ S \rightarrow \frac{98.1}{32.1}\ g\ H_2SO_4 = 3.1\,g\ H_2SO_4$$

$$\Rightarrow 1.0\,kg\ S \rightarrow 3.1\,kg\ H_2SO_4$$

So, 1 kg of pure sulfur can form 3.1 kg of sulfuric acid.

This is the maximum amount of sulfuric acid that can be obtained from 1 kg of sulfur. In practice, we never get the maximum amount of a product during chemical processes. Some of it may be lost when chemicals are transferred from one container to another. Or some of the reactant may not get converted to the product. You will learn more about this in Section 7.1.

⑩ a) What elements are present in sulfuric acid (H_2SO_4)?
  b) Calculate the relative formula mass of sulfuric acid.
  c) What masses of the different elements are present in the relative formula mass of sulfuric acid?
  d) Calculate the percentage of each of the different elements in sulfuric acid.

⑪ Sulfuric acid can be manufactured from sulfur in three stages.
  1 Sulfur burns in oxygen to form sulfur dioxide.
  2 Sulfur dioxide reacts with more oxygen to form sulfur trioxide.
  3 Sulfur trioxide reacts with water to form sulphuric acid.
  Write word equations for the chemical reactions in stages **1**, **2** and **3**.

Activity – Extracting tin from tinstone

Figure 5.14 A disused tin smelting building in Cornwall

The production manager at Stannie's Tin Smelter has to meet certain production targets. The smelter must produce 595 tonnes of tin every month. In order to achieve this, the manager must calculate how much purified tinstone (tin oxide) he must buy to produce 595 tonnes of tin. To do this he uses the equation:

tin oxide + carbon (coke) → tin + carbon monoxide
SnO_2 + 2C → Sn + 2CO

The equation shows that 1 mole of SnO_2 produces 1 mole of Sn. (Sn = 119, C = 12, O = 16.)

❶ Copy and complete the following statement.
  _____ g SnO_2 produces _____ g Sn.
❷ What mass of tinstone is needed to meet the production target of 595 tonnes of tin per month?
❸ Why should the production manager be concerned about the gases emitted from the smelter?
❹ The smelter normally operates all through the day and night. It can produce a maximum of 1 tonne of tin per hour. Is the production target of 595 tonnes per month possible? Explain your answer.
❺ In the first 6 months of 2006, the amount of tin produced each month to the nearest 5 tonnes was: 650, 630, 575, 585, 560 and 600.
  a) What is the range in the amount of tin produced per month?
  b) What is the mean (average) amount of tin produced per month?
  c) Has the monthly target been achieved on average over the first 6 months of 2006?
  d) What should the production manager do to get a more reliable value for the average amount of tin produced per month?
  e) What should the production manager do to get a more accurate value for the average amount of tin produced per month?
❻ Why did the smelters have tall chimneys?
❼ Why is tin no longer mined and produced in Cornwall?

Activity – Finding the percentage of copper in red copper oxide

George and Meera's teacher showed them a sample of red copper oxide and asked them to do an experiment to find the percentage of copper in it.

George and Meera took a weighed amount of red copper oxide and reduced it to copper (Figure 5.15). They carried out the experiment five times, starting with different amounts of red copper oxide. Their results are shown in Table 5.5.

Experiment number	Mass of red copper oxide taken in g	Mass of copper in the oxide in g
1	1.43	1.27
2	2.10	1.87
3	2.72	2.54
4	3.55	3.15
5	4.29	3.81

Table 5.5

❶ Look at the apparatus in Figure 5.15. What safety precautions should George and Meera take during the experiment?

❷ Write a word equation for the reduction of red copper oxide to copper using methane (CH_4) in natural gas. (*Hint*: The only solid product is copper.)

❸ What could George and Meera do to make sure that all the copper oxide is reduced to copper? (*Hint*: If all the copper oxide is not reduced, what would happen to the mass of substance remaining if George and Meera tried to reduce it further?)

❹ Make a table similar to Table 5.5 but with an extra column.
  a) Write the experiment number in the first column, the mass of copper oxide in the second column and the mass of copper in the oxide in the third column.
  b) In the extra (fourth) column, calculate the percentage of copper in the oxide for each experiment.

❺ Use the results in the second and fourth columns of your table to plot a graph of mass of red copper oxide taken (horizontal axis) against the percentage of copper in the oxide (vertical axis). Draw the line of best fit through the points on your graph.

❻ Which of the points is anomalous and should be disregarded in drawing the line of best fit?

❼ Look at your graph. What is the average value for the percentage of copper in red copper oxide?

❽ How did George and Meera improve the reliability of their result?

❾ Use the results in Table 5.5 to explain why a balance reading to only one decimal place would be useless for this investigation.

❿ a) What was i) the independent variable and ii) the dependent variable in this investigation?
  b) Are these categoric, continuous or ordered variables?

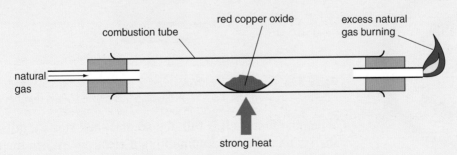

Figure 5.15 Reducing red copper oxide by heating in natural gas

5.4

How are the electrons arranged in atoms?

In science, ideas and theories change as scientists collect more information. New evidence is used to improve theories so that they give a better explanation of what scientists can see and what they can measure.

In 1911, Rutherford said that the electrons in atoms moved in a region surrounding the nucleus. Rutherford compared atoms to the solar system and said that electrons orbited the nucleus like planets orbiting the Sun.

In 1913, the Danish scientist Niels Bohr suggested a better idea (model) for the arrangement of electrons in atoms. Bohr said that electrons were grouped together in layers or **shells** at particular energy levels. Bohr's ideas about electrons in layers or shells have helped chemists to understand what happens when elements react.

> **Electron shells** are the regions occupied by electrons around the nucleus of an atom.
>
> **Electron structures** show the number of electrons in each shell (energy level). The structures can be drawn as shell diagrams or written as numbers of electrons in each shell, for example 2, 8.

Filling the shells

The number of electrons in an atom is the same as its atomic number. So, atoms with larger atomic numbers have more electrons and different atoms have different **electron structures**. The electrons always occupy the lowest energy levels first starting with the first shell nearest the nucleus.

The first shell can hold only two electrons. When it contains two electrons, it is full and the electrons in it are stable (Figure 5.16).

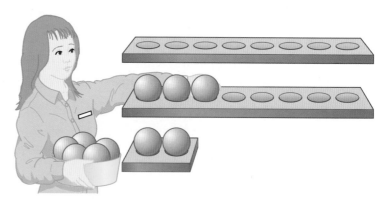

Figure 5.16 Filling shells with electrons is like filling shelves in a shop. The lowest shells (shelves) are filled first. Each shell (shelf) holds only a limited number of electrons (items).

When the first shell is full, the second shell starts to fill. The second shell can hold a maximum of eight electrons. When the second shell contains eight electrons, it is full (Figure 5.17). This electron structure is very stable.

Once the second shell is full, the third shell starts to fill. The third shell is also very stable when it contains eight electrons.

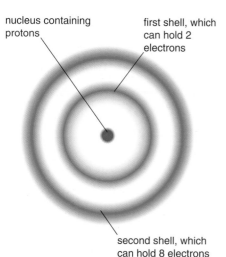

nucleus containing protons

first shell, which can hold 2 electrons

second shell, which can hold 8 electrons

Figure 5.17 A model for the arrangement of electrons in the first and second shells

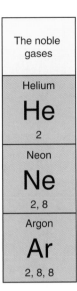

The noble gases
Helium
He
2
Neon
Ne
2, 8
Argon
Ar
2, 8, 8

Figure 5.18 The electron structures of the noble gases

Electron structures and the noble gases

The idea of electrons in shells or energy levels has helped chemists to understand why the noble gases (Group 0) are so unreactive. The first shell is full and the electrons in it are stable when the shell contains two electrons. This is exactly the electron structure of helium. Helium has two electrons. They both go into the first shell, which is then full and stable.

The second shell is full and the electrons in it are stable when the shell contains eight electrons. So, the next element to be unreactive like helium will have two electrons filling the first shell and eight electrons filling the second shell. This element is neon, the tenth element in the Periodic Table. Because neon has two electrons in the first shell and eight electrons in the second shell, we can write its electron structure as 2, 8 (Figure 5.18).

The third shell is also stable when it contains eight electrons. So, the next very unreactive element will have two electrons filling the first shell, eight filling the second shell and eight in the third shell. This is the electron structure of argon. We can write the electron structure of argon as 2, 8, 8 (Figure 5.18).

Figure 5.19 Electric light bulbs are filled with argon or krypton. These noble gases are very unreactive. Their electrons are so stable that the metal filament does not react with them even when it is white hot.

5.5 Electron structures and chemical reactivity

Figure 5.20 shows the first 20 elements in the Periodic Table. The atomic number and electron structure of each element is shown below its symbol.

When the first shell is full at helium, further electrons go into the second shell. Thus the electron structure of lithium is 2, 1; beryllium is 2, 2; boron is 2, 3 and so on.

Period 1 Atomic no.			H 1					He 2
Electron structure			1					2
Period 2 Atomic no.	Li 3	Be 4	B 5	C 6	N 7	O 8	F 9	Ne 10
Electron structure	2, 1	2, 2	2, 3	2, 4	2, 5	2, 6	2, 7	2, 8
Period 3 Atomic no.	Na 11	Mg 12	Al 13	Si 14	P 15	S 16	Cl 17	Ar 18
Electron structure	2, 8, 1	2, 8, 2	2, 8, 3	2, 8, 4	2, 8, 5	2, 8, 6	2, 8, 7	2, 8, 8
Period 4 Atomic no.	K 19	Ca 20						
Electron structure	2, 8, 8, 1	2, 8, 8, 2						

Figure 5.20 The electron structures of the first 20 elements in the Periodic Table

When the second shell is full at neon, electrons start to fill the third shell. The electron structure of neon is 2, 8. So, the electron structure of sodium is 2, 8, 1; magnesium is 2, 8, 2; and so on.

Electron structures help us to explain why elements in the same group of the Periodic Table have similar chemical properties.

The alkali metals	The halogens
Lithium Li 2, 1	Fluorine F 2, 7
Sodium Na 2, 8, 1	Chlorine Cl 2, 8, 7
Potassium K 2, 8, 8, 1	Bromine Br 2, 8, 18, 7

Figure 5.21 The electron structures of the first three alkali metals and the first three halogens

Group 1 – the alkali metals

All the alkali metals in Group 1 react with non-metals to form compounds containing ions (ionic compounds). In these ionic compounds, each alkali metal ion has one positive charge.

- Each of the alkali metals in Group 1 has one electron in its outermost shell (see Figure 5.21).
- Alkali metals can lose this outer electron very easily. This results in ions which have one more proton than electrons. The ions have one positive charge (Li^+, Na^+, K^+).
- These ions are very stable because they have electron structures like atoms of the noble gases.

For example, the electron structure of Na^+ is 2, 8, which is like neon. The electron structure of K^+ is 2, 8, 8, which is like argon. So, alkali metals have similar chemical properties because they have similar electron structures.

Group 7 – the halogens

The elements in Group 7 of the Periodic Table are called the halogens (Figure 5.21). All the halogens have similar chemical properties. They react with alkali metals to form ionic compounds. In these ionic compounds, the halide ions, such as chloride, Cl^- and fluoride F^-, have one negative charge.

- All the halogen atoms have seven electrons in their outermost shell.
- By gaining one electron, they form ions with one negative charge such as F^-, Cl^- and Br^-.
- These ions have stable electron structures like atoms of the next noble gas.

For example, fluoride ions have the electron structure 2, 8 like the noble gas neon, and chloride ions have the electron structure 2, 8, 8 like atoms of the noble gas argon. Halogens have similar properties because they have the same number of electrons in their outermost shell. The halogens are very reactive elements because they gain one electron very easily and form stable ions.

In general, elements in the same group of the Periodic Table have similar chemical properties because they have the same number of electrons in their outer shell (highest energy level).

Figure 5.22 Chlorine is the most useful and most common halogen. It is added in very small quantities to the water in swimming pools. This kills bacteria and other microorganisms.

---

⑫ Copy and complete the following sentences.

Atoms of the _____ metals are very _____. They have one electron in their _____ shell. This means they lose _____ electron very easily, forming _____ which are very _____. These ions have electron structures like atoms of the previous _____ _____ in the Periodic Table.

⑬ How many protons, neutrons and electrons are there in:

a) one $^{14}_{7}N$ atom;
b) one $^{14}_{7}N^{3-}$ ion?

⑭ Write the electron structure for:
a) Li; b) Li^+; c) O; d) O^{2-}.

⑮ a) Write down the electron structures of magnesium and calcium.
b) How many electrons are there in the outer shell of an atom of an element in Group 2?
c) Why do elements in Group 2 readily form ions with a charge of 2+?

Activity – Atoms, ions and the Periodic Table

Look carefully at Table 5.6. This shows the electron structures of the atoms and ions of elements in period 3 of the Periodic Table.

❶ What pattern can you see in the ions formed by elements in Groups 1, 2 and 3?
❷ Predict the ions formed by the following atoms.
a) Li; b) Be; c) K; d) Ca.

(If you need to check where these elements are in the Periodic Table, look at Figure 5.20.)

❸ We can write an equation for the formation of a sodium ion (Na^+) when a sodium atom (Na) loses an electron as:

$$Na \rightarrow Na^+ + e^-$$
$$(2, 8, 1) \quad (2, 8)^+ + \text{electron}$$

Write a similar equation for the formation of a magnesium ion (Mg^{2+}) from a magnesium atom (Mg).

4 What pattern can you see in the ions formed by elements in Groups 5, 6 and 7?

5 Predict the ions formed by the following atoms:
a) N   b) O   c) F

6 We can write an equation for the formation of a chloride ion (Cl⁻) when a chlorine atom (Cl) gains an electron as:

Cl	+	e⁻	→	Cl⁻
(2, 8, 7)		electron		(2, 8, 8)⁻

Write a similar equation for the formation of a sulfide ion (S^{2-}) from a sulfur atom (S).

7 Why does argon not form an ion?

8 Use your answer to question 7 to explain why argon is used to fill electric light bulbs.

Group	1	2	3	4	5	6	7	0
Elements in period 3	Na	Mg	Al	Si	P	S	Cl	Ar
Electron structure	2, 8, 1	2, 8, 2	2, 8, 3	2, 8, 4	2, 8, 5	2, 8, 6	2, 8, 7	2, 8, 8
No. of electrons in outer shell	1	2	3	4	5	6	7	8
Common ion	Na⁺	Mg²⁺	Al³⁺	No ion	P³⁻	S²⁻	Cl⁻	No ion
Electron structure of ion	2, 8	2, 8	2, 8	–	2, 8, 8	2, 8, 8	2, 8, 8	–

Table 5.6 Electron structures of the atoms and ions of elements in period 3

What happens to the electrons when elements react?

In Section 5.5, you learned that:
- metal atoms, like sodium and magnesium, lose electrons and form positive ions when they react to form compounds;
- non-metal atoms, like chlorine and sulfur, gain electrons and form negative ions when they react to form compounds. Non-metals can also share electrons when they react to form compounds.

These ideas form the basis of the **electronic theory of chemical bonding**.

When elements react to produce compounds, chemical bonds are formed. These chemical bonds result from either the transfer or the sharing of electrons in the outer shells of atoms. When the atoms react, they lose, gain or share electrons in order to get a more stable electron structure, like a noble gas.

Two kinds of bond are formed when atoms react – ionic bonds and covalent bonds.

Ionic bonds are formed when metals react with non-metals. Metals lose electrons and form positive ions. The electrons are transferred to non-metals which gain the electrons and form negative ions. The attraction of the opposite charges on the ions forms the ionic bond.

Covalent bonds are formed when non-metals react with each other. The non-metals share one or more pairs of electrons. The positive nucleus of each non-metal attracts the shared negative electrons and this forms the covalent bond.

The **electronic theory of chemical bonding** says that when atoms react, they lose, gain or share electrons in order to get a more stable electron structure.

An **ionic bond** results from the electrical attraction between oppositely charged ions.

A **covalent bond** is formed by the sharing of a pair of electrons between two atoms.

Ionic bonds – transfer of electrons

Figure 5.23 shows what happens to the electrons when sodium chloride (Na^+Cl^-) is formed. The electrons are shown as either dots or crosses.

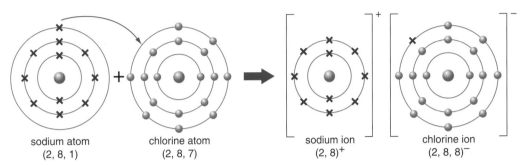

| sodium atom (2, 8, 1) | chlorine atom (2, 8, 7) | sodium ion (2, 8)$^+$ | chlorine ion (2, 8, 8)$^-$ |

Figure 5.23 Electron transfer during the formation of sodium chloride

The sodium atom has one electron in its outer shell and chlorine has seven. During the reaction, the sodium transfers its one electron into the outer shell of the chlorine atom. This produces:

● a sodium ion (Na^+) with the same stable electron structure as the noble gas neon and
● a chloride ion (Cl^-) with the same stable electron structure as the noble gas argon.

This formation of sodium chloride can be summarised by showing only the outer electrons, as shown in Figure 5.24.

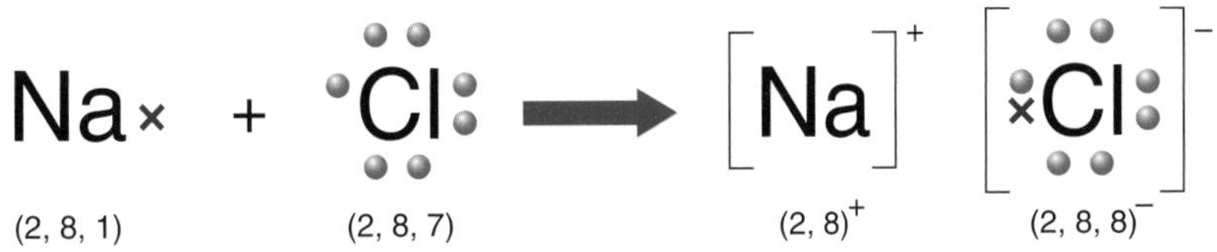

$$\text{Na} \times + \ ^{\bullet}\text{Cl}^{\bullet}_{\bullet} \longrightarrow \left[\text{Na}\right]^{+} \left[^{\bullet}_{\times}\text{Cl}^{\bullet}_{\bullet}\right]^{-}$$

| (2, 8, 1) | (2, 8, 7) | (2, 8)$^+$ | (2, 8, 8)$^-$ |

Figure 5.24 A 'dot-cross' diagram for the formation of sodium chloride

This is called a 'dot-cross' diagram because the electrons of the different atoms are shown as either dots or crosses. Although the sodium electron is shown as a cross and the chlorine electrons are shown as dots, the electrons are not really different. They have only been shown as dots or crosses in Figure 5.24 to help us understand what happens when the elements react.

Compounds containing ions are called ionic compounds. The ions are held together by strong forces of attraction between their opposite charges. This attraction between positive ions and negative ions is called ionic bonding. The structure, bonding and properties of ionic compounds are discussed further in Section 6.7.

Magnesium oxide

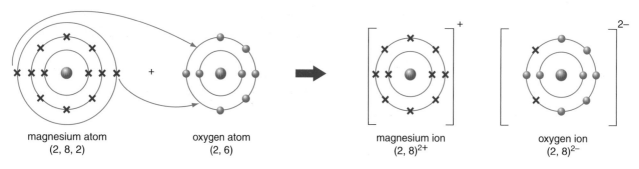

| magnesium atom (2, 8, 2) | oxygen atom (2, 6) | magnesium ion $(2, 8)^{2+}$ | oxygen ion $(2, 8)^{2-}$ |

Calcium chloride

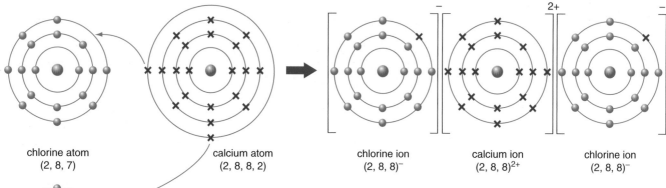

chlorine atom (2, 8, 7)

calcium atom (2, 8, 8, 2)

chlorine ion $(2, 8, 8)^{-}$

calcium ion $(2, 8, 8)^{2+}$

chlorine ion $(2, 8, 8)^{-}$

chlorine atom (2, 8, 7)

Figure 5.25 Electron transfers in the formation of magnesium oxide and calcium chloride

Figure 5.25 shows two more examples of electron transfer between a metal and a non-metal forming ionic compounds.

16 Look at the formation of magnesium oxide in Figure 5.25.
a) How many electrons do magnesium and oxygen atoms gain or lose in forming magnesium oxide?
b) What is the charge on:
i) a magnesium ion;
ii) an oxide ion?
c) What is the formula of magnesium oxide?
d) Which noble gas has an electron structure like the ions in magnesium oxide?

17 Look at the formation of calcium chloride in Figure 5.25.
a) How many electrons do calcium and chlorine atoms gain or lose in forming calcium chloride?
b) What is the charge on:
i) a calcium ion;
ii) a chloride ion?
c) What is the formula of calcium chloride?
d) Why does one calcium atom react with two chlorine atoms in forming calcium chloride?

Covalent bonds – sharing electrons

A chlorine atom is very unstable. Its outer shell contains seven electrons. At normal temperatures, chlorine atoms join up in pairs to form Cl_2 molecules by sharing electrons (Figure 5.26).

The two chlorine atoms share a pair of electrons and both of them now have eight electrons in their outer shell. This is a very stable electron structure exactly like that of argon.

The positive nuclei of both atoms attract the shared electrons and this holds the atoms together. This attraction forms a covalent bond.

Notice in Figure 5.26 that:
- the shared pair of electrons form part of the outer shell of both chlorine atoms;
- the chlorine atoms are bonded together forming an uncharged molecule.

Some covalently bonded substances such as chlorine, hydrogen chloride, water, ammonia and methane consist of simple molecules containing a small number of atoms.

Other covalently bonded substances, such as diamond and many polymers, have giant structures (giant molecules) containing thousands and sometimes millions of atoms. The structure and properties of these giant structures are discussed further in Section 6.5.

The covalent bonding and electron structures in some of the simple molecules are shown in Figure 5.27. Next to each 'dot-cross' diagram, the structures of the molecules have been drawn showing all the bonds in these molecules. Each covalent bond is shown as a line between atoms. For example, the bonds in water are drawn as H–O–H.

The structures can be worked out from the dot-cross diagrams by remembering that each shared pair of electrons is a covalent bond and then drawing a line between the atoms.
- So each hydrogen atom (H) always has one bond.
- Chlorine atoms (Cl) always have one bond.
- Nitrogen atoms (N) always have two bonds.
- Carbon atoms (C) have four bonds.

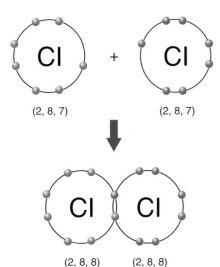

(2, 8, 7)   (2, 8, 7)

(2, 8, 8)   (2, 8, 8)

Figure 5.26 Electron sharing in the covalent bond in a chlorine molecule

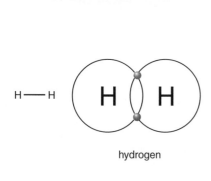

hydrogen

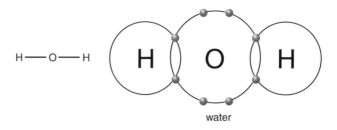

water

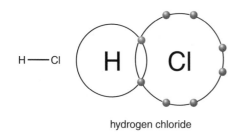

hydrogen chloride

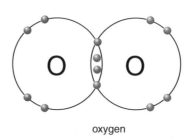

oxygen

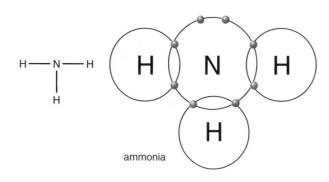

ammonia

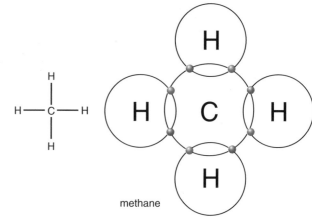

methane

Figure 5.27 The covalent bonding and electron structures in some simple molecules

⑱ Copy and complete the following statement using words from the box.

> bond   electron   pair   sharing   two

A covalent bond is formed by the _____ of a _____ of electrons between _____ atoms. Each atom contributes one _____ to the _____.

⑲ Look at Figure 5.27.
a) Which noble gas has an electron structure like the hydrogen atoms in H_2?

b) In oxygen, O_2, there is a double covalent bond between the two oxygen atoms. How many electrons are shared in a double covalent bond?

c) The structure for carbon dioxide is O=C=O. Draw the dot-cross diagram for carbon dioxide. (Remember that each line in the structure represents a shared pair of electrons. Also, each atom provides one electron for the shared pair.)

Summary

✓ Atoms have a small nucleus containing positive protons and uncharged neutrons surrounded by a large region of empty space in which there are negative electrons.

✓ In all atoms, the positive charges on the protons are just cancelled by the negative charges on an equal number of electrons.

✓ Ions are formed from atoms by the loss or gain of one or more electrons.

✓ The **atomic number** is the number of protons in an atom.

✓ The **mass number** is the total number of protons plus neutrons in an atom.

✓ **Isotopes** are atoms of the same element with the same atomic number, but different mass numbers.

✓ **Relative atomic masses** are used to compare the masses of the atoms of different elements.

✓ The **relative formula mass** of a compound is the sum of the relative atomic masses of all the atoms in its formula.

✓ The relative atomic mass of an element in grams and the relative formula mass of a compound in grams are sometimes called one **mole**.

✓ Using relative atomic masses it is possible to calculate the percentage of different elements in a compound.

✓ The electrons in an atom determine its chemical properties. Electrons are grouped together in **shells** at different distances from the nucleus and at particular energy levels. When the shells are full, the atoms or ions are stable.

✓ **Electron shells** are the regions occupied by electrons around the nucleus of an atom.

✓ **Electron structures** show the number of electrons in each shell (energy level). The structures can be drawn as shell diagrams or written as numbers of electrons in each shell – for example 2, 8.

✓ Elements in the same group of the Periodic Table have the same number of electrons in their outermost shell (highest energy level). This gives them similar chemical properties.

✓ When atoms react, they lose, gain or share electrons in order to get a more stable electron structure. This idea is called the **electronic theory of chemical bonding**.

✓ **Ionic bonds** are formed when metals react with non-metals. Electron transfer occurs. Metals lose electrons and form positive ions. Non-metals gain electrons and form negative ions. Ionic bonds result from the electrical attraction between ions with opposite charges.

✓ **Covalent bonds** are formed when non-metals react with each other. The non-metal atoms share electrons. The positive nucleus of each atom attracts the shared negative electrons and this forms the covalent bond.

EXAM QUESTIONS

❶ Many processed foods contain chemicals as additives.
  a) Sodium carbonate is used to control acidity in some tinned foods. Sodium carbonate contains sodium ions (Na^+) and carbonate ions (CO_3^{2-}). Which one of the following is the formula of sodium carbonate?
  A $NaCO_3$; B Na_2CO_3; C $Na(CO_3)_2$;
  D $Na_3(CO_3)_2$.   (*1 mark*)
  b) The electron structure of a sodium atom can be written as 2, 8, 1. Which one of the following is the electron structure of a sodium ion?
  A 2, 2; B 2, 8, 2; C 2, 8;
  D 2, 8, 8.   (*1 mark*)

  c) Calcium chloride is used as a firming agent in some tinned foods. Calcium chloride contains calcium ions (Ca^{2+}) and chloride ions (Cl^-). Which one of the following is the formula of calcium chloride?
  A $CaCl$; B Ca_2Cl; C Ca_2Cl_2; D $CaCl_2$.
                (*1 mark*)
  d) Copy and complete the following sentence by choosing words from the box.

  | electrons | gains | loses | neutrons |
  | protons | shares | | |

  A calcium ion (Ca^{2+}) is formed when a calcium atom _____ two _____. (*2 marks*)

EXAMQUESTIONS

❷ If people are anaemic and have a low concentration of red blood cells, they may be prescribed iron tablets (Figure 5.28). These tablets contain iron sulfate.

Iron Tablets
Fe

Active ingredient
Iron sulfate, FeSO₄

(One tablet contains
1.5g FeSO₄)

Figure 5.28

a) What elements are present in iron sulfate? *(3 marks)*
b) Iron sulfate contains iron ions (Fe^{2+}) and sulfate ions. Write the symbol and charge for a sulfate ion. *(2 marks)*
c) Calculate the relative formula mass (M_r) of iron sulfate.
(Fe = 55.8, S = 32.1, O = 16.0) *(2 marks)*
d) Calculate the percentage of iron in iron sulfate. *(2 marks)*
e) Calculate the mass of iron in one tablet. *(1 mark)*

❸ Toothpaste sometimes contains calcium fluoride, CaF_2, which helps to produce strong teeth and bones.
a) A fluoride ion can be written as $^{19}_{9}F^-$. How many protons, neutrons and electrons are there in one $^{19}_{9}F^-$ ion? *(3 marks)*
b) Why does one calcium ion combine with two fluoride ions in calcium fluoride? *(2 marks)*
c) Figure 5.29 shows the outer shell electrons and the full electron structures in brackets for a calcium atom and two fluorine atoms before reacting to form calcium fluoride. Copy and complete the diagram showing the outer shell electrons, charges and electron structures of the calcium and fluoride ions which form. *(8 marks)*

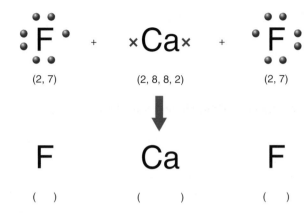

Figure 5.29

❹ Read the newspaper cutting below. Then answer the questions that follow.

Toxic gas scare at local factory

Workers were forced to leave the 'Cupromets' factory in Woodside Avenue last Tuesday. The factory was evacuated when fumes of highly toxic nitrogen dioxide filled the building.

The gas was produced when concentrated nitric acid spilled onto thin copper pipes.

a) What does 'toxic' mean? *(1 mark)*
b) Explain why the reaction was more dangerous because the acid spilled onto thin copper pipes rather than thick copper bars. *(2 marks)*
c) Water was sprayed onto the copper and nitric acid to slow down the reaction. Why did this slow down the reaction? *(2 marks)*

Chapter 6
How do the structures of substances influence their properties and uses?

At the end of this chapter you should:

✓ know that the arrangement of particles in a substance determines its structure;

✓ know that the forces between particles in a substance determine its bonding;

✓ understand that the structure and bonding of a substance determine its properties and that these properties determine its uses;

✓ know that the particles in substances may be atoms, ions or molecules;

✓ understand how these different particles result in four different types of structure (giant metallic, giant covalent, giant ionic and simple molecular) with very different properties;

✓ understand that the bonds between atoms in metals, between atoms in molecules and between ions in ionic compounds are strong, but the forces between molecules are much weaker;

✓ be able to relate the properties of substances to their uses;

✓ be able to identify the structure of a substance from its properties;

✓ understand that nanomaterials have different properties to normal-sized chunks of the same material because of their very small size and large surface area;

✓ be able to evaluate the benefits and risks of using nanomaterials.

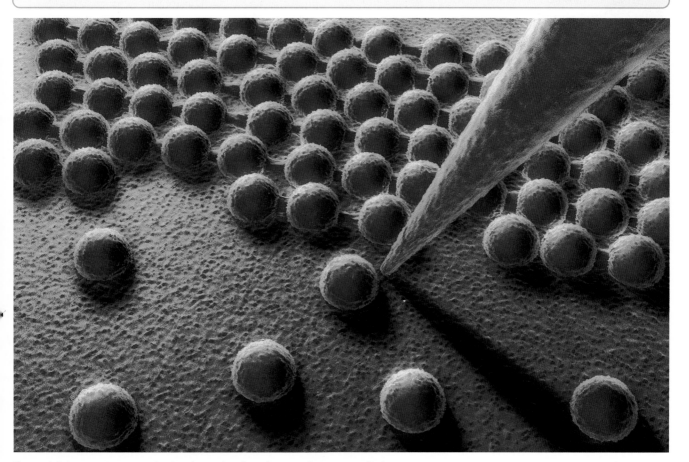

Figure 6.1 In recent years, scientists have developed new substances called nanomaterials with special properties because of the ultra-small size of their particles. This photo shows individual particles being moved around at the nano-level.

CHAPTER 6 How do the structures of substances influence their properties and uses?

Figure 6.2 Crystals of rock salt (sodium chloride, NaCl)

Figure 6.3 Crystals of quartz. Quartz is silicon dioxide (SiO_2).

 6.1 Studying the structures of substances

All substances are made up of particles. These particles can be atoms, ions or molecules. If we know how the particles are arranged in a substance, we can begin to understand its structure and properties.

Scientists have studied crystals to help us understand the structures and properties of materials.

> Look at the crystals of rock salt and quartz in Figures 6.2 and 6.3.
>
> ❶ Do most of the rock salt crystals have roughly the same shape?
>
> ❷ Do most of the quartz crystals have roughly the same shape?
>
> ❸ Describe the shape of:
>   a) the rock salt crystals;
>   b) the quartz crystals.

All the crystals of a substance have similar shapes. In Figure 6.2, you will see that individual crystals of rock salt are all cubic even though they are joined to each other.

The similar shapes suggest that particles inside the crystals always pack together in the same way. This gives the same overall shape to crystals of the substance. A similar thing happens with piles of apples and oranges. When they are stacked in piles, the piles form similar pyramid shapes.

Figure 6.4 shows how cubic crystals and hexagonal crystals can form. If the particles always pack in parallel lines or at 90° to each other, the crystals are cubic. If the particles are arranged in hexagons, the final crystal is hexagonal.

The shape of a crystal only gives a clue to the way in which its particles are arranged. Using X-rays, it is possible to get much better evidence for the arrangement of particles in a substance.

 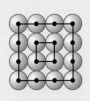 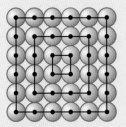 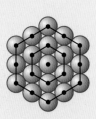 

When the particles are arranged in a cubic fashion, the final crystal will be cubic.

When the particles are arranged in hexagons, the final crystal will be hexagonal.

Figure 6.4

Using X-rays to study structures

Look through a piece of thin cotton fabric at a small bright light. You will see a pattern of bright dots. The pattern forms because the light is deflected as it passes between the closely spaced threads of the fabric.

From the pattern of bright dots which you can see, it is possible to work out the pattern of threads in the fabric which you cannot see.

The same idea is used to find out how particles are arranged in substances. Instead of light, scientists use a thin beam of X-rays (Figure 6.5).

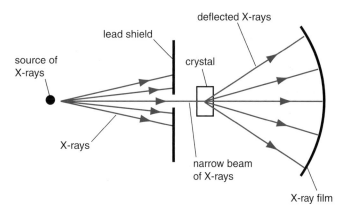

Figure 6.5 Using X-rays to study the particles in a crystal

The X-rays are deflected by particles in the crystal onto X-ray film. When the film is developed, a pattern of spots appears. From the pattern of spots which we can see, it is possible to work out the pattern of particles in the crystal which we cannot see. A regular arrangement of spots on the film indicates a regular arrangement of particles in the crystal. An X-ray photo is shown in Figure 6.6.

Figure 6.6 An X-ray photo of crystals of a protein found in egg white. Notice the general pattern in the dots.

> A **lattice** is a regular arrangement of particles in a solid, such as a metal or an ionic compound.

The regular arrangement of particles in a crystal is called a **lattice**.

Photos like this have been used to study the structures of thousands of different solids.

④ Look at Figure 6.7.
  a) What substance makes up snowflakes?
  b) What are the particles in snowflakes?
  c) What is (are) the angle(s) between branches on the snowflake?
  d) How do you think the particles are arranged in snowflake crystals? (*Hint*: Look at Figure 6.4)

Figure 6.7 Crystals on a snowflake

⑤ Copy and complete the following sentences using words from the box below.

> atoms   ions   metals   molecules
>   particles   solids

Crystals are _____ in which there is an orderly arrangement of _____. The particles in crystals can be _____, ions or molecules. In most _____, the particles are closely packed atoms. In common salt, the particles are sodium and chloride _____. In water, the particles are _____.

⑥ Why do all crystals of one substance have roughly the same shape?

6.2 From structure to properties and uses

If we know how the particles in a substance are arranged (the structure) and how they are held together (the bonding), we can explain the properties of the substance.

For example, copper is composed of close-packed atoms. Outer electrons in the close-packed atoms can move freely from one copper atom to another. These electrons move through the metal when copper is connected to a battery, so it is a good conductor of electricity.

Atoms in the close-packed structure of copper can slide over each other. Because of this, copper can be drawn into wires. These properties of copper lead to its use in electrical wires and cables.

Notice how:
● the structure and bonding of copper determine its properties;
● the properties of copper determine its uses.

⑦ Use words in the box below to complete the following sentences.

> bond   hard   molecules
>   moulded   water

Wet clay is soft and easily _____ because _____ molecules can get between its flat two-dimensional particles. When the clay is fired, all the water _____ are driven out. Atoms in one layer _____ to those in the layers above and below. This gives the clay a three-dimensional structure, making it _____ and rigid.

Figure 6.8 Wet clay is soft and easily moulded by the potter. After she has moulded the clay, it is heated (fired) in a furnace. This makes it hard and rigid and it can be used for pots and crockery.

The links from structure and bonding to the properties of a substance help us to explain its uses. They explain why metals are used as conductors and why clay is used to make bricks.

Although there are millions of different substances, they are all made up from only three kinds of particle – atoms, ions and molecules.

These three particles lead to four different solid structures:
- giant metallic;
- simple molecular;
- giant covalent (macromolecular);
- giant ionic.

Table 6.1 shows the particles in these four structures, the types of substances they form and examples of these substances. In the following sections, we will look at each of these structures in more detail.

Type of structure	Particles in the structure	Types of substance	Examples
Giant metallic	Atoms	Metals and alloys	Sodium, iron, copper, steel, brass
Simple molecular	Small molecules containing a few atoms	Non-metals or non-metal compounds	Iodine (I_2), oxygen (O_2), water (H_2O), carbon dioxide (CO_2)
Giant covalent (macromolecular)	Very large molecules containing thousands or millions of atoms	Non-metals or non-metal compounds	Diamond, graphite, polythene, sand (silicon dioxide, SiO_2)
Giant ionic	Ions	Compounds of metals with non-metals	Sodium chloride (salt, Na^+Cl^-), calcium oxide (quicklime, $Ca^{2+}O^{2-}$), magnesium chloride ($Mg^{2+}(Cl^-)_2$)

Table 6.1 The four types of solid structures and the particles they contain

Figure 6.9 A natural crystal of lead sulfide

8 Match each of the following substances to one of the solid structures in Table 6.1:
   a) chlorine (Cl_2);
   b) limestone (calcium carbonate, $CaCO_3$);
   c) gold (Au);
   d) PVC (polyvinylchloride);
   e) copper sulfate ($CuSO_4$);
   f) methane in natural gas (CH_4).

9 Look at the photo of a lead sulfide crystal in Figure 6. 9.
   a) What elements does lead sulfide contain?
   b) Is each of these elements a metal or a non-metal?
   c) What particles does lead sulfide contain – atoms, ions or molecules?
   d) What is the general shape of lead sulfide crystals?
   e) How do you think the particles are arranged in lead sulfide? Explain your answer.

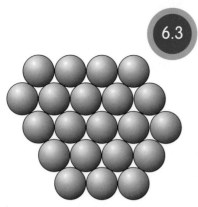

Figure 6.10 The close packing of atoms in one layer of a metal

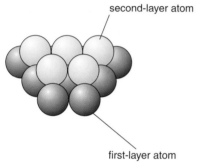

second-layer atom

first-layer atom

Figure 6.11 Atoms in two layers of a metal crystal

A **giant structure** is an arrangement of very large numbers (millions and millions) of atoms or ions held together by strong forces in a regular pattern.

In **giant metallic structures** metal atoms are close packed in a giant lattice, through which the outer shell electrons can move freely.

6.3 Giant metallic structures

Metals are very important and useful materials. Just look around you and notice the uses of different metals – vehicles, girders, bridges, pipes, taps, radiators, cutlery, pans, jewellery and ornaments.

X-ray studies show that the atoms in most metals are packed together as close as possible. This arrangement is called close packing.

Figure 6.10 shows a model of a few atoms in one layer of a metal crystal.

Notice that each atom in the middle of the layer 'touches' six other atoms in the same layer. When a second layer is added, atoms in the second layer sink into the dips between atoms in the first layer (Figure 6.11).

This close packing allows atoms in one layer to get as close as possible to those in their own layer and in the next layer. So, metals consist of **giant structures** of closely packed atoms in a regular pattern. In this **giant metallic structure** there are strong forces between the metal atoms in the lattice.

Figure 6.12 The forces between atoms of iron in steel are very strong. This allows thin steel cables to lift heavy loads.

⓾ Describe the packing of atoms in a giant metallic structure.

The properties of metals

In general, metals:
- have high densities;
- have high melting points and high boiling points;
- are good conductors of heat and electricity;
- are malleable (can be bent or hammered into different shapes).

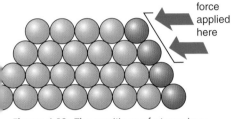

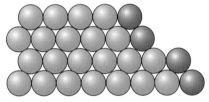

Figure 6.13 The positions of atoms in a metal before slip has occurred

The properties of metals can be explained by their close-packed structure with strong forces between atoms. For example:
- Metals have high density due to the close packing of their atoms.
- When a force is applied to a metal, the layers of atoms can slide over each other. This is known as 'slip'. After slipping, the atoms settle into close-packed positions again. Figure 6.13 shows the positions of atoms before slip and Figure 6.14 shows the positions after slip has occurred. This is what happens when a metal is bent or hammered into different shapes.

Figure 6.14 The positions of atoms in a metal after 'slip' has occurred

Figure 6.15 Blacksmiths rely on the malleability of metals to hammer and bend them into useful shapes.

Figure 6.16 Steel was used to make suits of armour in the Middle Ages.

❶❶ Explain in terms of atoms why blacksmiths get metals red hot before hammering them into different shapes (Figure 6.15).

❶❷ Which of the following properties show that copper is a metal and not a non-metal?
A Copper burns to form an oxide.
B Copper reacts with non-metals.
C Copper reacts only with non-metals.
D Copper is non-magnetic.
E Copper conducts electricity.
F Copper has two common isotopes.

❶❸ Look at the suit of armour in Figure 6.16.
a) What particles make up the structure of steel in the armour?
b) How are these particles arranged in steel?
c) What properties of steel are important for its use in the armour?

CHAPTER 6 How do the structures of substances influence their properties and uses?

Activity – Choosing metals for different uses

Various properties of five metals are shown in Table 6.2.

Metal	Density in g/cm³	Relative strength compared with iron	Melting point in °C	Relative electrical conductivity compared with iron	Relative thermal conductivity compared with iron	Rate of corrosion	Cost per tonne in £
Aluminium	2.7	0.33	660	3.7	3.0	Very slow	950
Copper	8.9	0.62	1083	5.8	4.8	Very slow	1100
Iron	7.9	1.00	1535	1.0	1.0	Quick	130
Silver	10.5	0.39	962	6.1	5.2	Very slight	250 000
Zinc	7.1	0.51	420	1.6	1.4	Very slow	730

Table 6.2 The properties of five commonly used metals

❶ Use the information in Table 6.2 to answer the following questions.
  a) Explain why the frames and poles of tents are made from aluminium.
  b) Explain why electrical cables in the National Grid are made of aluminium even though copper is a better conductor.
  c) Explain why bridges are built from steel which is mainly iron, even though it corrodes (rusts) faster than the other metals.
  d) Explain why gates and dustbins are made from iron coated (galvanised) with zinc.

  e) Explain why silver is no longer used to make our coins.
  f) Explain why high-quality saucepans have copper bottoms rather than steel (iron) bottoms.

❷ a) What is the range in values for:
    i) densities; ii) melting points in Table 6.2?
  b) Which values for density or melting point are anomalous (unusual or irregular)? Explain your answer.

Simple molecular substances

Oxygen and water are good examples of **simple molecular substances**. They have simple molecules containing a few atoms. Their formulae and structures are shown in Figure 6.17 along with those of hydrogen, methane, chlorine, hydrogen chloride, carbon dioxide and iodine.

Notice that all these substances are either non-metals or compounds of non-metals. Most non-metals and compounds of non-metals are simple molecular substances.

In these simple molecular substances, the atoms are held together in each molecule by strong covalent bonds (Figure 6.18). But there are only weak forces between the separate molecules

> **Simple molecular substances** are small molecules with only a few atoms compared with polymers or giant molecules.

Name and formula	Structure	Model of structure
Hydrogen, H_2	H—H	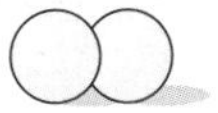
Oxygen, O_2	O=O	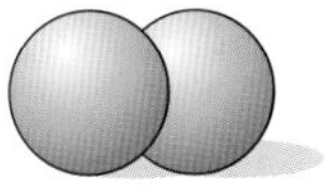
Water, H_2O	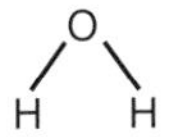 $\overset{\displaystyle O}{\underset{\text{H \quad H}}{\diagup\diagdown}}$	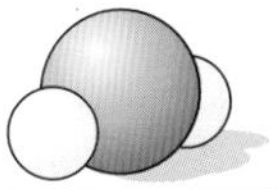
Methane, CH_4	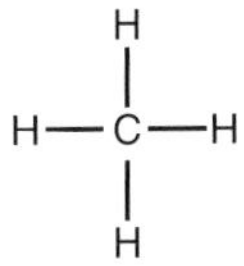 $\overset{\displaystyle H}{\underset{\displaystyle H}{\overset{\mid}{H—C—H}}}$	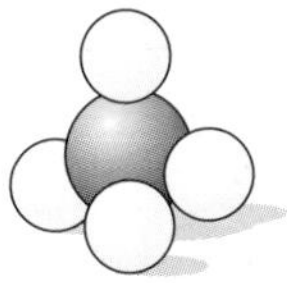
Hydrogen chloride, HCl	H—Cl	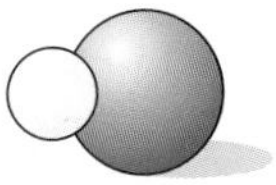
Chlorine, Cl_2	Cl—Cl	
Carbon dioxide, CO_2	O=C=O	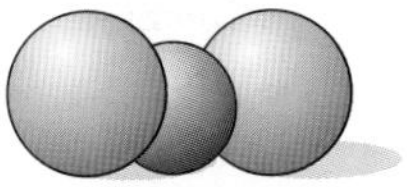
Iodine, I_2	I—I	

Figure 6.17 The formulae and structures of some simple molecular substances

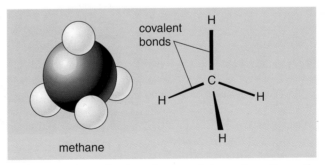

methane

Figure 6.18 Methane (CH_4) is a simple molecular substance. In methane, the carbon atom and four hydrogen atoms are held together by strong covalent bonds.

The properties of simple molecular substances

Simple molecular substances have the following properties:
- they have low melting points and low boiling points;
- they are often gases or liquids at room temperature. If the substance is solid, like iodine, it is soft;
- they do not conduct electricity.

These properties can be explained in terms of their simple structures and the weak forces between their molecules.
- There are only weak forces between the molecules in simple molecular substances. This means that the molecules can be separated easily when simple molecular substances are heated. They melt and evaporate easily with relatively low melting points and boiling points.
- The separate molecules in simple molecular substances are usually further apart than atoms in metals and ions in ionic structures. The forces between the molecules are weak and the molecules are easy to separate. Because of this, simple molecular solids such as iodine are softer than other materials.
- Simple molecules have no overall electric charge. They have no free outer electrons like metals and no ions like ionic compounds. This means they do not conduct electricity.

Figure 6.19 This butcher is using 'dry ice' (solid carbon dioxide) to keep meat cool during mincing. 'Dry ice' is a simple molecular substance. After mincing the 'dry ice' sublimes (changing directly from solid to gas) without spoiling the meat.

The formulae of molecular compounds

Figure 6.17 on page 103 shows the formulae and structures of some well-known simple molecular compounds. The structures are drawn to show the number of covalent bonds (drawn as a line −) to each atom.

> The **combining power** of an atom is the number of covalent bonds that it forms with other atoms.

Notice that each hydrogen atom always forms one bond with other atoms (H−). So, the **combining power** of hydrogen is 1. The combining powers of chlorine and iodine are also 1. Oxygen atoms always form two bonds to other atoms (single bonds −O− or double bonds O=). The combining power of oxygen is therefore 2. Carbon atoms form four bonds to other atoms, so the combining power of carbon is 4.

Using these ideas of combining power should help you to draw the structures of other simple molecular substances.

Figure 6.20 Butter contains a mixture of simple molecular substances. On hot corn on the cob butter starts to melt.

⑭ Look at the photo in Figure 6.20. What properties does butter have which show that it contains simple molecular substances?

⑮ Simple molecular substances often have a smell, but metals never have a smell. Why is this?

⑯ Solid X does not conduct electricity. It has a low melting point and a low boiling point. Could X be:
A a metal
B a non-metal

C a compound of a metal with a non-metal
D a compound of non-metals
E an ionic compound
F a simple molecular compound?

⑰ Using the usual combining powers of the elements carbon, chlorine and oxygen, draw structures for the following compounds. (Show each bond as a line.)
a) dichlorine oxide (Cl_2O);
b) tetrachloromethane (CCl_4).

6.5

Giant covalent structures

> **Giant covalent structures** contain very large numbers of atoms joined to each other by strong covalent bonds.

Atoms that share electrons in covalent bonds can also form **giant covalent structures** or macromolecules. One important group of compounds with giant covalent structures are polymers like polythene and PVC. Polythene and PVC have very long, thin molecules made by joining together smaller monomer molecules. These polymers can have hundreds and often thousands of atoms joined by strong covalent bonds.

Diamond, graphite and sand (silicon dioxide) are other examples of giant covalent structures, but these form lattices with billions of atoms.

Diamond and graphite are both pure carbon, but the two solids have very different structures, properties and uses. Diamond is hard and clear, whereas graphite is soft and black.

Diamond and graphite have different properties and different uses because they have different structures. They are both pure carbon, but the carbon atoms are packed in different ways. The structures of diamond and graphite have been studied using X-rays.

Figure 6.21 A saw with a diamond-studded blade can be used to cut through stone.

Diamond

In diamond, carbon atoms are joined to each other by strong covalent bonds. Inside the diamond structure (Figure 6.23), each carbon atom forms a covalent bond with four other carbon atoms. Check this for yourself in Figure 6.23. The strong covalent bonds extend through the whole diamond, forming a giant three-dimensional structure.

A perfect diamond, without flaws or cracks, is a single giant molecule. Only a small number of atoms are shown in Figure 6.23. In a real diamond, there are billions and billions of carbon atoms.

Figure 6.22 This artist is using a soft graphite pencil.

Diamond has the following properties:
- it is very hard;
- it has a very high melting point.

These properties can be explained by diamond's structure and the strong forces between atoms:
- It is very difficult to break the strong covalent bonds between carbon atoms in diamond. This makes diamond very hard.
- Carbon atoms in diamond are linked together by very strong covalent bonds. This means that the atoms cannot vibrate enough to break away from their neighbours (when the substance melts) until a temperature of about 3800 °C.

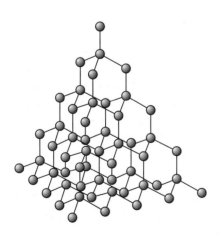

Figure 6.23 An 'open' model of the giant structure in diamond. Each black ball represents a carbon atom and each stick is a covalent bond.

Graphite

Figure 6.24 shows a model of part of the structure of graphite. Notice that the carbon atoms are arranged in layers. Each layer contains billions of carbon atoms arranged in hexagons. Each carbon atom is held in its layer by strong covalent bonds to three other carbon atoms. So, every layer is a giant covalent structure.

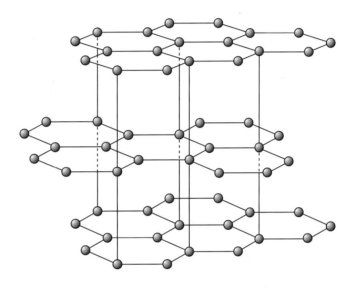

Figure 6.24 A model of the structure of graphite. Notice how graphite has layers of carbon atoms. In each layer, the carbon atoms are arranged in hexagons.

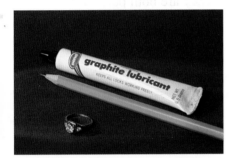

Figure 6.25 Graphite makes a good lubricant because the layers in graphite slide over one another very easily.

Figure 6.26 Graphite fibres are used to strengthen the shafts of badminton racquets, golf clubs and even broken bones.

Graphite has the following properties:
- it is soft and slippery;
- it has a high melting point.

Again, these properties can be explained by graphite's structure:
- Each carbon atom is linked by strong covalent bonds to three other atoms in its own layer. But the layers in graphite are more than twice as far apart as carbon atoms in the same layer. This means that the forces between the layers are weak. If you rub graphite, it feels soft and slippery as the layers slide over each other and onto your fingers.
- Although the layers of graphite can move over each other easily, it is difficult to break the strong covalent bonds between carbon atoms within one layer. Because of this, graphite does not melt until 3730 °C.

The uses of graphite relate to its properties. The softness of graphite has led to its use as the 'lead' in pencils and as a lubricant in engine oils. The strong bonds between carbon atoms in the layers of graphite mean that graphite fibres are very strong and can be used to strengthen badminton racquets and golf clubs. The high melting point of graphite means it can be used to make crucibles for hot molten metals.

⑱ a) Why is diamond called a 'giant molecule'?
  b) Why has diamond such a high melting point?

⑲ a) State two similarities and two differences between diamond and graphite.
  b) Why do diamond and graphite have some differences?

⑳ a) Explain why a zip-fastener moves more freely after rubbing with a soft pencil.
  b) Why is a pencil better than oil for freeing a zip-fastener?

㉑ Why is graphite better than oil for lubricating the moving parts of hot machinery?

㉒ Match the substances A, B, C and D below to the statements 1, 2, 3 and 4.
  A methane (CH_4) in natural gas
  B potassium nitrate (KNO_3) used as a fertiliser
  C polythene (polyethene) used for clingfilm
  D brass, an alloy of copper and zinc

  1 This substances contains ions.
  2 This substance contains atoms which have not combined.
  3 This substance has a giant covalent structure.
  4 This substance contains simple molecules.

6.6 Nanomaterials

Nanoparticles are particles with sizes measured in nanometres (nm).

Nanomaterials and nanotechnology are new to the twenty-first century. Very few people had heard of nanomaterials before the year 2000. Since then, a wide range of materials have been developed and used in the form of **nanoparticles**. These are particles between one and a hundred nanometres in size. That's between one millionth and one ten-thousandth of a mm in size.

Nanoparticles contain a few hundred atoms or less. They include metals, carbon, plastics and polymers. Nanoparticles show different properties from larger pieces of the same material because of their incredibly small size and large surface area.

Here are some of the applications of nanotechnology:
- Fabrics can now be coated with nano-thick polymers. Any liquid spilt on the fabric just turns into 'beads' and rolls off without staining the fabric.
- Ultra-thin coatings of scratch-resistant polymers are now used on lenses for spectacles, cameras and contact lenses. The coatings are so thin that the polymer material is transparent.
- New solar cells have been developed with nano-sized metal crystals on their surface. These have a much larger surface area on which to collect the Sun's energy.
- New catalysts containing nanoparticles are being developed. These have a much larger surface area than bulk materials and are therefore more efficient. For example gold nanoparticles catalyse the conversion of poisonous carbon monoxide to carbon dioxide. Their large surface area means you need only a tiny amount of gold – which is cheaper!

Figure 6.27 These polymer nanoparticles have been designed to carry drug molecules into the body. Just 100 nm to 500 nm across, they can pass across vein walls, and so the drug can be released into tissues in exactly the part of the body that needs treating.

Future nanotechnology applications could include:

- smaller and more sensitive sensors in electronic devices such as security lights and cameras;
- smaller and faster computers with layers of magnetic nanoparticles to increase the capacity for storing data;
- lighter yet stronger construction materials strengthened with long, ultra-thin carbon nanotubes. Carbon nanotubes are 10 times lighter than steel but 250 times stronger;
- 'smart' clothing with nano-sized sensors to measure our pulse rate and temperature.

The future

Nanomaterials are exciting new materials. However, there are concerns about the effects of nanoparticles when they get onto and inside our bodies. Nanoparticles could be more reactive and so more toxic than larger particles of the same material. Although most areas of nanotechnology have no risks, scientists have made the following recommendations:

- Nanoparticles should be treated as 'new chemicals'.
- More research is urgently needed into the health risks of nanomaterials.
- An independent scientific safety committee should approve new nanomaterials before they are marketed and used by the general public.
- Nanoparticles that have direct contact with our bodies, such as those in cosmetics and sunscreens, are the most likely to cause long-term damage.
- Workplace regulations are needed to protect workers who are exposed to nanoparticles.

Activity – Nanomaterials and the future

❶ Explain what is meant by nanotechnology in no more than 25 words.
❷ Describe three benefits from the development of nanomaterials.
❸ Describe two possible risks from the development of nanomaterials.
❹ Why is it important for the whole of society to make decisions about the development of nanomaterials? The decisions should not be left to scientists.

If you would like more information on these issues, go to www.news.bbc.co.uk and search on 'nanomaterials' and 'nanotechnology'.

6.7

Giant ionic structures

Ionic compounds form when metals react with non-metals. During these reactions, electrons are transferred from the metal to the non-metal forming positive metal ions and negative non-metal ions. For example, when sodium reacts with chlorine, sodium chloride is formed.

sodium	+	chlorine	$\rightarrow$	sodium chloride
2Na	+	Cl_2	$\rightarrow$	$2Na^+Cl^-$
2 sodium atoms		1 chlorine molecule		2 sodium ions + 2 chloride ions

Electrons are transferred from the sodium atoms to the chlorine atoms. Positive sodium ions and negative chloride ions are formed.

The structure and properties of ionic compounds

In ionic compounds, billions of positive and negative ions are packed together in a **giant ionic lattice**.

Figure 6.29 shows how the ions are arranged in one layer of sodium chloride (NaCl). Figure 6.30 is a three-dimensional model of the structure. Notice that Na^+ ions are surrounded by Cl^- ions and that Cl^- ions are surrounded by Na^+ ions. This means that there are strong forces of attraction between oppositely charged ions in the lattice. These forces of attraction are called ionic bonds (see Section 5.6).

Strong ionic bonds hold the ions firmly together in ionic compounds. This explains why ionic compounds:
- are hard substances;
- have high melting points and high boiling points;
- do not conduct electricity when solid, because their ions cannot move freely;
- conduct electricity when they are melted or dissolved in water, because the charged ions are then free to move. Positive ions move towards the negative terminal and negative ions move towards the positive terminal, carrying the current through the liquid

Figure 6.28 Chalk cliffs are made of calcium carbonate ($CaCO_3$). This is a giant ionic lattice of Ca^{2+} and CO_3^{2-} ions.

> **Giant ionic lattices** have billions of ions held together by forces between oppositely charged particles.

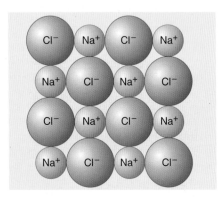

Figure 6.29 The arrangement of ions in one layer of a sodium chloride (salt) crystal

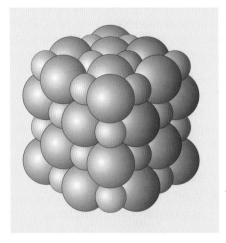

Figure 6.30 A three-dimensional model of the structure of sodium chloride. The larger green balls represent Cl^- ions. The smaller red balls represent Na^+ ions.

Name of compound	Formula
Aluminium nitrate	$Al^{3+}(NO^{3-})_3$ or $Al(NO_3)_3$
Zinc sulfate	$Zn^{2+}SO_4{}^{2-}$ or $ZnSO_4$
Magnesium carbonate	$Mg^{2+}CO_3{}^{2-}$ or $MgCO_3$
Potassium iodide	K^+I^- or KI
Iron(III) chloride	$Fe^{3+}(Cl^-)_3$ or $FeCl_3$
Copper(II) bromide	$Cu^{2+}(Br^-)_2$ or $CuBr_2$

Table 6.3 The names and formulae of some ionic compounds

The formulae of ionic compounds

The formulae of ionic compounds can be worked out by balancing the positive and negative charges on ions. For example, the two positive charges on one calcium ion (Ca^{2+}) are balanced by the single negative charges on two chloride ions (Cl^-). So the formula of calcium chloride is $Ca^{2+}(Cl^-)_2$, or simply $CaCl_2$.

The number of charges on an ion is a measure of its combining power (see Section 6.4). Ions with a single positive charge have a combining power of 1, whereas ions with two positive charges have a combining power of 2. Na^+ can combine with only one Cl^- ion to form Na^+Cl^- whereas Ca^{2+} can combine with two Cl^- ions to form $Ca^{2+}(Cl^-)_2$.

Table 6.3 shows the names and formulae of some other ionic compounds. Notice that the formula of calcium nitrate is $Ca(NO_3)_2$. The brackets around $NO_3{}^-$ show that it is a single unit. $NO_3{}^-$ contains one nitrogen atom and three oxygen atoms with one negative charge. Thus, two $NO_3{}^-$ ions balance one Ca^{2+} ion. Other ions like $SO_4{}^{2-}$, $CO_3{}^{2-}$ and OH^- should also be put in brackets when there are two or three of them in a formula.

23 Which of the substances listed below conduct electricity:
    a) when liquid;
    b) when solid?

       diamond   potassium chloride   copper   sulfur

24 Look carefully at Figures 6.29 and 6.30.
    a) How many Cl^- ions surround one Na^+ ion in one layer of the NaCl crystal?
    b) How many Cl^- ions surround one Na^+ ion in the three-dimensional crystal?
    c) How many Na^+ ions surround one Cl^- ion in the three-dimensional crystal?

25 Use the symbols and the charges on ions in Section 6.7 and Table 6.3 to write formulae for the following compounds:
    a) sodium carbonate;
    b) aluminium oxide;
    c) zinc chloride;
    d) magnesium sulfate.

Activity – Using models in science

Models are very important in science. They help us to think about the structure and properties of substances and how things work. They also help us to test new ideas and make predictions. Sometimes the models that scientists use are complex computer programs like those that help weather forecasters.

In this chapter we have been using models of the structures of different substances. These have helped us to understand their properties and uses.

Atomic models for giant metallic structures

You will need about 25 marbles or 25 polystyrene spheres for this activity. The marbles or polystyrene spheres represent atoms.

1 Put three books flat on a bench so that they form a triangle around 10 atoms.
2 Move the books carefully so that they enclose a layer of close-packed atoms like those in Figure 6.10 on page 100.
3 Now add another layer of atoms on top of the first one.
4 Then put further layers on top of this.

Look carefully at your structure. This represents a very good model for most metals.

❶ How many other atoms does one atom in the middle of the structure touch?
❷ Why is this called a close-packed structure?
❸ Why is this a giant structure?
❹ Describe how this model helps us to understand metals.

We used ball and stick models to represent the structures of diamond and graphite in Section 6.5. Ball and stick models are useful because the 'sticks' show the bonds which hold the atoms together.

Building a ball and stick model for silicon dioxide

Silicon dioxide (silica, SiO_2) has a giant covalent structure (Figure 6.31). Silica occurs in its pure form as large, beautiful crystals of quartz.

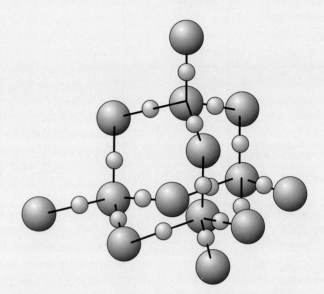

Figure 6.31 A ball and stick model of silicon dioxide, SiO_2

Use a ball and stick model kit to build a structure of silicon dioxide like that in Figure 6.31. Use black balls from the kit to represent silicon atoms and red balls to represent oxygen atoms.

❺ a) How many covalent bonds are formed by silicon atoms in the middle of your structure?
  b) How many covalent bonds are formed by oxygen atoms in your structure?
❻ Explain why silicon dioxide:
  a) is hard;
  b) has a very high melting point.
    (*Hint*: Silicon dioxide is a giant covalent structure similar to diamond.)

Silicon is the second most common element in the Earth's crust. Most rocks including sandstones and clays contain silicon and oxygen. The structures of these rocks are based on that of silicon dioxide. Sand is ground up pieces of these rocks.

Although models are usually helpful, it is important to remember that they are not real representations. For example, metal atoms are not really like marbles or polystyrene spheres, and silicon dioxide doesn't have tiny balls and sticks.

❼ Give two reasons why models are helpful to scientists.

Summary

✓ The regular arrangement of particles in a crystal is called a **lattice**.

✓ The structure and bonding of a substance determine its properties and these properties determine its uses.

✓ All substances are made up from only three kinds of particle – atoms, ions and molecules.

✓ These three particles result in four different solid structures – **giant metallic**, **giant ionic**, **giant covalent** and **simple molecular**.

✓ The atoms in most metals are packed together as close as possible. This arrangement is called close packing.

✓ A **giant structure** is an arrangement of very large numbers (thousands or even billions) of atoms or ions held together by strong forces in a regular pattern.

✓ **Simple molecular substances** are small molecules with just a few atoms.

✓ The **combining power** of an atom is the number of covalent bonds that it forms with other atoms.

✓ The **combining power** of an ion is the number of charges on the ion.

✓ **Nanoparticles** are particles with sizes measured in nanometres (nm).

✓ The particles, bonding, structure and properties of the four different solid structures are summarised in Table 6.4.

Type of structure	Particles in the structure	Type of substance	Structure	Bonding	Properties
Giant metallic	Atoms close-packed	Metals e.g. Na, Fe, Cu and alloys such as steel		Atoms are held in a close-packed giant structure by strong bonds	• High melting points and boiling points • Conduct electricity • High density • Hard but malleable
Giant covalent (macro-molecular)	Very large molecules containing thousands or billions of atoms (giant molecules)	A few non-metals (e.g. diamond, graphite) and some non-metal compounds (e.g. polythene, PVC, silicon dioxide (sand))		Large numbers of atoms are joined together by strong covalent bonds to give a giant 3D structure or a very long, thin molecule	• High melting points and boiling points • Do not conduct electricity (except graphite) • Hard but brittle (3D structures) or flexible polymers
Simple molecular	Small molecules containing a few atoms	Most non-metals and non-metal compounds e.g. O_2, I_2, H_2O, CO_2, sugar		Atoms are held together in small molecules by strong covalent bonds. The bonds between molecules are weak	• Low melting points and boiling points • Do not conduct electricity • Soft when solid
Giant ionic	Ions	Metal / non-metal compounds e.g. Na^+Cl^-, $Ca^{2+}O^{2-}$, $Mg^{2+}(Cl^-)_2$		Positive and negative ions are held together by the attraction between their opposite charges – ionic bonds	• High melting points and boiling points • Conduct electricity when melted or dissolved in water • Hard but brittle

Table 6.4 The particles, structure, bonding and properties of the four different solid structures

❶ Table 6.5 shows some properties of diamond and graphite.

Diamond	Graphite
Colourless crystals	Shiny black solid
Hardest natural substance	Soft and slippery

Table 6.5

a) Why would you expect diamond and graphite to have the same properties? *(1 mark)*

b) Why do diamond and graphite have different properties? *(1 mark)*

c) Explain why graphite is soft and slippery. *(2 marks)*

d) Explain why diamond is hard. *(2 marks)*

❷ This question is about aluminium oxide and how it is formed from atoms of aluminium and oxygen.

a) Copy and complete the following sentences by choosing the most suitable words from the box below to fill in the blank spaces.

> atoms   covalent   giant   hard   high
> ionic   ions   low   simple   soft

Aluminium oxide is a substance with _____ bonding. It has a _____ structure composed of _____. Strong forces between particles in the structure of aluminium oxide make it very _____ with a _____ melting point. *(5 marks)*

b) The electron structure in an aluminium atom is 2, 8, 3 and the electron strucutre in an oxygen atom is 2, 6.

  i) Describe the change in electron structure of an aluminium atom when aluminium oxide forms. *(2 marks)*

  ii) Describe the change in electron structure of an oxygen atom when aluminium oxide forms. *(2 marks)*

c) Explain why the formula of aluminium oxide is Al_2O_3. *(2 marks)*

❸ Copy and complete Table 6.6 for methane and sodium chloride. *(5 marks)*

	Methane	Sodium chloride
Formula		NaCl
Particles in the substance	Molecules	
Appearance at room temperature		White solid
Type of bonds	Covalent	
One use		In cooking

Table 6.6

❹ Substance Y melts at a high temperature and the liquid which forms conducts electricity. Three of the following substances could be Y. Which are they?

> calcium chloride   starch   copper
> polythene   brass   carbon disulfide

(3 marks)

❺ a) Carbon dioxide is used in fire extinguishers. When an extinguisher is used, carbon dioxide gas pours out and smothers the fire.

  i) Explain why carbon dioxide smothers the fire. *(2 marks)*

  ii) Explain why carbon dioxide puts out the fire. *(2 marks)*

b) Solid carbon dioxide is used for refrigerating ice-cream, soft fruit and meat. The solid carbon dioxide is called 'dry ice' or 'Dricold'.

  i) What kind of structure does solid carbon dioxide have? *(1 mark)*

  ii) Why is 'dry ice' better than ordinary ice for refrigeration? *(2 marks)*

Chapter 7
How do we control the rate of chemical reactions and measure energy transfer?

At the end of this chapter you should:

✓ be able to use the symbols (s), (l), (g) and (aq) to mean solid, liquid, gas and aqueous (watery) solution;
✓ understand that in chemical reactions, not all the reactants always turn into products;
✓ know about the principle of atom economy (atom utilisation) and how a high atom economy helps the sustainability of chemical processes;
✓ be able to plot graphs of amount of products formed or reactants used over time in a reaction;
✓ know that the amount of a reactant used or the amount of product formed over time is the rate of reaction;
✓ know that the rate of a chemical reaction increases:
  – if the temperature increases;
  – if the concentration of dissolved reactants or pressure of gases increases;
  – if solid reactants are in smaller pieces;
  – if a catalyst is used;
✓ be able to explain how colliding particles react if the energy of the collision is greater than the activation energy;
✓ explain how faster collisions or more collisions per second increase the rates of reactions;
✓ know that catalysts can be useful in industry to make reactions faster;
✓ know that reactions can release or take in energy;
✓ understand the words exothermic and endothermic;
✓ know about reversible reactions that can go both ways;
✓ know that the Haber process is used to manufacture ammonia.

Figure 7.1 Cooking involves chemical changes. These chemical reactions change the flavour and texture of food – making potatoes soft and turning meat brown and tender. But if the temperature is too high, the reactions happen too fast. The meat gets burnt and dark on the outside, but is uncooked inside. You need to control the speed of the cooking reactions. This is important when making new materials in industry too.

CHAPTER 7 How do we control the rate of chemical reactions and measure energy transfer?

How much useful product do chemists get from chemical changes?

In a chemical reaction you start with some materials called 'reactants' and end up with new materials called 'products'. A simple equation, like the one below, is used to show the progress of the reaction. This is written as an equation because all the atoms in the reactants must still be there in the products – no atoms can be created or destroyed, lost or gained.

$$\text{reactants} \xrightarrow{\text{in certain conditions}} \text{products}$$

State symbols

It makes equations much clearer if the states of the reactants and products are given. Usually solid, liquid and gas are shown by (s), (l) and (g) after the formula. If you see (aq) it means an aqueous solution was used in the reaction.

Example

Methane burns by reacting it with oxygen in the air.

The word equation is:

methane + oxygen → carbon dioxide + water

The symbol equation is:

$$CH_4(g) + 2O_2(g) \rightarrow CO_2(g) + 2H_2O(l)$$

on the reactants side	on the products side
1 carbon atom	1 carbon atom
4 hydrogen atoms	$2 \times 2 = 4$ hydrogen atoms
$2 \times 2 = 4$ oxygen atoms	$2 + (2 \times 1) = 4$ oxygen atoms

Useful changes

A chemical reaction can turn 'reactants' (raw materials) into useful 'products' such as nylon or copper. When you burn a chemical such as methane the reaction can produce heat. Other reactions can do a useful process, such as using chlorine bleach to make a stained tea mug white again.

All of these are useful changes that have different products. Sometimes the products are 'waste products'. Gases from a combustion reaction or dirty watery mixtures from a cleaning reaction are waste products.

These waste products can cause pollution if they get into the wrong place.

❶ a) Give the names of two man made materials that are made from a chemical reaction (they should not occur naturally).
b) Give the names of two substances that can be burnt in air to release energy.
c) Give the names of two chemicals that can be used for useful jobs like cleaning.

❷ Write out the numbers of each different atom in the reactants and the products in each of these reactions.
(See page 232 for a Periodic Table to give the symbols and names of the elements.)
a) $CaCO_3(s) \rightarrow CaO(s) + CO_2(g)$
b) $TiO_2(s) + 4Na(s) \rightarrow 2Na_2O(s) + Ti(s)$
c) $C_6H_{12}O_6(aq) \rightarrow 2C_2H_5OH(aq) + 2CO_2(g)$

Some chemical reactions are **reversible reactions**. This means the products can react to produce the original reactants. The equation can be represented by:

$$A + B \rightleftharpoons C + D$$

The arrow symbol with the two tails is a special sign to show it is a reversible reaction.

Reversible and irreversible reactions

Many chemical reactions are irreversible – once the products are formed they do not go back to the reactants. For example:

magnesium	+	oxygen	→	magnesium oxide
$2Mg(s)$	+	$O_2(g)$	→	$2MgO(s)$

cannot be reversed.

Some chemical reactions go forwards and backwards easily. But this can depend on the conditions when the reaction happens, such as the temperature when the reaction happens. These are called **reversible reactions**.

An example is the reaction between ammonia and hydrogen chloride gases. If you mix the gases at room temperature a white cloud of ammonium chloride forms.

ammonia	+	hydrogen chloride	→	ammonium chloride
$NH_3(g)$	+	$HCl(g)$	→	$NH_4Cl(s)$

Your teacher can collect this white solid ammonium chloride and heat it to a higher temperature. The compound decomposes (falls apart) and you get the ammonia and hydrogen chloride gases back:

ammonium chloride	→	ammonia	+	hydrogen chloride
$NH_4Cl(s)$	→	$NH_3(g)$	+	$HCl(g)$

Figure 7.2 The white smoke is a solid, ammonium chloride. This is made when ammonia reacts with hydrogen chloride.

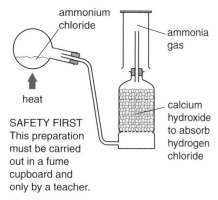

Figure 7.3 The reverse reaction: ammonium chloride decomposes, making ammonia gas and hydrogen chloride. This is one way of making ammonia.

Getting the sums right

You read in Chapter 5 about the amount of product that can theoretically be obtained in a chemical reaction from a given amount of starting material. The amount of product you can make is important, but there are also other important calculations.

Figure 7.4 Pharmacists need to know exactly how much of a product they are producing.

These things are important to industrial chemists when making new materials:

- Getting as much product as possible from the reactants – the more product made, the less waste there is and the greater the profit.
- Being able to control the speed of reactions – time is money.
- The cost of equipment – equipment costs can be high if the reaction needs a high temperature or pressure.
- The cost of fuel – reducing the amount of energy input can save money.

You cannot always get all the product predicted from a reaction. Here are some possible reasons:

- The reactants may not be totally pure, so there is a smaller amount of material to react.
- Some of the product may get lost in the separation process. For example, some very fine particles may get through filter paper or some liquid may be left on the sides of containers.
- Not all of the reactants may react, or may react in a different way from expected and not give the product you want. Forming different products reduces the amount produced of the main product.
- With reversible reactions, some of the products may change back to reactants again.

Example

Slaked lime or calcium hydroxide ($Ca(OH)_2$) is used as a weak alkali to neutralise acid soil. Slaked lime can be made by heating limestone (calcium carbonate) to make lime (calcium oxide). Then calcium oxide is reacted with water to make slaked lime (calcium hydroxide).

Chemists can calculate how much slaked lime should be produced from the reactants. They know that adding this amount of lime to acid soil will neutralise it.

A group of chemists made some slaked lime using this process. This product was measured out and added to the acid soil. The soil was found to be still slightly acid when tested.

Possible explanations for the slaked lime not doing its job:

1 The starting material (marble chips) was not pure calcium carbonate and contained some stone dust.
2 Some of the calcium hydroxide may be lost in the dissolving and filtering and drying processes.
3 The heating did not turn all the marble chips (calcium carbonate) into lime. Some remained as calcium carbonate.

> ❸ Describe in detail how would you test the soil to show it was still acidic after treatment with slaked lime.

4 a) Here is a description of a common process – making mashed potato from real potatoes. Describe how some of the starting material gets wasted at each stage.
Stage 1 – buying a kilogram of potatoes from a farm and washing them.
Stage 2 – peeling the potatoes.
Stage 3 – boiling the potatoes and draining away the water.
Stage 4 – mashing the potatoes with a masher.
Stage 5 – serving the potatoes from a dish.

   b) Is there any way that any of the waste of potato can be avoided, or are all of these 'little wastes' at each stage an unavoidable part of any process?

> **Atom economy** (also called atom utilisation) refers to the proportion of atoms in the reactants that ends up in the useful product. Atom economy is calculated as the mass of atoms in the desired product divided by the mass of atoms of all the reactants, expressed as a percentage.

Atom economy

Not all atoms of the reactants always end up in the product you want. Sometimes by-products are formed. If you want information about the overall waste in a chemical reaction you would find out the **atom economy**.

Example

Glucose can be fermented to produce ethanol (this reaction is also used to make ethanol fuel from renewable plant resources).

This is the equation:

$$\text{glucose} \xrightarrow{\text{yeast}} \text{ethanol} + \text{carbon dioxide}$$

$$C_6H_{12}O_6(aq) \rightarrow 2C_2H_5OH(aq) + 2CO_2(g)$$

You may hear TV adverts that say 'all the sugar turns to alcohol'. If this were true the atom economy would be 100%. But some sugar turns to carbon dioxide. So there are some waste products from this process.

In fact nearly half the sugar is 'wasted' in this process. Not all of the reactant atoms (carbon, hydrogen and oxygen) end up in molecules of ethanol – some carbon and oxygen atoms are released as carbon dioxide.

Atom economy and sustainability – green chemistry

Some reactions and processes involve several stages. This can give rise to several by-products. So these reactions score low on atom utilisation. Other reactions score highly because there are fewer by-products.

Chemists in all the industries now look for alternative ways to make the same product with a high atom economy. This is more efficient and minimises waste.

> A system is **sustainable** if it meets present needs without compromising those of future generations. For example, a reaction will be more sustainable if we can reduce the amount of resources used, including energy.

High atom economy reactions are more **sustainable**. They use less chemicals and energy, and reduce the amount of waste material.

It's much better to produce less waste in the first place than to treat waste afterwards to remove even harmless by-products. This reduces energy used in waste processing.

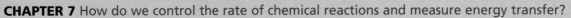
Chemistry in industry

People who work in industry have to think carefully about the consequences of what they do.

They have to think about these environmental issues:
- How much energy is used in a reaction or a process including separating the useful products from the waste products?
- Does the reaction use hazardous substances?
- Does the reaction produce by-products that are toxic to human health and the environment?
- Can the starting materials be made from renewable resources?

To answer these questions they need to know about all the chemical properties of the materials they produce, and any waste material.

---

5 a) Explain what is meant by atom economy or atom utilisation.
   b) Is 100% atom utilisation a good or a bad feature of a process? Explain your answer.

6 Would you expect a reaction with a high atom economy to be:
   A a cheaper way of producing a product;
   B a faster way of producing a product;
   C a less wasteful way of producing a product?
   Explain your answer.

7 Design an illustration or a poster to explain this idea:
   'It's better to produce less waste in the first place, than to treat waste afterwards.'

Activity – Manufacturing processes

Use a computer and a search engine such as www.ask.com to find out about one of these processes. Choose one from:
- how steel is made;
- how soap is made;
- how plastic is made.

Use the computer search and your information to try to answer some of the following questions about the process. You may not be able to answer all of them.

1 What are the environmental issues for the process?
2 Is a lot of energy used in the process, including separating the useful products from the waste products?
3 Does the reaction use hazardous substances?
4 Does the reaction produce by-products that are toxic to human health and the environment?
5 Can the starting materials be from renewable or recycled resources?

7.2 How do we measure the rate of a chemical change?

Speed of reactions

Figure 7.5 The reactants are used up very quickly – an explosion is a fast reaction.

Figure 7.6 Sometimes you have to wait a long time to see the products form in a chemical reaction – rusting is a slow reaction.

Chemical changes happen at different speeds. The speed of a chemical change is called the **rate of reaction**.

The rate of reaction can be very different, depending on the reactants. You can control the rate of reaction by controlling the conditions.

> The **rate of reaction** is the speed at which a reaction takes place. It can be measured as the rate of formation of a product or the rate of removal of a reactant.

Examples

- Dynamite – this is made from a very dangerous material called nitroglycerine. The nitroglycerine is absorbed onto dry clay and wrapped in paper. The clay dilutes the nitroglycerine and makes it explode less easily. You need a detonator to set it off.
- Eggs –You need to be careful about timing to produce the perfect soft-boiled or fried egg.
- Rusting – oil stops the reactive oxygen getting to the steel and slows down rusting.

Figure 7.7 When cooking egg you can control the outcome carefully by controlling the temperature and how long you let the reaction continue. This is a medium-speed reaction.

Figure 7.8 Reaction time is very important in cooking. There are several factors that change the rate of cooking reactions and the cook has to control the reactions so the parts of the meal are ready at the same time.

You need to control the speed of a chemical reaction by controlling the conditions (such as the temperature) of the reaction.

Cooking needs a lot of careful temperature and time control – or the food is undercooked and nasty, or burnt. Chips need to be thin to cook quickly. If your chips are very fat they don't cook in the middle. So the size of the solid lumps in a reaction matters.

How can you measure a rate of reaction?

A 'rate' is a speed. You calculate a rate as a measured quantity divided by time taken. For example, your pulse rate is the number of heart beats in one minute.

Measuring the time taken for a reaction is straightforward. Use a stop clock – or a calendar for very slow reactions.

But the quantity you measure in a chemical change can be:
- mass lost (if the reaction produces a gas);
- time for all the solid reactants to vanish from sight;
- amount of unreacted solid left at any time;
- the temperature change;
- change in colour;
- change in transparency of a solution.

All of these can be measured to find the rate. You choose one that is suitable.

In the laboratory, we measure rates of reaction by the amount of reactant used up or the amount of product formed:

or

$$\text{rate of reaction} = \frac{\text{amount of reactant used}}{\text{time taken}}$$

$$\text{rate of reaction} = \frac{\text{amount of product formed}}{\text{time taken}}$$

Example
When magnesium reacts with acid, hydrogen gas is formed. How could the rate of reaction be measured?

magnesium + sulfuric acid → magnesium sulfate + hydrogen

$$Mg(s) + H_2SO_4(aq) \rightarrow MgSO_4(aq) + H_2(g)$$

You can choose.
- You could measure the volume of gas collected.
- If the gas was allowed to escape, you could measure the loss in mass of the flask at regular intervals.

---

8 a) Explain what is meant by the rate of a reaction.
   b) Give examples of fast and slow reactions

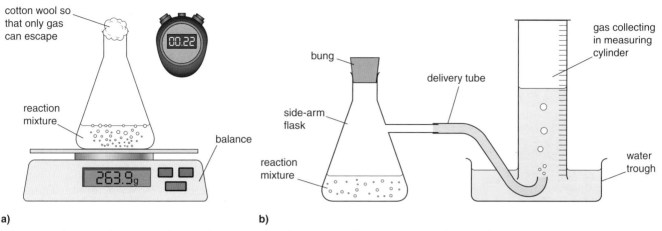

Figure 7.9 The rate of a reaction that produces a gas can be measured by **a)** measuring the mass lost as the gas escapes, or **b)** by collecting the gas produced.

> ⑨ Describe three things that you could measure to show the progress of a reaction.
>
> ⑩ Draw the apparatus you could use to measure the gas given off by a reacting mixture as time proceeds.

Graphs of reactions

Measurements from rates of reaction experiments are often shown as line graphs. The variables are continuous. The independent variable is most often time and this is usually the horizontal axis. The dependent variable is the mass lost or the volume of gas, or whatever you measure to follow the progress of the reaction.

Graphs of rates of reaction follow the same rules as the distance–time graphs you have studied. A steep graph line shows a fast reaction. A flat graph line shows the reaction has stopped.

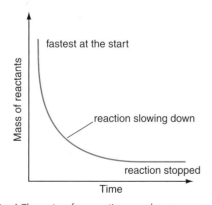

Figure 7.10 a) The rate of a reaction can be measured by recording the change in mass over time. When the graph levels off, one of the reactants is used up and the reaction stops.

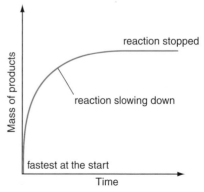

b) This graph shows the volume of gas formed over time. The rate of reaction is highest when the gradient is steepest.

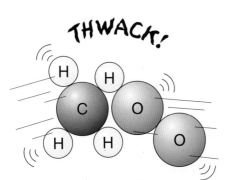

Figure 7.11 When two molecules meet, they react only if the collision is hard enough.

> **Collisions** between atoms or molecules that successfully transfer enough energy for the atoms or molecules to react together are called effective collisions.
>
> The **activation energy** is the minimum energy needed if molecules are to react when they collide.

What makes a reaction happen, and how can we control it?

A collision model for chemical reactions

For a chemical change to happen, the groups of atoms in the reaction have to collide. Reactions are not over instantaneously, but they start with the atoms banging together.

The **collision** model says that molecules react only if the collision is hard enough for the energy to break the bonds between atoms. The minimum energy needed for the reaction to happen is called the **activation energy**.

The collision theory is a thinking model used to predict rates of reaction. This thinking model says:

- Atoms or molecules can react only if they collide with each other.
- Some of the atoms or molecules have to be a liquid or a gas. If they are, they can move about randomly. So they can bang together.
- For solids, only the atoms or molecules on the surface can react.
- Not all collisions result in a reaction. There has to be enough energy in the collision to make the reaction happen. These are the effective collisions.

Only the molecules that collide with sufficient energy to overcome the activation energy react. Most of the collisions are not effective.

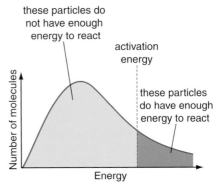

Figure 7.12 In a mixture of methane and oxygen molecules, all the molecules are moving and may collide. Only the molecules that transfer enough energy when they collide will react and form new molecules.

⓫ Draw a large annotated illustration to show what is meant by the collision theory for reactions. Add words to explain what could happen when atoms collide.

⓬ Explain what is meant by an 'effective collision' and why not all collisions are 'effective'. Use the idea of activation energy to help explain.

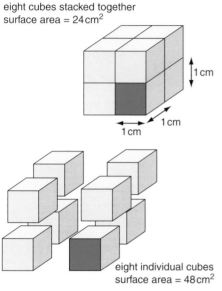
eight cubes stacked together
surface area = 24 cm²

1 cm
1 cm
1 cm

eight individual cubes
surface area = 48 cm²

Figure 7.13 Making the pieces of reactant smaller increases the surface area and the number of particles exposed on the surface.

Making reactions go faster

You can do any of these things to increase the rate of reaction.
- Increase the number of collisions.
- Make the collisions have more energy.

You can change the conditions to cause a faster reaction. These conditions increase the number of collisions (A) or they make the collisions more effective (B):
- increased temperature (A and B);
- increased concentration of a reactant (A);
- increased pressure (A);
- smaller particle size, so more surface area exposed (A);
- presence of a catalyst (B).

The collision model explains how these factors increase the number or energy of collisions:
- Increasing the temperature of the reactants makes the particles move about faster so they collide more often. The collisions are also faster with more energy. Both increase the number of effective collisions.
- Increasing the concentration means a greater number of particles in a certain volume of a solution. This means the particles are crowded more closely together, so there are more collisions.
- Increasing the pressure of a reacting gas is like increasing the concentration of a solution; there are more collisions.
- If a solid reactant is cut up into more pieces then there are more reactant particles on the surface area that are exposed and able to react.

Rates of reaction graphs

1 Rate and concentration

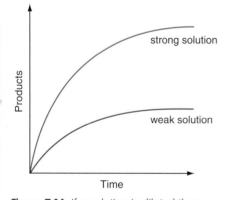

Products

strong solution

weak solution

Time

Figure 7.14 If a solution is diluted there would be fewer collisions in a certain time.

2 Rate and temperature

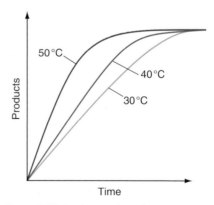

Products

50 °C

40 °C

30 °C

Time

Figure 7.15 Each time the solution becomes 10 °C hotter the rate roughly doubles.

3 Rate and particle size

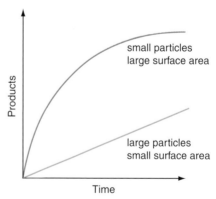

Products

small particles
large surface area

large particles
small surface area

Time

Figure 7.16 If more surface particles are exposed then the reaction rate increases.

⑬ 'If you halve the average size of solid particles you should double the speed of the reaction.'
Copy Figure 7.13 on page 125 and add words to explain the conclusion above.

⑭ List as many different ways as you can for making a reaction happen faster.

⑮ Use the collision model to explain why temperature has a large effect on rates of reaction.

⑯ Michaela collected data from a reaction that produced a gas as a product.

Time in minutes and seconds	Volume of gas given off in cm³		
	A	B	C
0 15	3	10	20
0 30	6	19	40
0 45	9	28	51
1 00	12	35	54
1 15	15	42	55
1 30	18	49	55
1 45	20	54	55
2 00	23	55	55
2 15	25	55	55
2 30	28	55	55

Table 7.1

a) Plot graphs for these three sets of results on the same piece of graph paper.
b) If these results were for different temperatures of reaction, which of A, B or C was the coldest? Explain your answer.
c) If these results were for different concentrations of reaction, which of A, B or C was the strongest concentration? Explain your answer.
d) If these results were for different particle size of a solid reactant reaction, which of A, B or C was for the smallest particles? Explain your answer.

Visualisation – the blind mice and rice crispy bar

This is a thinking model for collision theory. This will help you imagine what the collisions would be like for different factors. For magnesium reacting with hydrochloric acid you have to visualise the mice (acid particles) moving and 'reacting' with the rice crispy bar (the magnesium).

Figure 7.17 The acid particles (the mice) react with the magnesium (rice crispy bar) and gradually the magnesium is used up (the rice crispy bar is eaten).

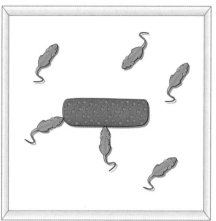

Figure 7.18 Slow-moving mice (low temperature) take all day to find and eat the rice crispy bar (slow reaction).

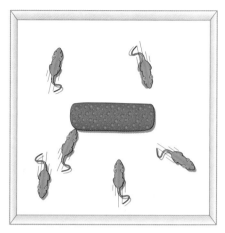

Figure 7.19 Fast scurrying mice (higher temperature) eat the bar up much more quickly (faster reaction).

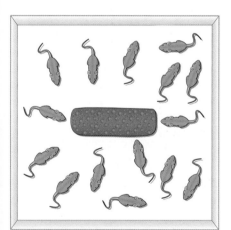

Figure 7.20 Lots more mice in the same space (higher concentration) eat the bar more quickly than a small number of mice.

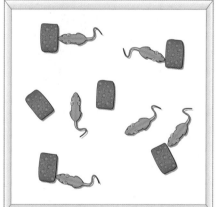

Figure 7.21 Even with a few mice, if the rice crispy bar is cut up into pieces it's more likely the mice will bump into a piece.

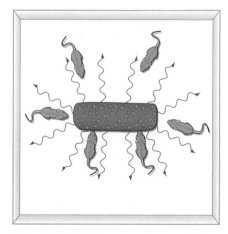

Figure 7.22 Explaining catalysts with this thinking model is difficult. But if a vibration attracted the mice to the crispy bar, then it would get eaten much more quickly.

The mice are not clever. For a mouse to take a bite out of the rice crispy bar it has to bump its nose into the bar first (this is like an effective collision). If the mouse just brushes past the bar (unsuccessful collision) then no rice crispies get eaten.

⑰ Explain why chips that are deep-fried in oil cook in 8 minutes, but boiling potatoes takes about 20 minutes.

⑱ Explain why if you cut the potatoes up smaller they cook faster. Crisps take only 20–30 seconds to deep fry.

⑲ Explain why crinkle cut chips cook faster than straight chips.

Figure 7.23 Cooking potatoes is a chemical change that sometimes takes ages and sometimes only a minute or two. The cooking process breaks down the strong cell walls, making the food easier to digest. Cooking also releases the starch from inside the cells.

Catalysts

> A **catalyst** is a material that speeds up the rate of a chemical change, without it being used up itself.

Catalysts speed up chemical reactions. The catalyst substance is not one of the reactants. It is not used up in the reaction. At the end of the reaction the catalyst is unchanged. This is why the formula for the catalyst does not appear in the equation for the reaction.

(See Chapter 3, p. 36 for more details.)

Figure 7.24 Hydrogen peroxide (H_2O_2) decomposes very slowly at room temperature to form water and oxygen. A catalyst such as manganese(IV) oxide or peroxidase (an enzyme found in raw liver) makes the decomposition reaction much faster.

⑳ Name two catalysts that make hydrogen peroxide decompose more quickly.

㉑ Write a word equation for the decomposition of hydrogen peroxide.

㉒ Suggest how you could measure the rate of a reaction to decompose hydrogen peroxide with a manganese oxide catalyst.

㉓ Sketch the graph that you would plot of your results, and show the point at which the reaction stops.

Figure 7.25 Hydrogen peroxide is found in highlight kits and permanent hair dyes. It doesn't just bleach – it also releases oxygen, which combines with the dye molecules and helps them deposit colour.

Industrial uses of catalysts

Industries use catalysts a lot. The catalysts are used to increase the rate of reaction of some important reactions to make useful products from raw materials.

Without the catalyst, some reactions would happen only very slowly. Other reactions would have to be carried out at a higher temperature. So the catalyst helps the process by saving time or by saving on heating costs.

One disadvantage of a catalyst is it needs to be separated from the product after the reaction. This is easy if the catalyst is a solid and the reactants are gases. But if both the catalyst and reactants are liquids, this could be difficult.

Different catalysts speed up different reactions, so each catalyst has only one use. Researchers have to test new catalysts for new industrial processes.

Reactants	Catalyst	Product
Nitrogen and hydrogen	An iron mesh to give large surface area	Ammonia
Sulfur dioxide and oxygen	Little lumps of vanadium oxide	Sulfur trioxide
Hydrogen and unsaturated fats or oils	Tiny particles of nickel	Margarine
Car exhaust polluting gases	Platinum on honeycomb of metal to increase surface area	Carbon dioxide and nitrogen (less polluting gases)
Ethene and steam	Phosphoric acid absorbed on to sand	Ethanol
Cracking of hydrocarbons	Zeolite rock crystals	More useful hydrocarbons
Ammonia and oxygen	Platinum metal mesh	Nitric acid for fertilisers and explosives

Table 7.2 Industrial reactions and catalysts

24 Use Table 7.2 to describe three examples that show that a catalyst should have a large surface area.

25 Catalysts are used in industrial processes to reduce costs.
a) Name three catalysts used in industry.
b) Name the materials that are made using each of these catalysts.
c) How can catalysts reduce energy costs in industrial processes?

26 Some catalysts are supported on an inert substance so they stay in one place. Other catalysts are mixed up with the reacting mixture. Give one example of each type of catalyst from the table.

27 a) Margarine has catalyst particles in it when it is manufactured. What has to happen to these catalyst particles before the margarine can be sold?
b) What does this processing do to the cost of making margarine?

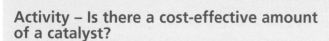

CHAPTER 7 How do we control the rate of chemical reactions and measure energy transfer?

Activity – Is there a cost-effective amount of a catalyst?

Lyubov investigated the question above as part of her GCSE practical work. She chose the decomposition reaction of hydrogen peroxide (H_2O_2) catalysed by manganese(IV) oxide.

$$2H_2O_2(aq) \xrightarrow{MnO_2} 2H_2O(l) + O_2(g)$$

She used $60\,cm^3$ of 2 volume hydrogen peroxide solution in all her tests. All the tests were carried out at room temperature and atmospheric pressure. She used similar apparatus each time.

Lyubov eventually produced the table of results below (Table 7.3).

She needs to analyse the data to reach a conclusion.

1 Materials such as platinum are used as catalysts in several chemical processes. Explain why it is important to be cost-effective in the use of catalysts.

2 List and draw the apparatus that Lyubov could have used to carry out this investigation.

3 Copy and complete Table 7.4 to summarise how Lyubov dealt with the many possible factors that would affect this investigation.

Factor	Type of variable	Range chosen	Controlled by Lyubov
Type of catalyst used		Manganese (IV) oxide	
Temperature and pressure			
Concentration of peroxide solution		2.0 volume solution	yes
Amount of catalyst			
Volume of oxygen given off			

Table 7.4

4 a) What is the maximum amount of oxygen gas produced in this experiment?
   b) What is the longest time measured?
   c) Use these answers to produce a scale for the horizontal axis (time) and a scale for the vertical axis (oxygen gas given off) for a set of graphs.

5 Plot a line graph for each set of results. Plot them all on the same axes on one piece of graph paper.

6 Write a conclusion answering the question in the title. Suggest, for this set of reaction conditions, which is the best amount to use.

Grams of catalyst used	0 g	5 g	10 g	15 g	20 g	25 g
Time in seconds	Total volume of oxygen gas released in cm³					
0	0	0	0	0	0	0
10	0	5	12	20	22	24
20	0	10	20	37	40	43
30	0	15	30	55	57	60
40	1	20	39	72	74	76
50	1	25	47	86	87	88
70	1	35	65	110	110	110
100	2	48	90	115	115	115
150	2	70	118	120	120	120
200	2	92	120	120	120	120

Table 7.3

Calculating concentrations of reactants in solution

In a well-mixed solution the solute particles are spread out evenly through the whole mixture. The solvent chemists use most often is water. We refer to solutions in water as aqueous solutions.

Chemicals are easy to handle in solutions. They are easy to measure, pour, heat and mix.

Using the mice model

As you can see from the diagrams showing reacting particles, the **concentration** of a solution is how many reactant particles there are in each unit of volume.

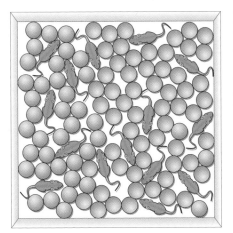

Figure 7.26 This is the 'mice thinking model' for solutions. The mice represent the acid particles. The ping-pong sized balls are the water molecules. In a very concentrated solution, there would be many more mice (acid particles) in the same volume of solution.

Concentration is the quantity of a chemical dissolved in each unit of volume.

28 Draw a particle picture to show both the solvent particles and the acid particles in a weakly acid solution. Use the mice model.

29 Explain why you get a much stronger taste on your tongue when you drink more concentrated orange squash.

30 Even if orange squash is very dilute, it still tastes a bit orangey. Explain this using a particle model.

Energy change in reactions

All chemical changes happen because there is an energy transfer that makes them happen.

To 'stay in control' of chemical reactions, you need to know the answers to these questions.
- How much energy gets transferred?
- Is the energy transfer 'in' or 'out' of the reactants when they make products?
- What energy transfer happens, and how can you make use of the energy transfer?

Exothermic means energy transferred out

Many chemical reactions transfer energy to the surroundings. Usually the energy heats up the surroundings. Sometimes the energy is transferred as light (glow sticks) or sound (explosions). These energy changes are called **exothermic reactions**. Combustion is an example of an exothermic reaction between a fuel and oxygen in the air.

Figure 7.27 Combustion reactions give out energy

Here is an example of an exothermic change you can try in the laboratory. During neutralisation, energy is given out when the new bonds in water molecules are formed and this causes the solution to be heated.

$25 \, cm^3$ of acid solution + $25 \, m^3$ of alkali solution	
Before mixing	**After mixing**
20 °C	29 °C

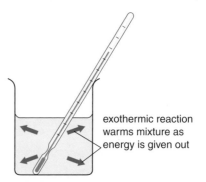

exothermic reaction warms mixture as energy is given out

Figure 7.28 An exothermic reaction transfers energy to the surroundings.

Endothermic means energy taken in

Not all chemical reactions cause a temperature increase. Some chemical changes cool down the reactants and their surroundings. To do this the reaction takes in energy from the surroundings and transfers it to the reactants. This is called an **endothermic reaction**. Thermal decomposition is an endothermic reaction, as the energy must be transferred to the reactant before it breaks down.

Here is an example of an endothermic change you can try in the laboratory. When sodium carbonate reacts with ethanoic acid, this causes cooling.

An **exothermic reaction** is a chemical change where energy is transferred to the surroundings, often causing heating.

An **endothermic reaction** is a chemical change where energy has to be absorbed from the surroundings, often as a heat transfer that causes cooling of the surroundings.

$100 \, cm^3$ of ethanoic acid + $10 \, g$ sodium carbonate	
Before mixing	**After mixing**
20 °C	6 °C

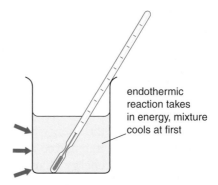

endothermic reaction takes in energy, mixture cools at first

Figure 7.29 An endothermic reaction absorbs energy from the surroundings.

Figure 7.30 A self-warming can of coffee heats the coffee with an exothermic reaction. A reaction occurs in a sealed compartment inside the can. The reaction gives out energy. This energy is transferred to the coffee, causing it to heat up.

Figure 7.31 Twist the pack and it gets cold enough to numb the pain of a sports injury. Injuries such as sprains or bruises hurt because of the swelling; cold helps to reduce swelling. The chemicals combine to take in energy, so the pack gets cold.

Figure 7.32 Glow sticks contain luminol, a chemical that gives out light energy when it reacts with another liquid in the glow stick.

31 When would 'self-heating coffee' be useful?

32 The can is heated by the reaction between calcium oxide and water. The only product of this reaction is calcium hydroxide. Write a word equation for the reaction.

33 What type of injuries are treated with cold packs?

34 Copy and complete Table 7.5 below.

Chemical change	Endothermic or exothermic?
Acid–alkali reaction	
Methane burning in a Bunsen burner	
Sodium reacting with water	
Calcium carbonate decomposing to calcium oxide and carbon dioxide	
Making aluminium metal	
Luminol reacting	

Table 7.5

CHAPTER 7 How do we control the rate of chemical reactions and measure energy transfer?

Energy changes in a reaction that goes both ways

Figure 7.33 Hydrated (blue) copper sulfate crystals have a formula of $CuSO_4.5H_2O$. They can be turned into anhydrous copper sulfate on heating. The anhydrous copper sulfate is slightly blue because it has absorbed water from the air.

Copper sulfate is blue crystals. But this substance actually has water in the crystal structure. It is called hydrated copper sulfate. If these crystals are heated they give off water vapour. The crystals turn into a white powder with no water in the crystal structure. This is called anhydrous copper sulfate.

When you add water to anhydrous copper sulfate, it heats up and the blue colour of the crystals returns. The anhydrous copper sulfate is turning back into hydrated copper sulfate. So the reaction is reversible.

The forward reaction (hydrated to anhydrous) is endothermic. Energy from the heating is taken in for the reaction to happen.

So the reverse reaction has to be exothermic. Energy is given out, and this heats up the substances.

Exactly the same amount of energy is transferred in each case.

$$\text{hydrated copper sulfate} \xrightarrow{\text{endothermic}} \xleftarrow{\text{exothermic}} \text{anhydrous copper sulfate} + \text{water}$$

(blue)   (white)

$CuSO_4.5H_2O(s)$ $CuSO_4(s) + 5H_2O(g)$

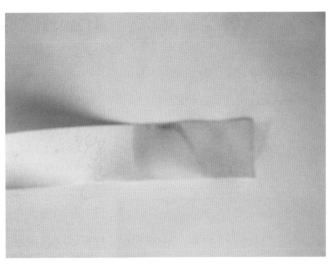

Figure 7.34 Testing for water. Filter paper is soaked in copper sulfate solution and dried in a hot oven. When the paper comes in contact with water, the anhydrous copper sulfate turns blue.

35 When 5 g of anhydrous copper sulfate are dissolved in 50 g of water the temperature rises by 10 °C.
Predict the rise in temperature in the reactions below.

Reaction	Temperature rise in °C
10 g of anhydrous copper sulfate are dissolved in 50 g of water	
10 g of anhydrous copper sulfate are dissolved in 100 g of water.	
20 g of anhydrous copper sulfate are dissolved in 100 g of water	

Table 7.6

36 Describe a procedure to test a few drops of a mystery colourless liquid, to see if it is water.

7.6 Equilibrium in reversible reactions

In a reversible reaction the forward reaction turns the reactants into products and the reverse reaction turns these products back into the reactants again. Sometimes all the reactants are changed to products. But sometimes the amounts of reactants and products reaches a balance, or equilibrium. The amounts of each chemical do not change.

CHAPTER 7 How do we control the rate of chemical reactions and measure energy transfer?

 7.7 ## The Haber process

Making ammonia

> **Ammonia** is a common compound of nitrogen. It is a smelly alkaline gas. Ammonia has the formula NH_3.

Plants need nitrates in the soil as one of their nutrients. The nitrates are used to make proteins. We eat the plants, or animals that feed on the plants. We use the proteins for growth and repair of our bodies.

Farmers add fertiliser to the soil to help plants grow. **Ammonia** compounds are needed to make nitrates for the fertilisers.

Just before the First World War, Fritz Haber invented a process to manufacture ammonia for fertilisers. Ammonia is also used to make the nitrates for the explosives in shells and bullets. Haber's invention allowed Germany to fight the First World War even though it was cut off from the ammonia deposits.

Using ammonia and its compounds can both sustain life (as fertilisers) and destroy it (as explosives). But Fritz Haber did not have either reason in mind when carrying out his research. He was just doing research.

From Haber's invention, industry developed a large-scale process for making ammonia. The reactants are the elements, hydrogen and nitrogen gas. These are easy to obtain and cost very little:
- hydrogen from natural gas (methane, CH_4) or from cracking other hydrocarbons;
- nitrogen obtained from the air.

Figure 7.35 Fritz Haber is known for making ammonia from its elements. He was born in Prussia in 1868. Haber won a Nobel prize for his work.

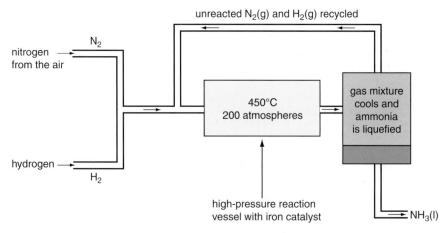

Figure 7.36 Flow diagram for the Haber process. Not all the hydrogen and nitrogen react. The remaining gases are recycled. An iron catalyst is used to speed up the reaction, so that ammonia can be produced quickly.

An iron catalyst is also used to speed up the reaction:

nitrogen   hydrogen   ammonia

$$N_2(g) + 3H_2(g) \rightleftharpoons 2NH_3(g)$$

The forward reaction is exothermic and the reverse reaction is endothermic.

Industrial chemistry and sustainable development

The atom economy of the Haber process is 100% because there are no by-products. Atom economy is very important for sustainable development, because all of the starting material is used and there are no waste products. It is also important for sustainable development to have industrial processes that waste little energy.

'Sustainable' processes also need:
- catalysts to reduce energy costs by carrying out the reaction at a lower temperature;
- new technology to recycle unreacted materials that could be reused;
- new ways to turn unwanted by-products (waste) into useful products;
- new reactions with higher atom economy to reduce waste and preserve resources.

The Haber process is run as a continuous reaction. This has benefits:
- The unused reactants can constantly be recycled. This is an efficient use of materials.
- The ammonia can be easily extracted from the mixture. It liquefies easily. This is an efficient use of energy and materials.

However, even with the use of a catalyst the Haber process uses a lot of energy because the reaction happens at a high temperature. Also, a lot of energy is also needed to extract nitrogen from the air.

In the 1930s when Jewish academics were persecuted, Haber realised that it was time to emigrate. He was offered a position in Britain at Cambridge and he left Germany in 1933.

Look at Figure 7.36 on page 136.

37 Describe what the Haber process is. What reactants does it use and what product does it make?

38 The Haber process resulted in damage because of warfare from explosives, and benefits for agriculture. Think about whether these factors balance out – or if the balance tips in favour of one or the other.

a) Make a list of the points for and against the uses of explosives and fertilisers.
b) Explain where you think the overall balance of benefit and damage ends up.

39 Make a list of the points where the Haber process scores well for atom economy and sustainability.

40 The Haber process does not score well for energy economy. Make a list of the points why this is.

CHAPTER 7 How do we control the rate of chemical reactions and measure energy transfer?

Summary

✓ Chemical reactions do not always turn all the reactants into useful products. Some of the material is wasted as by-products.

✓ In **reversible reactions** the products can react to form the original reactants, depending on the conditions.

✓ The fact that a reversible reaction does not go to completion is another reason why not as much product as expected is made.

✓ **Atom economy** is a measure of how many atoms of all the reactants end up as the product you want. This gives an idea of how much waste a process produces. This is important for **sustainable** development.

✓ The collision theory can be used to explain how different factors affect the **rate of reaction**.

✓ Reactions occur when reacting particles collide with more than the **activation energy**.

✓ The number and rate of **collisions** can be used to explain how different factors, such as heat, affect reaction rate.

✓ The **concentration** of a solution is the quantity of chemical dissolved in each unit of volume.

✓ **Exothermic reactions** give out energy; **endothermic reactions** take in energy.

✓ The Haber process turns nitrogen and hydrogen into **ammonia** using an iron **catalyst**, high pressure and moderate temperatures.

✓ Industrial processes should choose sustainable methods that minimise energy and material waste. Improved processes could also recycle unreacted materials, use renewable starting materials and discover ways of converting waste to useful by-products.

EXAM QUESTIONS

❶ a) Show how this symbol equation indicates that atoms are not created or destroyed in a chemical change. *(4 marks)*

b) Complete the table to show the meaning of the symbols.

Symbol	Meaning
(s)	Solid substance
(l)	
(g)	
(aq)	

Table 7.7
(3 marks)

❷ Copy and complete the sentences below, using the words in the box.

transferred	endothermic	light
exothermic	energy	chemical

When _____ changes happen _____ is always transferred. An _____ reaction gives out energy and an _____ reaction takes in energy. The energy is often _____ as heat. But it can be transferred as _____ or sound. *(6 marks)*

❸ Identical lumps of magnesium metal were dropped into two different concentrations of hydrochloric acid. After a certain time the magnesium had disappeared. The hydrogen gas given off was measured using an inverted measuring cylinder.

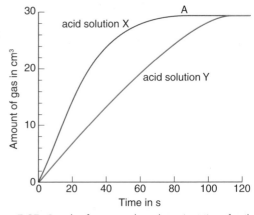

Figure 7.37 Graph of gas produced against time for the reaction between magnesium and acid

This graph (Figure 7.37 on page 138) was plotted of the results.

a) Write a word equation for this reaction.
    (2 marks)

b) When was the rate of reaction fastest? Explain your answer. *(3 marks)*

c) Which solution X or Y was more concentrated? Explain your answer.
    (3 marks)

d) Explain what happened at point A for the reaction with solution X. *(2 marks)*

e) Draw a simple sketch of the graph above and add a line to show the results you would expect for a solution Z. Solution Z is stronger acid than either solution X or Y.
    (3 marks)

f) Draw a simple sketch of the apparatus you would use for this experiment. *(3 marks)*

4 Two clear solutions, P and Q, are mixed in a conical flask. They gradually go cloudy until a cross under the conical flask can no longer be seen. The time for the cross to disappear is measured for different temperatures of the reacting solutions.

Temperature in °C	22	27	35	43	50	58
Time taken in seconds	327	260	198	175	118	100

Table 7.8

a) Draw a line graph of the data. Use temperature as the horizontal axis (from 20 °C to 60 °C) and time as the vertical axis (from 0 to 360 seconds). *(6 marks)*

b) One of the results was anomalous. Identify it. *(1 mark)*

c) Use your graph to find how long it takes for the cross to become obscured at 30 °C.
    (2 marks)

d) Use collision theory to explain the shape of the graph. *(5 marks)*

5 In the Contact process, sulfur dioxide is turned into sulfur trioxide. This is reacted with water to make sulfuric acid. Vanadium pentoxide is used as the catalyst.

$$2SO_2(g) \quad + \quad O_2(g) \quad \rightleftharpoons \quad 2SO_3(g)$$

exothermic reaction

sulfur dioxide   oxygen   sulfur trioxide

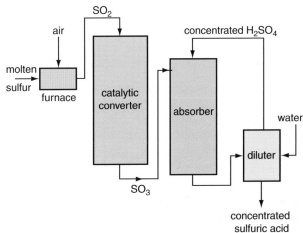

Figure 7.38 Flow diagram for making sulfuric acid

a) What are the reactants in this process?
    (2 marks)

b) What is the product in this process?
    (1 mark)

c) What important material is made from this product? *(1 mark)*

d) What is the purpose of the catalyst?
    (2 marks)

e) Explain what is meant by this sign: $\rightleftharpoons$.
    (2 marks)

f) Explain what is meant by the words **exothermic reaction**. *(2 marks)*

g) Explain why it is important to make best use of energy and materials in an industrial process. (*Hint*: Think about atom economy and sustainable development.) *(4 marks)*

Chapter 8
How can we use ions in solutions?

At the end of this chapter you should:

✓ know that when an ionic substance is melted or dissolved in water it breaks up into particles called ions;

✓ know that ions are particles that carry a permanent electrical charge;

✓ know that these ions can move about within the molten substance or in solution;

✓ know that salt solutions can be crystallised to produce a solid salt;

✓ know how to predict what salt is produced in a reaction;

✓ know how ammonium salts are produced and their uses as fertilisers;

✓ be able to choose methods to make a named salt;

✓ know that electrolysis breaks down liquid ionic compounds to produce elements;

✓ know about oxidation and reduction in electrolysis;

✓ know if there is a mixture of ions, the products formed depend on the reactivity of the elements involved;

✓ understand that electrolysis of sodium chloride solution produces important substances for the chemical industry;

✓ know that copper can be purified by electrolysis.

Figure 8.1 Common salt – it's for more than chips! It's a raw material for many useful products. Salt is used to make bleach, soap, caustic soda (sodium hydroxide), water softeners, chlorine and glass. Salt is also used for preserving meat and dyeing. Every cell of your body contains salt, a total of 250 g per person. Salt in body fluids is essential for muscle action – too little and you get cramp. For many of these uses and products, a solution of salt is needed. If salt did not dissolve, none of these uses would be possible.

What are ions – and what does melting and dissolving do to ions?

Ions are particles formed when atoms react by losing or gaining electrons. They have an electrical charge, so they have to exist as positive ions balanced by negative ions. (Refresh your memory of ionic bonds in Section 5.6 and giant ionic structures in Section 6.7.)

Ions can be made from a single atom (e.g. a magnesium ion Mg^{2+}) or from a group of atoms (e.g. a nitrate ion NO_3^-). Pure ionic substances are all solids at room temperature.

> A solid, liquid or gas dissolved in a solvent is a **solution**.
>
> A **solvent** is a substance (usually a liquid) that dissolves another substance to form a solution.

When you melt a substance made of ions, the ions are free to move about in the molten liquid. Ions that are dissolved in water can also be free to move about randomly in the **solution**. When you put an ionic solid into water, the water molecules can get in between the particles of the ionic solid and separate them. This makes them dissolve. Water is a **solvent**.

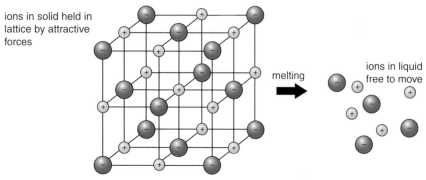

ions in solid held in lattice by attractive forces

melting

ions in liquid free to move

Figure 8.2 Melting an ionic compound means the ions are free to move.

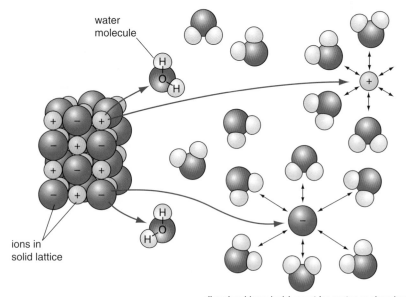

water molecule

ions in solid lattice

dissolved ions held apart by water molecules

Figure 8.3 In a solution of an ionic compound the positive and negative ions are free to move about separately, kept apart by water molecules round the ions. There are equal numbers of positive and negative charges.

Figure 8.4 The colourless solutions are two separate mixtures, one of barium and chloride ions, the other of sodium and sulfate ions. When the solutions are mixed the barium and sulfate ions react together to form a white precipitate.

A **precipitation reaction** is a reaction that produces an insoluble solid from solutions. The solid produced is called a precipitate.

A **salt** is an ionic compound. Most salts are made up of positively charged metal ions and negatively charged non-metal ions. Salts form when an acid neutralises an alkali.

Crystallisation

When the water in a solution evaporates, the solution becomes more concentrated. Eventually there will not be enough water to keep the ions in solution. The positive and negative ions join back together to form a solid. If the evaporation of the water is slow, the ionic solid forms as large, evenly shaped crystals.

Precipitation

If two solutions are mixed and one pair of ions reacts to form an insoluble substance as a solid this is called a **precipitation reaction**. For example:

$$BaCl_2(aq) \quad + \quad Na_2SO_4(aq) \quad \rightarrow \quad BaSO_4(s) \quad + \quad 2NaCl(aq)$$

| barium chloride (solution) | sodium sulfate (solution) | barium sulfate (solid) | sodium chloride (solution) |

The solid barium sulfate precipitates out (Figure 8.4), leaving the sodium ions and chloride ions still in solution. (Remember, (aq) means aqueous or in solution.) The sodium and chloride ions are called 'spectator ions' because they do not take part in the reaction.

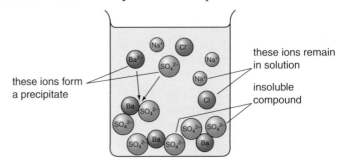

these ions form a precipitate

these ions remain in solution

insoluble compound

Figure 8.5 When two ionic solutions are mixed, one pair of ions forms a solid precipitate that can be removed from the solution, but the other ions remain in solution.

Uses of precipitation reactions

Precipitation can be used to remove unwanted ions from solution.

Drinking water contains dissolved iron and other metal ions that are not harmful to human health. However, they can form brown stains on sinks, and darken cups when combined with tea. These ions are removed in water treatment plants by adding a lime (calcium hydroxide) solution (rock 'lime', not fruit lime). A precipitate forms and can be filtered out.

The same precipitation reaction can be used to remove dissolved metal ions from waste water in mines and factories. Metals such as cadmium and lead are poisonous so must be removed before the waste water gets into drinking water. They are precipitated out when the waste water is mixed with lime.

Fertilisers can contaminate rivers and cause weeds to grow a lot. The weeds then rot and take all the oxygen out of the water. Adding a metal **salt** (such as aluminium sulfate) to the waste water precipitates out the fertiliser.

❶ Use the data from page 231 to write the formulae of:
a) sodium nitrate;
b) aluminium chloride;
c) magnesium sulfate;
d) ammonium carbonate;
e) calcium hydroxide.

❷ Explain why a dissolved metal ion can form a solid when you mix a colourless sample solution with another colourless solution.

❸ Draw a diagram to represent particles in a solution of sodium chloride.

❹ Copy the sentences below. Use the words in the box to fill in the gaps.

charged	copper	crystals	chloride
cubes	dissolve	evaporate	ion
molecules	opposite	paired	shape

Some substances are not made of _____ – they are made of ions. An _____ is a _____ particle that can exist on its own. In a compound each ion is always _____ up with an ion of the _____ charge. Many ionic compounds, such as sodium _____ and _____ sulfate, will _____ in water. When a solution is left to _____, the solid compound reappears as regularly shaped _____. All the crystals of the same compound are the same _____. Sodium chloride crystals are tiny regular _____.

❺ Two solutions will form a precipitate when mixed if one pair of the ions mixed together makes an insoluble compound. Here are some data from mixing different solutions.

Solutions mixed	Colour of precipitate
Sodium chloride and calcium nitrate	No precipitate
Silver nitrate and sodium chloride	White precipitate
Silver nitrate and calcium chloride	White precipitate

Table 8.1

What is the white precipitate? Explain how you worked this out.

8.2 How do acids and alkalis react?

Oxygen is a very reactive element. It reacts with both metal and non-metal elements. It combines with them to form oxides.

Non-metal oxides make acids if they dissolve in water. Metal oxides make alkalis if they dissolve in water. That's where many acid and alkali solutions come from.

Acid solutions all contain hydrogen ions. Hydrogen ions (H^+) are the acid particles. **Alkali** solutions all contain hydroxide ions (OH^-). These are the alkali particles.

When an acid or alkali dissolves in water, the substance splits up to make hydrogen ions or hydroxide ions. The other dissolved ion formed is a 'spectator ion'. It is there but takes no part in the reaction between the acid and the alkali.

$$HCl(aq) \rightarrow H^+(aq) + Cl^-(aq)$$

hydrochloric acid → hydrogen ion + chloride ion

$$NaOH(aq) \rightarrow Na^+(aq) + OH^-(aq)$$

sodium hydroxide → sodium ion + hydroxide ion

An **acid** is a substance that produces H^+ ions to make an acidic solution with a pH less than 7.

An **alkali** is a substance that releases OH^- ions to make an alkaline solution with a pH greater than 7.

All acids react in similar ways. This is because only the hydrogen ion in the acid reacts. The alkali reactions of the hydroxide ion are all the same for a similar reason. The spectator ions take no part in acid or alkali reactions.

Explaining neutralisation

> **Neutralisation** of an acid with an alkali produces water molecules.

In a **neutralisation** reaction, hydrogen ions react with hydroxide ions to produce water.

$$H^+(aq) \quad + \quad OH^-(aq) \quad \rightarrow \quad H_2O(l)$$

$$\text{hydrogen ion} \quad + \quad \text{hydroxide ion} \quad \rightarrow \quad \text{water}$$

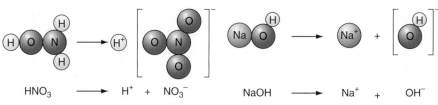

$$HNO_3 \longrightarrow H^+ + NO_3^-$$

$$NaOH \longrightarrow Na^+ + OH^-$$

Figure 8.6 Nitric acid HNO_3 splits into H^+ (hydrogen ions) and NO_3^- (nitrate ions).

Figure 8.7 Sodium hydroxide NaOH splits into Na^+ (sodium ions) and OH^- (hydroxide ions).

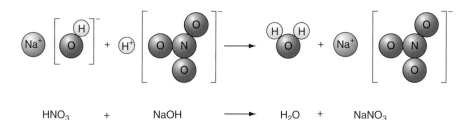

$$HNO_3 \quad + \quad NaOH \quad \longrightarrow \quad H_2O \quad + \quad NaNO_3$$

Figure 8.8 A neutralisation reaction. When sodium hydroxide (an alkali) reacts with nitric acid the H^+ and OH^- ions react to form water, but the Na^+ and NO_3^- ions stay dissolved.

> **6** Some acids in are so reactive that they are dangerous to eyes and flesh. Design a warning poster for using strong acids. On the poster:
> a) say what safety equipment should be used when handling acids;
> b) use the warning symbol for corrosive materials;
> c) write a list of rules for safety with strong acids.

Example

$$\{H^+(aq) \text{ and } NO_3^-(aq)\} + \{Na^+(aq) \text{ and } OH^-(aq)\} \rightarrow \{Na^+(aq) \text{ and } NO_3^-(aq)\} + H_2O$$

    nitric acid   sodium hydroxide   sodium nitrate (dissolved) + water

Note that:
- If you remove the spectator ions from the picture, then all neutralisation equations become the same:

$$H^+(aq) + OH^-(aq) \rightarrow H_2O(l)$$

- So only one change happens in any acid/alkali reaction – hydrogen ions join with hydroxide ions to make water molecules.
- The spectator ions are left over. They form the salt in the reaction, and stay dissolved.

pH scale

The pH scale is used to measure the acidity or alkalinity of a solution:
- pH 7 is the value for neutral solutions;
- pH 1 is a strong acid;
- pH 14 is a strong alkali.

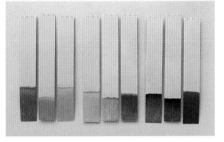

Figure 8.9 Universal indicator is a mixture of substances that reacts to the pH of a solution by turning different colours. This range of colours matches the pH scale.

8.3 How can we make different salts by neutralisation?

When a solution of an ionic compound evaporates, the solid crystallises out. A solid salt is formed. When acids are neutralised the spectator ions are left as ions in solution. If all the water is evaporated just the spectator ions are left behind and they make a solid salt.

An acid plus an alkali forms a salt plus water. The acid and alkali used determine the type of salt made (Table 8.2).

Acid or alkali	Salt made
Nitric acid	Nitrates
Hydrochloric acid	Chlorides
Sulfuric acid	Sulfates
Ethanoic acid	Ethanoates
Sodium hydroxide	Sodium salts
Potassium hydroxide	Potassium salts
Ammonia solution (alkali)	Ammonium salts

Table 8.2

The pattern is the same for other acids and alkalis. You can work out the formula of the salt formed if you know the charges on the ions that make it (see page 231).

Using indicators to prepare a salt

Acid and alkali solutions are usually both colourless. When you are making a salt by neutralisation you must measure the pH to show when the solution is exactly neutral. In a neutral solution only the dissolved salt will be present, and no left over acid or alkali.

Figure 8.10 You can use a pH meter to test when the solution is neutral.

To see if the solution is neutral:
- you can use a pH meter;
- you can add the acid or alkali solution a little at a time and check the pH after each addition by dropping a sample onto indicator paper;
- you can leave the indicator in the reaction flask as the solutions are mixed. Keep adding the neutralising solution until the indicator colour just changes. The indicator is removed by adding two spatulas of charcoal and heating. The charcoal absorbs the indicator and can be filtered off, leaving a colourless solution.

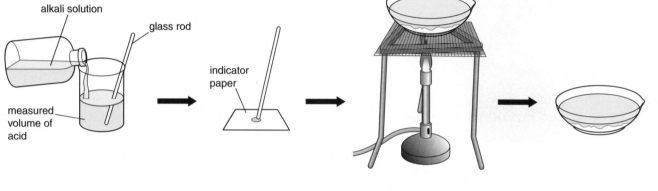

1 Add alkali a little at a time to the acid. Stir well.

2 Check pH after each addition.

3 When the acid is just neutralised, evaporate the salt solution to crystallising point.

4 Set aside to cool and crystallise.

Figure 8.11 Preparing a pure soluble salt by neutralisation

Figure 8.12 Measuring the volume of acid accurately for a neutralisation reaction

Ammonia

Ammonia (NH_3) is a very smelly gas. It is very soluble in water. Water will dissolve 1500 times its own volume of ammonia gas. When ammonia dissolves in water it makes an alkaline solution.

Ammonium salts are made by neutralisation and are important as fertilisers. The ammonia is the source of nitrogen for plants to make proteins.

7 a) What substances dissolve in water to produce acids?
   b) What substances dissolve in water to produce alkalis?

8 What is a hydrogen ion? Explain as much as you can about the reactions of a hydrogen ion.

9 a) What is a hydroxide ion?
   b) Explain what happens when a hydroxide ion neutralises a hydrogen ion.

10 What is meant by a 'spectator ion'?

What other ways are there of making salts?

> A **base** is a compound that will neutralise an acid by forming water molecules as one of the products.

In chemistry, a **base** is a metal oxide or hydroxide. If a base reacts with water to form a hydroxide solution, it is an alkali, but some bases are insoluble. Don't confuse the chemical word 'base' with all the other meanings of the word base, e.g. in sports, in apparatus, in mountain climbing, in 'back to base', etc.

Acid plus insoluble base forms a soluble salt

Figure 8.13 Copper oxide dissolves in hydrochloric acid to give a blue solution of copper chloride. Unreacted copper oxide has settled to the bottom.

$$2 \times (H^+ \text{ and } Cl^-)(aq) \quad + \quad CuO(s) \quad \rightarrow \quad (Cu^{2+} \text{ and } 2 \times Cl^-)(aq) \quad + \quad H_2O(l)$$

hydrochloric acid   copper oxide   copper chloride   water

To make copper chloride solution:
- Add copper oxide to hydrochloric acid until no more will react.
- The oxygen in the oxide combines with the hydrogen ions in the acid and water molecules are formed.
- The 'spectator ions' are left in solution to make copper chloride.
- All the acid is neutralised and the remaining (excess) copper oxide can be filtered off.
- Heat the mixture gently for a few minutes.
- This evaporates the water from the copper chloride solution.
- The copper chloride starts to crystallise out.

Acid plus metal forms a soluble salt plus hydrogen

> A **displacement reaction** is a reaction where a more reactive metal displaces a less reactive from a solution of its compound.

Many reactive metals also make salts when added to acids. The reaction is a **displacement reaction,** not a neutralisation reaction. The reaction does not work for the less reactive metals such as copper or gold.

Only the metals above hydrogen in the reactivity series react with an acid to make a salt.

To make a salt from a metal plus an acid:
- Add an excess of metal.
- Leave the reaction for a length of time – don't heat since hydrogen gas forms an explosive mixture with air.
- When the reaction is finished, filter off the unreacted metal.
- The salt solution is left.

For example, you can make zinc sulfate by adding zinc to sulfuric acid:

Reactivity series for metals
Potassium
Sodium
Lithium
Calcium
Magnesium
Aluminium
Zinc
Iron
Lead
<u>Hydrogen</u>
Copper
Silver
Gold

$$Zn(s) \quad + \quad H_2SO_4(aq) \quad \rightarrow \quad ZnSO_4(aq) \quad + \quad H_2(g)$$

zinc metal   sulfuric acid   zinc sulfate   hydrogen gas

Insoluble salts

When two ionic solutions are mixed a precipitate can form. The precipitate is an insoluble salt and can be filtered off. The solid is washed with pure water to remove any remaining salt solution, and dried to give the pure dry insoluble salt.

Figure 8.14 Soluble zinc sulfate is formed when zinc reacts with sulfuric acid. The fizz is hydrogen being released.

⑪ What is the difference between a base and an alkali?

⑫ Name three chemical 'bases'.

⑬ Magnesium chloride could be made by reacting magnesium granules with hydrochloric acid.
  a) Draw the apparatus you would use.
  b) Hydrogen is produced in this reaction. Why could it be dangerous if you heated the mixture?
  c) Write a step-by-step way of making magnesium chloride crystals by this method.

⑭ Copy and complete the sentences using the words in the box.

> acid   base   carbonate   copper   gas
> neutralised   solution   unreacted

When an insoluble _____ is reacted with an _____ it neutralises the acid. Sometimes there is a _____ given off if the base is a _____. Sometimes the _____ goes coloured, for example when you are making _____ salts.

You can tell when the acid is _____ because the reaction stops and the _____ base settles at the bottom of the mixture.

8.5 Electrolysis

Ions are free to move about when an ionic substance is molten or dissolved in water.

Electrolysis is the process of splitting up a chemical compound into its elements. This can be done by passing an electric current through a solution, or through a molten material containing ions.

The electrolyte is the liquid containing ions that conducts electricity.

The **electrode** is the physical connection between an electric circuit and another material. It is usually made from a material that won't corrode such as a carbon rod or platinum foil.

An electric circuit can be connected to the liquid by using conducting sticks of graphite or metal called **electrodes.** Then the electrically charged ions move towards the electrodes with the opposite charge.

Chemical changes take place at the electrodes as the ions gain and lose electrons. The electricity can turn ions back into elements.

Figure 8.15 Electrolysis does many jobs in science. These batteries are used in a chemical factory to electrolyse brine.

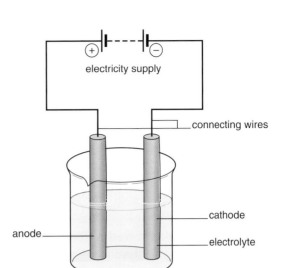

Figure 8.16 Electrolysis

For example, in the electrolysis of molten lead bromide:
- At the negative electrode (**cathode**) – positive charged lead ions are attracted to the cathode. Lead ions gain electrons so they become lead metal again.

lead ions + 2 electrons → lead metal

- At the positive electrode (**anode**) – negative charged bromide ions are attracted to the anode. Electrons are pulled away from the bromide ions to turn them into atoms again, so they become bromine as an element.

bromide ions + 2 electrons → bromine gas

Electrolysis is the method we use to extract most reactive metals, such as sodium and aluminium, from their molten metal ores.

> The **cathode** is the negative electrode in a solution and attracts positive ions.
>
> The **anode** is the positive electrode in a solution and attracts negative ions.

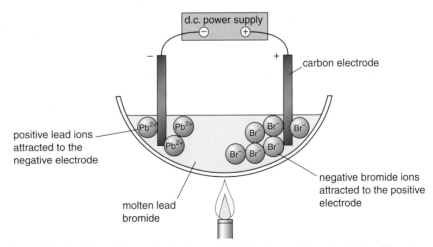

Figure 8.17 Lead bromide can be broken up into its elements, lead metal and bromine gas, by electrolysis.

Oxidation is loss of electrons. In electrolysis this happens at the positive electrode when a negatively charged ion loses electrons.

Reduction is gain of electrons. In electrolysis this happens at the negative electrode when a positively charged ion gains electrons.

OIL RIG

When oxygen reacts with a metal and oxidises it, the oxygen atoms remove electrons from the metal to make negatively charged oxide ions. The metal atoms become positively charged ions. When any other non-metal reacts with a metal, electrons are also transferred from the metal to the non-metal. This process is also called **oxidation**.

For example, oxygen oxidises magnesium to form a compound with Mg^{2+} and O^{2-} ions. In the same way, chlorine oxidises magnesium to form a compound with Mg^{2+} and Cl^- ions. In both cases the magnesium atom loses electrons.

Reduction with carbon or hydrogen is the reverse process. The carbon pulls the oxygen away from the less reactive metal ion and gives the electrons back, so the metal ion becomes a metal atom again.

For example, carbon monoxide reduces iron oxide to iron. The Fe^{2+} ions gain electrons, so we say the iron is reduced.

We can define oxidation and reduction as follows:

Oxidation Is Loss (of electrons)

Reduction Is Gain (of electrons)

This gives us the memory clue OIL RIG.

Electrolysis of solutions

In a solution, the ions are attracted to the electrode that has the opposite charge. There the ions are turned into atoms of elements.

Sometimes the water of the solution gets broken down instead. This means a different substance can be produced at the electrode. This happens for solutions of the more reactive metals, such as potassium, sodium, lithium, calcium and magnesium.

Example

When sodium chloride solution is electrolysed, hydrogen is formed at the negative electrode. Hydrogen ions in the water gain electrons at the cathode to form molecules of hydrogen gas. The positive ions from the salt (Na^+) stay in solution. At the positive electrode, chloride ions lose an electron to form molecules of chlorine gas. Hydroxide ions (OH^-) from the water stay in solution.

This means the original sodium chloride solution forms three products: hydrogen, chlorine and sodium hydroxide solution.

Mixtures of ions in solution

In solutions containing a mixture of ions, the products formed depend on the reactivity of the elements. If a mixture of positive ions is present, then the ion of the element with the lowest reactivity will form an atom first. For example, in a mixture of magnesium chloride and hydrochloric acid, hydrogen is produced, not magnesium.

15 Explain what these terms mean:
   a) electrolyte;
   b) electrolysis;
   c) anode;
   d) cathode.

16 Draw a particle picture for the electrolysis of molten lead bromide.
   Show the positive lead ions moving to the negative electrode and becoming lead atoms.
   Show the negative bromide ions moving to the positive electrode and becoming molecules of bromine gas.

17 Copy and complete the table.

Liquid being electrolysed	Product at negative electrode (cathode)	Product at positive electrode (anode)
Molten lead bromide		
Molten aluminium oxide		
Copper chloride solution		
Potassium iodide solution		

Table 8.3

8.6 Uses of electrolysis

Electrolysis of water

Pure water is a very poor conductor. But if you add a little acid to the water, then it will conduct electricity. This reaction breaks down water into hydrogen and oxygen gases. It is the basis of making the hydrogen used in fuel cells for electric vehicles.

Making aluminium metal

Aluminium is high in the reactivity series. You can't get aluminium from aluminium ore in a blast furnace. Aluminium is too reactive.

Aluminium metal is produced by the electrolysis of molten aluminium oxide (from bauxite ore). The aluminium oxide has a high melting point and is dissolved in a molten substance called cryolite.

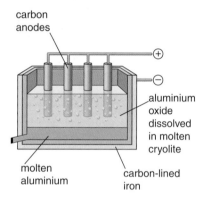

Figure 8.19 Aluminium oxide is decomposed by electrolysis in this industrial plant. The molten aluminium is siphoned out of the bottom of the cell.

Figure 8.18 The statue of Eros in Piccadilly Circus, London, was one of the first statues made out of aluminium.

Purification of copper metal by electrolysis

When it is made, copper metal contains many impurities (lead, nickel, zinc, gold, silver) that make it a poor electrical conductor. This impure copper is purified by electrolysis.

Large impure slabs of copper are used as the positive electrode and pure sheets of copper are used as the cathode. During electrolysis copper from the impure anode turns into copper ions and these ions go into solution. The positive copper ions are attracted to the cathode, where they turn into copper atoms. These copper atoms are added onto the cathode. As the impure copper anode crumbles away, all the impurities collect at the bottom of the cell as sludge.

Figure 8.20 To be used as copper wire, the copper has to be very pure.

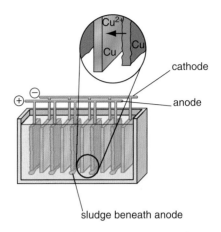

Figure 8.21 The impure copper anode dissolves away and pure copper is deposited on the cathode.

Electrolysis of sodium chloride solution

Concentrated brine (salt solution) is electrolysed to produce chlorine, hydrogen and sodium hydroxide in a membrane cell. These chemicals have many industrial uses. Hydrogen gas is a by-product of the process.

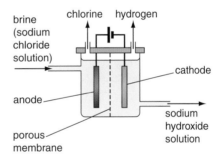

Figure 8.22 The membrane cell used to make chlorine and sodium hydroxide

⑱ Name three products we can make from the electrolysis of sodium chloride solution.

⑲ a) Why can't you make aluminium in a blast furnace?
   b) What is the name of the aluminium ore from which we obtain aluminium oxide?
   c) For what purpose is cryolite used?
   d) Write a word equation for the production of aluminium metal from ore.

⑳ a) Aluminium is a metal that takes a lot of energy to produce. List five reasons why we should recycle as much aluminium as we can.
   b) Aluminium cans for drinks can easily be recycled. Draw up a simple flow chart for a system to collect and recycle these cans.

Summary

✓ There are several types of substances that will neutralise acids and form a **salt**:

$$acid + alkali \rightarrow salt + water$$

$$acid + metal\ oxide\ (base) \rightarrow salt + water$$

$$acid + reactive\ metal \rightarrow salt + hydrogen$$

✓ Ions are free to move in a molten ionic compound or in a **solution**.

✓ Evaporation crystallises the solid salt out of solution.

✓ Ions dissolved in solutions can form an insoluble precipitate when two solutions are mixed. This is called a **precipitation reaction**.

✓ Acid solutions contain hydrogen ions (H^+); alkalis contain hydroxide ions (OH^-).

✓ Metal oxides and hydroxides are **bases**, and form alkalis if they dissolve in water.

✓ **Neutralisation** of an acid with an alkali produces water molecules.

✓ Ammonium salts are important as fertilisers.

✓ Liquids that contain ions conduct electricity.

✓ Positive ions (such as metal ions) are attracted to the **cathode**, while non-metal negative ions are attracted to the **anode**.

✓ When electricity passes through liquids there are chemical changes at the **electrodes**. The ions are oxidised or reduced.

✓ **Oxidation** is loss of electrons. In electrolysis this happens at the positive electrode when a negatively charged ion gains electrons.

✓ **Reduction** is gain of electrons. In electrolysis this happens at the negative electrode when a positively charged ion loses electrons.

✓ Electrolysis is an important industrial process. It can be used to:
   - produce hydrogen fuel;
   - extract aluminium and other reactive metals from their ores;
   - purify copper metal for electrical use;
   - produce chlorine and sodium hydroxide from the electrolysis of salt (sodium chloride).

1 Copy and complete this table to show the chemicals needed for making each salt, or the salt produced.

Name of acid	Name of alkali	Name of salt
Sulfuric acid	Sodium hydroxide	
Hydrochloric acid		Lithium chloride
		Calcium nitrate
		Magnesium chloride

Table 8.4

(*6 marks*)

2 Draw a flow chart and the apparatus needed for a method to produce clean dry salt crystals by neutralising sulfuric acid with potassium hydroxide solution, using universal indicator.
(*10 marks*)

3 Making salts is about neutralising acids. How would you make sure that all the acid had been exactly neutralised in each of these reactions?
a) an acid plus soluble metal carbonate reaction; (*2 marks*)
b) an acid plus metal oxide reaction; (*2 marks*)
c) an acid plus alkali reaction. (*2 marks*)

4 a) What is the formula of ammonia? (*1 mark*)
b) i) Is ammonia a liquid or a gas? (*1 mark*)
ii) Is it an acid or an alkali? (*1 mark*)
iii) What elements does it contain? (*1 mark*)
iv) How soluble is it in water? (*1 mark*)
c) Why is ammonia or its compounds useful to farmers? (*2 marks*)

5 Explain what the products would be from the electrolysis of these liquids:
a) acidified water (H_2O); (*2 marks*)
b) molten zinc chloride ($ZnCl_2$); (*2 marks*)
c) sodium chloride solution ($NaCl(aq)$). (*2 marks*)

6 The apparatus in the diagram is used in industry to purify copper. The anode and cathode are made out of copper and the electrolyte is copper sulfate solution.

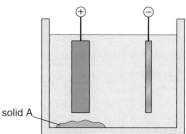

Figure 8.23

a) Explain why the anode is made of a large block of impure copper. (*2 marks*)
b) Explain why the cathode is made of a thin sheet of pure copper. (*2 marks*)
c) What is the difference in properties of pure and impure copper? (*1 mark*)
d) What is the solid A that accumulates below the anode? (*2 marks*)
e) Copy and complete the sentences using the words below

building	conduct	copper
electrical	electrolysis	impurities
	manufacturing	pure

_____ is a very useful metal. Its main use is in _____ wire. Copper wire has to be very _____ or it does not _____ well. Raw copper from the _____ plant has a lot of _____ in it such as other metals. It is purified so it can be used in wires for _____ houses. The purification is done by _____.

(*8 marks*)

Chapter 9
How can we describe and change the way things move?

At the end of this chapter you should:

✓ be able to use a distance–time graph or velocity–time graph to describe the movement of a body;

✓ know that the slope of a distance–time graph represents speed;

✓ know that the slope of a velocity–time graph represents acceleration;

✓ know that the area under a velocity–time graph represents distance travelled;

✓ understand that if a resultant force acts on a body, the body will accelerate;

✓ know that the force of gravity causes a falling body to accelerate but the body reaches a terminal velocity when the resultant force is zero;

✓ be able to describe factors that affect the stopping distance of a vehicle;

✓ understand that work is done when a force transfers energy;

✓ know that the kinetic energy of a body depends on both its mass and its speed;

✓ know that momentum is conserved in any collision or explosion, provided no external forces act on the colliding or exploding bodies;

✓ be able to use the equations for acceleration, force, weight, work done and momentum;

✓ be able to explain safety features using the idea of momentum.

Figure 9.1 The safety features of a car include crumple zones, seat belts and air bags. In an accident, these features make the time taken to slow down and stop longer. This makes the forces on you smaller. A small force gives you a better chance of not being seriously injured.

What's the difference between speed, velocity and acceleration?

Speed

A journey takes less time when you travel at a high speed than when you travel at a low speed. Some trains are so fast they travel 92 metres in just one second. This is a speed of 92 metres per second (92 m/s) and is the average speed of the train.

Velocity

When you go somewhere it's not just speed that is important: direction also counts.

The two joggers in Figure 9.3 have the same speed but they are running in opposite directions. One has a **velocity** of 3 m/s to the right and the other has a velocity of 3 m/s to the left. Instead of writing right or left, we can use arrows to show direction.

Figure 9.2 The average speed of a snail is just 0.0005 m/s. How far would a snail go in 60 seconds?

The **velocity** of a body is its speed and direction.

speed = 3 m/s	speed = 3 m/s
velocity = 3 m/s ←	velocity = 3 m/s →

Figure 9.3 Where you end up depends on your speed and direction.

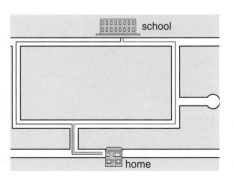

Figure 9.4 Stacey's routes to school

Figure 9.4 shows two routes that Stacey can take to school.

The two routes are the same distance and take Stacey the same time. This means that Stacey goes at the same speed on both routes. But the two routes are in different directions. Each time Stacey changes direction her velocity changes.

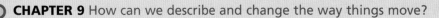

❶ Figure 9.5 shows the speed and direction of four animals.

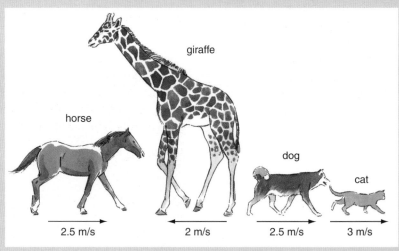

Figure 9.5

Which two animals have the same velocity? Give a reason for your answer.

The **acceleration** of an object is how quickly its velocity changes.

Figure 9.6 Olympic runners accelerating off the blocks

❷ A falcon hovering in the sky sees its prey and dives downwards. The falcon reaches a velocity of 9 m/s in just 1.5 s. Calculate the acceleration of the falcon.

Acceleration

Something accelerates when its velocity changes.

Acceleration is calculated using this equation:

$$\text{acceleration} = \frac{\text{change in velocity}}{\text{time taken for change}}$$

If velocity is measured in metres per second (m/s) and time in seconds (s), the unit of acceleration is metres per second per second, which is usually written as m/s^2.

Example
At the start of a 100 metre race, an Olympic runner accelerates to 12 m/s in 2 seconds. What is the acceleration of the runner?

starting velocity = 0 m/s
final velocity = 12 m/s
time taken = 2 s

$$\text{acceleration} = \frac{\text{change in velocity}}{\text{time taken}} = \frac{12 - 0}{2} = 6 \text{ m/s}^2$$

❸ A train travelling along a straight track accelerates from 10 m/s to 35 m/s in 100 seconds. Calculate the acceleration of the train.

Deceleration

A car slows down when you put on the brakes. A car that slows down is decelerating.

> ❹ Copy and complete the following sentence by choosing the correct word or words from the brackets. The speed of a decelerating car is [increasing / not changing / decreasing].

Figure 9.7 On landing a jet fighter uses its brakes and a parachute to produce a large deceleration.

> ❺ A motorbike decelerates from 20 m/s to rest (0 m/s) in 4 seconds. Calculate the deceleration of the motorbike.

9.2 Using graphs to describe the motion of a body

Two types of graph can be used to describe how a body moves.

Distance–time graphs

A **distance–time graph** can be used to describe the speed of a body.

Figure 9.8 shows the distance–time graph for a short car journey.

The car is travelling the same distance, 600 metres, every 60 seconds. So the car is moving at a constant speed.

Steve and his horse, Rocket, take part in a long-distance ride. Figure 9.9 shows the distance–time graph for the ride. The graph has been divided into three parts.

> The slope of a **distance–time graph** gives the speed of a body.

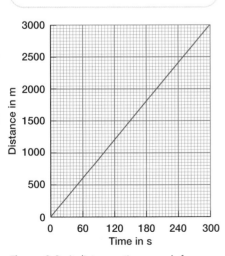

Figure 9.8 A distance–time graph for a short car journey

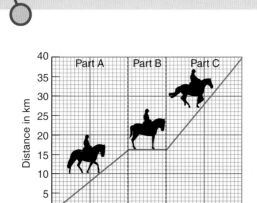

Figure 9.9 Distance–time graph for a horse ride

- Part A – Steve and Rocket move at a constant speed. They travel 16 kilometres in 2 hours.
- Part B – The distance moved does not change. Steve and Rocket have stopped to take a rest.

When a body is stationary (not moving), the line on a distance–time graph is horizontal.

- Part C – Steve and Rocket move at a constant speed. They travel 24 kilometres in 2 hours. This means their speed was the greatest during this part of the ride.

A steeper slope means a greater speed.

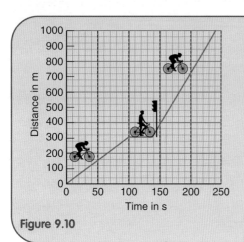

Figure 9.10

6 Copy and complete the following sentence.

The _____ the slope of a distance–_____ graph, the greater is the _____.

7 Curtis cycles to school. Figure 9.10 shows the distance–time graph for his journey.
   a) How far does Curtis live from school?
   b) How long did Curtis stop at the traffic lights?
   c) During which part of the journey was Curtis cycling the fastest?

Velocity–time graphs

A **velocity–time graph** can be used to describe the velocity and acceleration of a body. These graphs look very similar to distance–time graphs, but they mean different things. Always look at the axes.

Figure 9.11 shows the velocity–time graph for a car moving at a constant speed along a straight road. This means the car is moving with a constant velocity

Figure 9.12 shows the velocity–time graph for a car with a constant acceleration. The **slope** of the graph shows how quickly the velocity is changing. This means the slope shows the acceleration of the car.

The area below the graph line in a **velocity–time graph** represents distance travelled.

The **slope** (gradient) of a velocity–time graph gives the acceleration of a body.

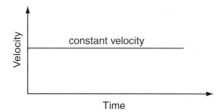

Figure 9.11 The velocity–time graph for something moving with a constant velocity is a flat line.

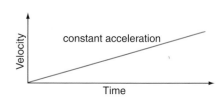

Figure 9.12 The slope of a velocity–time graph gives acceleration. A steeper slope means a greater acceleration.

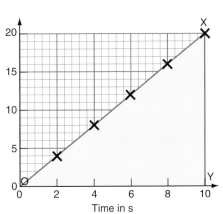

Figure 9.13 The bigger the area under the graph line, the further Ravi has travelled.

Figure 9.13 shows how Ravi's velocity changes as he cycles downhill. The straight line means that Ravi has a constant acceleration. The shaded area below the graph line represents the distance Ravi travels.

8 Copy and complete the following sentences.

The steeper the slope of a velocity–time graph, the _____ is the acceleration. The bigger the area under the graph line, the greater is the _____ travelled.

9 a) Describe the motion of the cheetah whose velocity–time graph is shown in Figure 9.15
b) Which part of the graph represents the distance the cheetah runs?

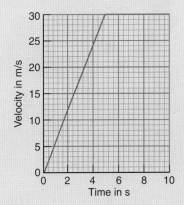

Figure 9.14   **Figure 9.15**

10 Table 9.1 gives some data for a speed skier travelling in a straight line down a steep slope.
a) Draw a velocity–time graph for the skier.
b) Describe the motion of the skier.

Time in s	0	2	4	6	8	10	12	14
Velocity in m/s	0	12	24	32	38	40	40	40

Table 9.1

How do forces affect the movement of a body?

Moving a supermarket trolley is simple. You push and the trolley moves forward. You pull and the trolley moves backwards. But as you push or pull on the trolley, the trolley will push or pull on you with the same size force. This is because forces always come in pairs. You just can't have one force without another.

Whenever two bodies interact, the forces they exert on each other are always equal in size and opposite in direction.

Remember

In diagrams an arrow is used to show a force. The length of the arrow represents the size of the force. The direction of the arrow shows the direction of the force.

⓫ Copy and complete the following sentences.

When a book rests on a shelf its ____ pushes down on the shelf. The shelf pushes _____ on the book, with the same ____ force.

force of the person on the trolley

force of the trolley on the person

Figure 9.16 When you push on the trolley it pushes equally hard on you.

athlete exerts a force on the starting blocks

starting blocks exert a force on the athlete

push up from the skateboard

push down on the skateboard

Figure 9.17 When two objects touch, they interact. There are always equal and opposite forces between the two objects.

What happens when more than one force acts on the same body?

The **resultant force** is a single force that has the same effect on a body as all the original forces together.

To find out what happens when more than one force acts on a body we imagine all the forces being replaced by one force that has the same effect. This single force is called the **resultant force**. The size and direction of the resultant force determine how or even if the body moves.

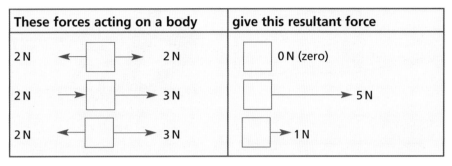

These forces acting on a body	give this resultant force
2 N ← ▢ → 2 N	▢ 0 N (zero)
2 N → ▢ → 3 N	▢ → 5 N
2 N ← ▢ → 3 N	▢ → 1 N

Table 9.2 Two forces acting in the same direction add to give the resultant force. Two forces acting in opposite directions subtract to give the resultant force.

⑫ Tom and Sam are pulling on the opposite ends of a rope. Tom pulls with a force of 70 N and Sam pulls with a force of 100 N.
  a) What is their resultant force?
  b) Jim now joins in pulling the rope. The new resultant force is zero. What force does Jim pull with and does he help Tom or Sam?

What happens when the forces are balanced?

If the resultant force on a body is zero, the forces are **balanced.** The body does not move or it continues moving at the same speed and in the same direction.

Figure 9.18 shows the forces on a toy bird. The weight of the toy causes the spring to stretch. The spring stretches until the forces are **balanced.** The resultant force is zero and the toy does not move.

⑬ Copy and complete the following sentences.
  a) Two forces that are balanced must be _____ in size and _____ in direction.
  b) When the forces on a body are balanced, the body could be moving at a _____ speed in a _____ line or it may not be _____ at all.

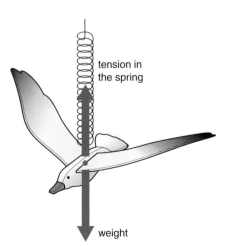

tension in the spring

weight

Figure 9.18 When the toy bird is not moving, the resultant force on the toy is zero.

CHAPTER 9 How can we describe and change the way things move?

⑭ What would happen to the tightrope walker if the forces did not balance?

weight

upward force from the rope

Figure 9.19

What happens when the forces are unbalanced?

If both teams in a tug of war pull equally hard, the resultant force is zero and the rope does not move. But when one team starts to pull with a larger force the rope moves. The resultant force is not zero. The rope and both teams start to move in the direction of the resultant force.

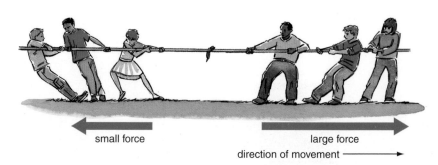

small force

large force

direction of movement ⟶

Figure 9.20 When forces are unbalanced, the resultant force is not zero.

An engine produces the force needed to move a car forwards. Pushing the accelerator pedal produces a resultant force forwards. The car accelerates forwards in the same direction as the resultant force.

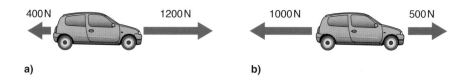

400N   1200N   1000N   500N

a)   b)

Figure 9.21 a) The car accelerates in the direction of the resultant force. **b)** The car decelerates in the direction of the resultant force.

When the resultant force on a body is not zero, the body will accelerate in the direction of the resultant force.

If the car engine stops or the driver puts the brakes on, the car slows down (decelerates). This happens because the frictional forces backwards are now larger than the force forwards. The resultant force is in the opposite direction to the way the car is moving.

When a body is moving in the opposite direction to the resultant force it will decelerate.

Force, mass and acceleration

Pushing a broken-down car is not easy. If you are the only person pushing, the car moves only slowly. The more people that push the bigger the force on the car and the bigger the acceleration.

The bigger the force on a body, the bigger is the acceleration of the body.

Figure 9.22 The acceleration of the car depends on the force.

Figure 9.23 A large resultant force acting on the small mass of the drag car gives it massive acceleration.

Common sense tells us that it is much harder to give a van the same acceleration as a car. A much larger force is needed. This is because the mass of the van is bigger than the mass of the car. Pushing a larger and larger mass with the same force gives a smaller and smaller acceleration.

The bigger the mass of a body, the bigger is the force needed to make it accelerate.

The force needed to accelerate a mass can be calculated using this equation:

$$\text{force} = \text{mass} \times \text{acceleration}$$

Units
- Force in newtons (N)
- Mass in kilograms (kg)
- Acceleration in metres/second² (m/s²)

Figure 9.24 A huge force is needed to accelerate this mass.

Figure 9.25 More force is needed to give a van the same acceleration as a car.

CHAPTER 9 How can we describe and change the way things move?

Example

Calculate the force needed to give a 2 kg ball an acceleration of 6 m/s².

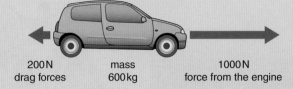

force = mass × acceleration
force =   2   ×   6   = 12 N

⑮ What force is needed to make a ball of mass 0.5 kg accelerate at:
a) 3 m/s²; b) 2 m/s²; c) 0.4 m/s²?

⑯ Figure 9.26 shows the forces acting on a moving car.

| 200 N | mass | 1000 N |
| drag forces | 600 kg | force from the engine |

Figure 9.26

Copy and complete the following sentences.

The resultant force on the car is _____ newtons in a forward direction. This force makes the car ____. When the drag forces increase to 1000 N, the car will move at a _____ speed.

⑰ Gurpal is cycling along a flat road when he stops pedalling. Gurpal decelerates at 0.5 m/s². The mass of Gurpal and his bicycle is 90 kg. Calculate the resistance force slowing Gurpal down.

9.4

Mass and weight – are they the same thing?

The simple answer is no!

> **Gravity** is a force of attraction between bodies.

If you want to know your weight, you will probably stand on some bathroom scales.

But most bathroom scales give a number in kilograms, which is mass not weight.

Weight is a force so it is measured in newtons. Weight is the force of **gravity** on a mass.

On Earth, gravity pulls on every kilogram of mass with a force of about 10 newtons. This is called the gravitational field strength (g).

$$g = 10 \, \text{N/kg}$$

So Sakhib, who has a mass of 50 kilograms, weighs:

$$50 \times 10 = 500 \, \text{N}$$

Figure 9.27 To measure your weight, the bathroom scales must measure in newtons.

You can use this equation to calculate the weight of an object:

weight (N) = mass (kg) × gravitational field strength (N/kg)

⑱ Kathy, Jon and Cary go on a diet. Table 9.3 shows the mass of each person at the start and end of the month
  a) How many kilograms did each person lose in one month?
  b) How much weight did each person lose in one month?

	Start of month	End of month
Kathy	72 kg	70.5 kg
John	115 kg	110.0 kg
Cary	68 kg	66.0 kg

Table 9.3

⑲ Gorese thinks he weighs 45 kg. Why is Gorese wrong?

Figure 9.28 Galileo tests out his ideas on gravity.

Activity – Investigating the acceleration of a falling body

Liam has read the story about Galileo's famous experiment with falling bodies. Galileo believed that gravity makes all falling bodies accelerate at the same rate. But most people had seen with their own eyes that different-sized bodies took different times to fall the same distance, so they did not believe Galileo.

To show that his idea was right Galileo is supposed to have dropped a small iron ball and a large iron ball from the top of the Leaning Tower of Pisa, in Italy.

Reports on the experiment say that the two objects hit the ground at almost, but not quite, the same time.

❶ Before doing his experiment, Galileo had a theory about gravity and had made a prediction.
  a) What was Galileo's theory about gravity?
  b) What did Galileo predict would happen in his experiment?
❷ What was the observation that made people say Galileo's theory was wrong?

Liam decided to investigate the acceleration of falling bodies, to see if Galileo's prediction was right. The apparatus Liam used is shown in Figure 9.29.

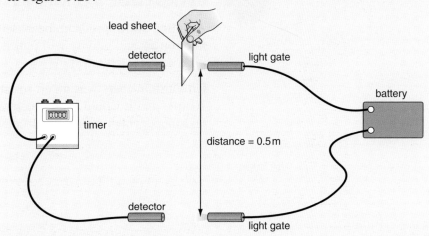

Figure 9.29 The apparatus used by Liam to measure the acceleration of a falling body

Liam started with a small sheet of lead. He used the electronic timer to measure how long it took the lead to fall 0.5 m. Liam repeated this four times. The four timer readings are written in Table 9.4.

Result	Time in s
1	0.326
2	0.330
3	0.465
4	0.319

Table 9.4

❸ Why did Liam repeat the time measurement?
❹ Liam did not use the third value when he calculated the mean (average) time. Why was this?
❺ What was the mean time calculated by Liam?

Liam repeated the experiment using lead sheets of different sizes. The average time for each sheet to fall the same distance is given in Table 9.5.

Sheet	Size	Average time
A	Small	0.320 s
B	Medium	0.325 s
C	Large	0.322 s

Table 9.5

❻ Draw a bar chart to show the results of Liam's experiment.
❼ Explain why the results from Liam's experiment agree with Galileo's ideas about gravity.

9.5

When does a falling body stop accelerating?

A falling body speeds up because of the force of gravity. Throw a ball into the air and gravity will pull it back down. As the ball falls, gravity makes it accelerate.

On Earth, if there was no air resistance, the ball would accelerate at 10 m/s^2 and it would keep accelerating. But on Earth there is air resistance which makes the acceleration of the ball smaller.

Joss is a sky-diver. She understands how important air resistance is in keeping her alive. At the moment when Joss jumps from a plane the only force acting on her is her weight. So she starts to accelerate downwards and her speed increases.

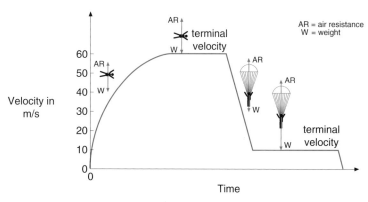

Figure 9.30 The velocity–time graph of a sky-diver

Figure 9.31 The hull of a hydrofoil lifts out of the water. This reduces the water resistance so the hydrofoil can accelerate to a higher speed.

> **Terminal velocity** is the constant velocity reached by a moving body when the resultant force acting on it is zero.

> Liquids and gases are both **fluids**.

But as soon as she starts to fall, air resistance begins to act upwards on her. Since her weight is bigger than the air resistance, she still accelerates and gets faster.

As Joss's speed increases, the air resistance on her increases until it equals her weight. Now the resultant force on Joss is zero and she stops accelerating. But she doesn't stop falling! She carries on falling but at a constant speed. Joss is falling at her **terminal velocity**.

When Joss opens her parachute, the increased surface area causes air resistance to increase. So Joss decelerates and slows down. Once again the two forces, weight and air resistance, become balanced. Joss then falls with a new, slower terminal velocity until she lands on the ground.

It's not just sky-divers that have a terminal velocity. All objects falling or moving through a **fluid** have a terminal velocity.

If you have ever paddled a canoe, you will know that no matter how hard you paddle you cannot keep increasing your speed. Eventually the force you paddle with forwards and water resistance backwards will be equal. The resultant force is zero and you have reached your terminal velocity.

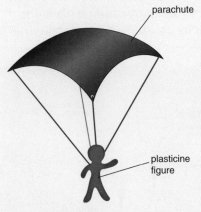

parachute

plasticine
figure

Figure 9.32

Activity – Investigating terminal velocity

Figure 9.32 shows a simple model parachute made from a sheet of plastic. When dropped, the Plasticine figure soon reaches its terminal velocity.

1 Plan an experiment to find out if the terminal velocity of the Plasticine figure depends on the area of the parachute. Think about where you could do this experiment, how you could try out your ideas and what you could do to make it a fair test.

2 What measurements would you take?

3 Which one of the following is the independent variable in this experiment?
   A   Distance the parachute falls
   B   Area of the parachute
   C   Weight of the Plasticine figure
   D   Time taken to fall

4 What are the control variables in this experiment?

9.6

Stopping safely

If a dog runs out in front of a car, the driver puts the brakes on as quickly as possible. But the average driver takes about three-quarters of a second to react. During this time the car carries on moving at a steady speed and covers a distance we call the **thinking distance**.

Once the brakes are on, the car slows down and stops. The distance moved by the car once the brakes are on we call the **braking distance.**

The **thinking distance** is how far a vehicle travels during the driver's reaction time, before the brakes are put on.

The **braking distance** is how far a vehicle travels before stopping, once the brakes have been put on.

thinking
distance

braking
distance

Figure 9.33 First you react. Then you brake.

stopping distance = thinking distance + braking distance

If the braking force doesn't change, the greater the speed of a vehicle the greater the stopping distance.

To stop a vehicle in the shortest distance a large braking force is needed. As the vehicle goes faster, a greater braking force is needed to make the vehicle stop in the same distance. But drivers need to be careful; too great a braking force can make the vehicle skid. Even with the same car and the same driver, stopping distances can change. This can be caused by lots of different conditions.

If the driver's reactions are slower than usual the thinking distance is longer. A driver's reactions are slower if they:
● have been drinking alcohol;
● have been taking certain types of drug;
● are tired;
● are talking on a mobile phone.

Braking distance can be changed by:
● weather conditions – on wet or icy roads the friction between the car tyres and road goes down. This makes the braking distance longer.
● the vehicle being in poor condition – worn brakes or worn tyres make the braking distance longer.
● the road surface – on a smooth road the friction between the road and the tyres goes down. This makes the braking distance longer.

20 Copy and complete the following sentences;
  a) The distance a car travels during the driver's ___ time is called the ___ distance.
  b) A driver's reactions are ___ when they are tired.
  c) Too big a braking ___ may make a car ___.

21 Why should people not drive a car after drinking alcohol?

22 An off duty policeman caught driving at 160 mph was found not guilty of dangerous driving. The court was told that the policeman was a trained advanced driver practising his driving skills.

Do you think that high-speed driving should sometimes be allowed? Give reasons for your answer.

23 Table 9.6 gives the thinking distance and braking distance for a car at different speeds.

Speed in m/s	0	9	13	18	26	36
Thinking distance in m	0	6	9	12	18	24
Braking distance in m	0	6	14	24	56	96

Table 9.6

  a) Plot a graph of thinking distance (on the vertical axis) against speed (on the horizontal axis).
  b) Copy and complete the following sentence.

  Doubling the speed of a car will ___ the thinking distance.

  c) Plot a graph of braking distance (on the vertical axis) against speed (on the horizontal axis).
  d) Use the graphs to find the stopping distance for a car travelling at 30 m/s.

9.7 Are you working?

What is work?

Ask anyone what work is and you are likely to get a lot of different answers. But the answers usually involve doing something – maybe mowing the lawn, or lifting a box, or even writing an essay.

In science, **work** has an exact meaning. Work is done when a force makes a body move. The bigger the force and the further the force makes the body move, the more work is done.

> **Work** is done when a force makes something move. Work is measured in joules.

Figure 9.34 These cranes can do more work than a human.

24 Calculate the work done in each of following.
a) a shopper pushing a trolley with a force of 40 N for 75 m;
b) a pole-vaulter lifting her own weight of 520 N a height of 3.6 m;
c) a car using a braking force of 700 N to stop in 23 m;
d) a crane lifting a crate weighing 14 000 N a height of 12 m.

Work, like energy, is measured in joules (J).

The work done in moving a body can be calculated using the equation:

work done = force applied × distance moved in the direction of the force
(joules, J)   (newtons, N)   (metres, m)

Example
Calculate the work done by a weightlifter when he lifts a weight of 750 N to a height of 2.4 m.

work done = force × distance moved
= 750 × 2.4 = 1800 J

Work and energy

Richard has a job on a building site. Sometimes he has to move sand in a wheelbarrow. When he starts pushing the wheelbarrow, it moves, so work is done and the wheelbarrow gains kinetic energy. This energy has been transferred from the chemical energy in Richard's muscles.

Figure 9.35 Pushing the wheelbarrow involves transferring energy.

Whenever a force makes a body move, work is done and energy must be transferred.

Work and energy are linked by the equation:

work done = energy transferred

If Richard does 1000 J of work to move the wheelbarrow and sand, 1000 J of energy must be transferred.

㉕ The Falkirk Wheel is a rotating boatlift. It lifts 600 000 kilograms through a height of 35 metres.
  a) Calculate the weight that the Falkirk Wheel lifts.
  b) Calculate the work done by the Wheel in one lift.

Figure 9.36 The Falkirk Wheel in action

Work done against frictional forces

Imagine pushing a heavy crate across the floor. It's hard work! As you push, friction acts with an equal force but in the opposite direction to your push. Since the resultant force on the crate is zero the crate will move across the floor at a constant velocity.

Although you are doing work, the kinetic (movement) energy of the crate is not changing. The work you do is against the frictional forces that are trying to stop the crate moving. Where the crate rubs against the floor both the crate and the floor get a little hotter. Chemical energy from your muscles has been transformed into heat.

When work is done against frictional forces, energy is mainly transformed into heat.

Figure 9.37 When work is done against frictional forces, energy is mainly transformed into heat.

Example
Ahmed uses a force of 225 N to drag a heavy box 5 m across a rough wooden floor. The box moves at a steady speed. Calculate the work done against friction.

work done = force × distance moved
= 225 × 5 = 1125 J

26 Copy and complete the following sentences.
   a) When a _____ moves an object, _____ is done and _____ is transferred.
   b) When work is done against friction, most energy is transferred as ___.

27 Matthew pulls a heavy sack up a ramp. Copy and complete the following sentences.

   Matthew does work to _____ the sack. He also does work against _____. Some of the chemical energy from his muscles is transferred into _____ in the sack and in the ramp.

28 Ray, a survival expert, is able to light a fire by rubbing two pieces of wood together. Explain why this works.

Elastic potential energy

If you apply a force to an elastic object, it may change shape but it does not break. When the force is taken away the object goes back to the way it was.

Imagine bending a ruler. As long as the force is not too big, the ruler pings back into shape when the force is removed.

The energy stored in an elastic object when work is done to change its shape is called **elastic potential energy**. In Figure 9.39 chemical energy from the person's muscles is transformed into elastic potential energy and stored in the stretched springs.

Figure 9.38 Bending the ruler and letting go makes it vibrate up and down. When the ruler stops it is straight again. The ruler is an elastic object.

Elastic potential energy is the energy stored in an elastic object that has been temporarily squashed, stretched, bent or twisted.

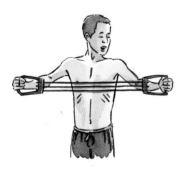

Figure 9.39 Using a chest expander involves doing work and transferring energy.

29 Each of the objects in Figure 9.40 has had its shape changed.

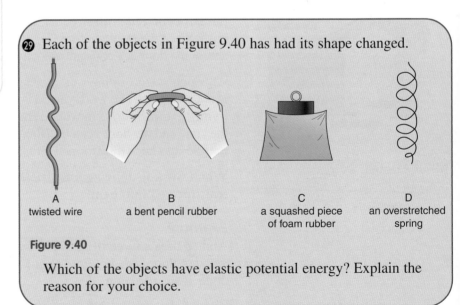

A
twisted wire

B
a bent pencil rubber

C
a squashed piece of foam rubber

D
an overstretched spring

Figure 9.40

Which of the objects have elastic potential energy? Explain the reason for your choice.

Work and kinetic energy

When a force makes a body move, the force does work and energy is transferred to the body. Moving bodies have kinetic energy. The kinetic energy of a body increases when a force makes it speed up and decreases when a force makes it slow down.

But kinetic energy is not just to do with the speed of a body; it is also to do with the mass of the body. A lorry with a large mass moving at 20 m/s will have more kinetic energy than a car with a small mass moving at 20 m/s.

So, the kinetic energy of a moving body depends on:
- its mass;
- its speed.

Units

- Mass in kilograms (kg)
- Velocity in metres per second (m/s)
- Momentum in kilogram metres per second (kgm/s)

Figure 9.41 A charging rhino can reach speeds of up to 11 m/s. That's a lot of momentum!

Figure 9.42 A bungee rope stretches as work is done to slow the jumper down. Some work is also done against air resistance, so some of the jumper's energy is transformed into heat. This is just as well, or the bungee jumper would bounce up and down forever.

 9.8

What is momentum?

A moving body has **momentum**. The greater the mass of the body and the faster it moves, the more momentum it has.

We can calculate the momentum of a body using the equation:

$$\text{momentum} = \text{mass} \times \text{velocity}$$

There is no short name for the unit of momentum, but you can remember it as the unit of mass (kilogram) multiplied by the unit of velocity (metre/second).

Momentum has a size and a direction. So, if two bodies move in opposite directions one will have a positive momentum and the other a negative momentum.

Momentum is the mass of a body multiplied by the velocity of the body.

Example
A lorry and a car are travelling in opposite directions. Use the data in the box to calculate the momentum of each vehicle.

Figure 9.43

Lorry		**Car**	
mass	= 9000 kg	mass	= 900 kg
velocity	= 14 m/s →	velocity	= 25 m/s ←
momentum	= mass × velocity	momentum	= mass × velocity
	= 9000 × 14		= 900 × 25
	= 126 000 kg m/s		= 22 500 kg m/s
momentum of the lorry	= +126 000 kg m/s	momentum of the car	= −22 500 kg m/s

Saying the momentum of the lorry is positive makes the momentum of the car negative.

> **30** Copy and complete the following sentences:
> a) A body that is not moving has _____ momentum.
> b) Momentum, like velocity, has both _____ and _____.
> c) Momentum is worked put by multiplying _____ and _____.
>
> **31** Calculate the momentum of:
> a) a 60 kg cyclist pedalling at 8 m/s;
> b) a football of mass 0.4 kg moving at 7 m/s;
> c) a rhino of mass 2000 kg charging at 11 m/s;
> d) a 500 kg horse galloping at 16 m/s;
> e) an elephant of mass 1800 kg walking at 2 m/s.

Figure 9.44 A cricketer pulls his hands back to reduce the force.

How do unbalanced forces affect momentum?

Unbalanced forces change the momentum of a body.

Catching a fast cricket ball can be painful. A large force used to stop the ball quickly produces an equally large force on the player's hands. By pulling his hands backwards as he catches the ball, the cricketer takes longer to reduce the momentum of the ball to zero. This reduces both the force needed to stop the ball and the force on the player's hands.

Momentum and saving lives

Increasing the time that bodies are in contact makes the force needed to change the momentum smaller. Many different types of safety devices use this idea.

Figure 9.45 A horse rider wearing a helmet and body protector

If you ride a bicycle or go horse riding you should always wear a helmet. Often horse riders also wear a body protector.

A helmet and body protector work in the same way. If you fall off your bicycle and hit your head, the padding inside the helmet will start to crush.

If you fall off a horse, the padding inside the body protector will start to crush. In both cases the time taken for your body to stop moving increases and the force which could cause an injury is smaller.

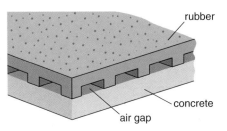

Figure 9.46 A safe surface for a children's play area can be made from rubber tiles.

The surface of a child's play area needs to be tough but it also needs to be flexible. This is so that if a child falls, the surface will squash. The child will slow down more gradually than if it fell on a hard surface. This makes the force on the child smaller, reducing the risk of injury.

32 Explain the reason for each of the following.

Figure 9.47 This trainer has a gas-filled heel. (*Hint*: gas is easily squashed)

Figure 9.48 A climbing rope is designed to stretch a little. (*Hint*: How does the rope slow down the climber if they accidentally fell?)

Figure 9.49 The goalkeeper kit is well padded. (*Hint*: Players often collide into the goalkeeper.)

Activity – Safety surfaces

Rakesh has bought a children's slide and swing. Before putting them in his garden he wants to put down a safety surface.

The chart in Figure 9.50 shows some data Rakesh found from a manufacturer. The data give the average height a child can fall onto different surfaces without seriously hurting themselves.

The data were obtained using a dummy fitted with electronic sensors.

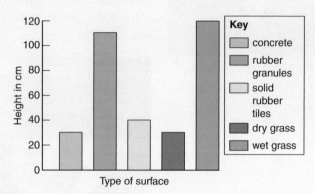

Figure 9.50

1 Are these categoric or continuous variables?
  a) the height the child falls;
  b) the type of surface.
2 Copy and complete the following sentences.
  The data are reliable because another manufacturer using the same _____ and following the same method would get the same _____.
3 Which type of surface would you tell Rakesh to use? Give the reason for your choice.

Car safety

Figure 9.51 This car has been in a serious collision but the important part, where the passengers and driver sit, is undamaged.

Car design is not all about performance and looks – buyers also care about safety.

A modern car, even in a small accident, is easily damaged. The car has 'crumple zones' at the front and back. In a collision the crumple zones crush. As they crush, the car slows down and stops gradually. The longer it takes the car to stop, the smaller is the force on the driver and passengers, so the more likely they are to walk away from the accident without serious injury.

In a crash a seat belt stretches slightly. This is very important. It increases the time taken for your momentum to go down to zero. So the force on your body and the risk of injury are reduced.

33 In a crash an air bag inflates. A fraction of a second later the driver's head hits the air bag. The bag, which has tiny holes in it, will start to go down as the force from the driver's head pushes some of the gas out.

Figure 9.52

a) Copy and complete the sentences by choosing the correct words from the box.
When the driver's head hits the air bag it will

slow down   move at a steady speed
speed up

b) The air bag reduces the risk of serious injury by

decreasing   increasing

the time it takes the driver's head to stop moving.

Activity – Investigating the idea of a crumple zone

Tracy investigated crumple zones. The trolley and test material shown in Figure 9.53 are like a car with a crumple zone.

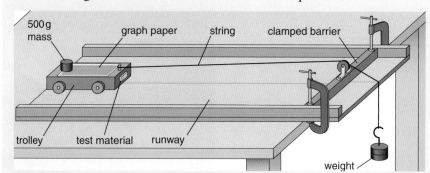

Figure 9.53 Using a trolley and test material to model a car with a crumple zone

The trolley was pulled by a falling weight. When the trolley hit the barrier, it slowed down and stopped. The 500 g mass kept moving forward, just like the passengers in a car that suddenly stops.

Tracy marked the graph paper to show how far the 500 g mass slid forwards.

Tracy tested five different types of material for the crumple zone. Each material had the same area and thickness.

Because the falling weight was kept the same, the trolley always hit the barrier at the same speed. This was one way that Tracy made the investigation a fair test.

❶ Write down one more way that Tracy made this investigation a fair test.

❷ In Tracy's investigation, which one of the variables, A, B or C was:
   a) the independent variable;
   b) the dependent variable;
   c) a control variable?
   A   Thickness of the material used for the crumple zone
   B   Distance the 500 g mass slides
   C   Type of material used for the crumple zone

Reminder

In a fair test only the independent variable affects the dependent variable.

Figure 9.54 shows two sets of data obtained using two different falling weights.

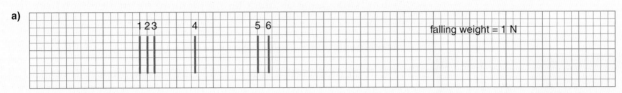

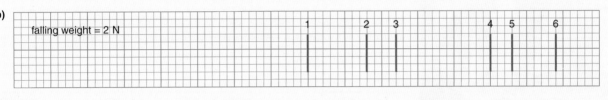

Key

1 = no material; 2 = polystyrene; 3 = foam rubber; 4 = carpet; 5 = fibre wool; 6 = rubber underlay

Figure 9.54 **a)** Stopping distance using a 1 N falling weight
b) Stopping distances using a 2 N falling weight

Remember

The range is from the maximum to the minimum value.

❸ Which falling weight gave the biggest range of results?
❹ Draw a bar chart for each set of data.
❺ Copy and complete the sentence by choosing one of the words in the box.

It is better to draw a bar chart rather than a line graph because the 'type of material' is a

continuous   categoric   variable

After she had looked at all her data, Tracy wrote:

'Of the five materials that I tested rubber underlay made the best crumple zone.'

❻ Do both sets of data agree with what Tracy has written? Give a reason for your answer.

CHAPTER 9 How can we describe and change the way things move?

Momentum is **conserved** in a collision. The total momentum before a collision is the same as the total momentum after the collision.

Figure 9.55 Understanding forces and momentum can make the difference between winning and losing a game of snooker.

Collisions and explosions

Collisions

When two bodies collide, the total momentum of the bodies after the collision is the same as the total momentum of the bodies before the collision.

> total momentum after a collision = total momentum before a collision

So, the total momentum is not changed by the collision. It doesn't go up and it doesn't go down. The total momentum is **conserved**.

Look at the white snooker ball in Figure 9.56. It is moving with velocity *v* towards a red snooker ball. Before they collide, the red ball is not moving. The red ball has zero momentum.

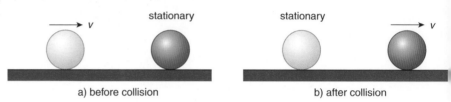

a) before collision　　　　　　b) after collision

Figure 9.56

After the collision the white ball will stop. So now the white ball has zero momentum. The red ball will move with a velocity *v* in the same direction as the white ball was moving.

So, although momentum has gone from the white ball to the red ball, the total momentum has been conserved.

Explosions

An explosion is the opposite of a collision. Instead of moving together, bodies move apart. But the total momentum of the bodies involved in an explosion remains constant.

In an explosion momentum is conserved.

> total momentum after an explosion = total momentum before an explosion

34 A 2 kg trolley, moving at 3 m/s, collides with and sticks to a stationary 1 kg trolley.
   a) Before the collision what is the momentum of:
      i) the moving trolley;
      ii) the stationary trolley;
      ii) the two trolleys added together?
   b) After the collision what is:
      i)   the momentum of the two trolleys
      ii) the total mass of the moving trolleys;
      iii) the speed of the two trolleys?

35 Jackie and Jasmin are on roller blades. They stand facing each other, and then give each other a gentle push. Figure 9.57 shows what happens next.

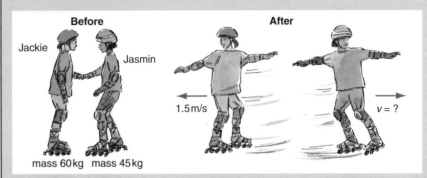

Figure 9.57

   a) What is the total momentum before they push each other?
   b) Calculate Jackie's momentum immediately after the push.
   c) What is Jasmin's momentum immediately after the push?

CHAPTER 9 How can we describe and change the way things move?

Summary

✓ **Velocity** is the speed of a body and its direction.

✓ **Acceleration** is how fast the velocity of a body changes.

✓ **Distance–time graphs** and **velocity–time graphs** can be used to show the motion of a body.

✓ The **slope** of a distance–time graph represents the speed.

✓ The slope of a velocity–time graph represents acceleration.

✓ The area under a velocity–time graph line represents distance travelled.

✓ Two interacting bodies exert forces on each other that are always equal in size and opposite in direction.

✓ The **resultant force** is a single force that has the same effect on a body as all the original forces acting together.

✓ Weight is the force of gravity on a mass.

✓ **Gravity** is a force of attraction that acts between all bodies.

✓ When the resultant force on a body is zero, the movement of the body does not change because the forces are **balanced**.

✓ When the resultant force on a body is not zero the body will accelerate because the forces are **unbalanced**.

✓ The greater the resultant force the greater is the acceleration of the body.

✓ The bigger the mass of a body the bigger is the resultant force needed to make it accelerate; force and mass are linked by:

resultant force (N) = mass (kg) × acceleration (m/s²)

✓ **Air resistance** (or drag) is a force of friction. The direction of air resistance is always opposite to the direction of the moving object.

✓ When the resultant force on a falling body is zero the body falls at its **terminal velocity**.

✓ When a vehicle travels at a steady speed the frictional forces balance the driving force.

✓ **Stopping distance = thinking distance + braking distance**.

✓ The stopping distance of a vehicle depends on the braking force, the driver's reaction time, the condition of the road and the vehicle, weather conditions, the speed and the mass of the vehicle.

✓ Whenever a force makes a body move, **work** is done and energy is transferred.

✓ When work is done against frictional forces, energy is transformed into heat.

✓ The faster a body moves through a **fluid**, the greater are the frictional forces.

✓ **Elastic potential energy** is the energy stored when work has been done to change the shape of a body.

✓ Kinetic energy is the energy of moving bodies.

✓ **Momentum** is defined by the equation:

momentum (kg m/s) = mass (kg) × velocity (m/s)

✓ A resultant force acting on a body causes a change in momentum.

✓ In any collision or explosion, the total momentum is **conserved**.

1 Bill and Veneeta took part in a sponsored run. The distance–time graph for Bill's run is shown in Figure 9.58. Veneeta did not start the run until 500 seconds after Bill. She completed the whole run at a constant speed in 3000 seconds.

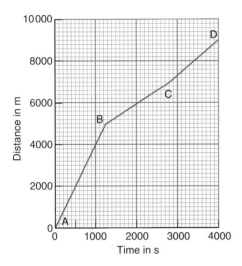

Figure 9.58

a) Describe how Bill's speed changes during the race (*2 marks*)

b) Copy the distance–time graph for Bill's run. Draw on the same axes a distance–time graph for Veneeta's run. (*2 marks*)

c) How far had Bill run when Veneeta overtook him? (*1 mark*)

2 Amrita has investigated how different forces stretch a spring. The results of her investigation are given in Table 9.7.

Force in N	Length of spring in cm	Extension of spring in cm
0	5.0	0.0
2	7.5	2.5
4	10.0	5.0
6	11.0	6.0
8	15.0	
10	17.5	12.5

Table 9.7

a) Copy and complete Table 9.7. (*1 mark*)

b) Plot a graph of force against extension. (*3 marks*)

c) Which result does not fit the pattern? (*1 mark*)

d) What length would the spring be were a 3 N force used? (*1 mark*)

e) What was the range of force used by Amrita? (*1 mark*)

3 Figure 9.59 shows three racing cars.

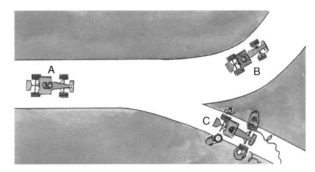

Figure 9.59

Car A has a mass of 500 kg and is moving at 85 m/s along a straight part of the track.

Car B is moving at constant speed around a curved part of the track.

Car C is in the pits and not moving.

a) Which, if any, of the cars has zero momentum? (*1 mark*)

b) Calculate the momentum of car A. (*2 marks*)

c) Which of the following is the unit of momentum?

   N m   kg m/s   J/kg   (*1 mark*)

d) The momentum of one of the cars is changing. Which one? Give a reason for your answer. (*2 marks*)

EXAMQUESTIONS

Chapter 10
What is static electricity and how is it used?

At the end of this chapter you should:

✓ know that certain insulating materials become electrically charged when they are rubbed against each other;

✓ understand that electrons are rubbed off one material onto another when materials become charged by friction;

✓ understand that the material that gains electrons becomes negatively charged and the material that loses electrons becomes positively charged;

✓ know that objects (bodies) with the same type of charge repel one another and objects with different types of charge attract;

✓ understand that an electric current is a flow of charge;

✓ understand that a spark may jump across a gap between a charged body and an earthed conductor if the charge on the body becomes high enough;

✓ understand how static charges are useful in photocopiers, smoke precipitators and electrostatic paint spray guns;

✓ be able to explain why static electricity is dangerous in some situations;

✓ understand how electrostatic charge can be discharged safely.

Figure 10.1 A flash of lightning is a gigantic spark. Billions and billions of electrons shoot from the bottom of the cloud to Earth. So much heat is produced that there is a flash of light. The air expands so rapidly that it causes a clap of thunder.

What is static electricity?

People often call static electricity just 'static' for short. 'Static' results in lightning flashes (Figure 10.1). It makes your hair stand on end and it makes dust stick to TV screens. The word 'static' is normally used to mean 'stationary'. **Static electricity** results when materials have stationary charges.

> **Static electricity** is the formation of stationary (static) positive and negative charges on materials. The materials become charged when they are rubbed against each other or move over each other.
>
> The materials become positive or negative and we say they are electrically **charged**.

Invisible electrostatic forces

Try this simple experiment. Comb your hair briskly with a plastic comb. Then use the comb to pick up tiny pieces of paper. (It works only if your hair is dry and not gelled.) When you comb your hair, the comb becomes negatively **charged** (Figure 10.2). The charged comb can now pick up bits of paper.

You may have noticed some other effects of electric charges.
- When you take off a shirt or top, it tends to cling to your body or your vest.
- A balloon can stick to the wall and possibly the ceiling after rubbing it against your sweatshirt or fleece.

These effects show that when certain materials are rubbed against each other or move over each other they become electrically charged. People sometimes say the materials have 'static electricity' on them.

Figure 10.2 A plastic comb gets charged when you comb your hair briskly.

Where do the charges come from?

When certain materials are rubbed against each other, friction causes negatively charged electrons to be rubbed off one material onto the other.

Combing your hair with a plastic comb makes electrons move off your hair and onto the comb (Figure 10.2). The comb now has more electrons than protons so it has an overall negative charge. Your hair has lost the electrons. It now has more protons than electrons and so it has an overall positive charge.

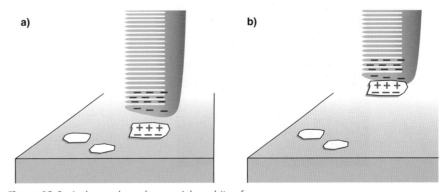

a)

b)

Figure 10.3 A charged comb can pick up bits of paper.

When electrically charged objects are close together, they exert electrostatic forces on each other:

- objects with opposite (different) charges **attract** each other;
- objects with the same type of charge **repel** each other.

If you put the negatively charged comb close to a tiny bit of paper, it repels negative electrons from the area of the paper nearest to it (Figure 10.3a on page 187). This part of the paper therefore becomes positive. It is attracted to the comb because objects with different charges **attract**. If the paper is small enough, it can be picked up with the comb (Figure 10.3 b).

Have you noticed that your hair sometimes stands up when it is combed? (but probably not as much as the boy's hair in Figure 10.2). This is more likely to happen if your hair is clean and dry. It happens because each hair becomes positively charged and objects with the same charges **repel**.

❶ Copy and complete the following sentences using words from the box below.

> charge electrons neutrons negative
> positive protons rubbed static

When a polythene rod is _____ with a cloth, the cloth loses _____ to the rod, so the rod gets a _____ charge. The cloth has more _____ than electrons, so it has a _____ charge.

❷ When certain materials are rubbed against each other, electrons move from one material to the other, but protons and neutrons never move. Explain why electrons move from one material to another, but not protons and neutrons.

❸ When a Perspex rod is rubbed with a cloth, the Perspex rod becomes positively charged. Explain how the rod gets its charge.

Figure 10.4 A hair-raising experience!

❹ Look at Figure 10.4. The dome on which the boy is resting his hand has a large negative charge and the boy is standing on a rubber mat.
a) What is the charge on the boy's hand?
b) What is the charge on the boy's hair?
c) Why is the boy's hair sticking out?
d) Why is he standing on a rubber mat?

❺ Figure 10.5 shows two identical lightweight plastic balls attached to the same hook by nylon threads. The balls are charged.
a) What can you say about the charges on the balls?
b) Make a copy of Figure 10.5.
   i) Draw arrows to show the electrostatic force acting on each ball.
   ii) Draw arrows to show the force of gravity acting on each ball.

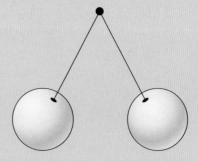

Figure 10.5

Insulators and conductors

Materials like plastic, paper and hair can hold their charge. The charges on them are 'static' (stationary) and electrons do not flow through them. These materials are called **insulators**. Plastics like polythene and PVC are used to insulate electrical wires and cables (Figure 10.6).

In contrast to insulators, electrons flow easily through metals and alloys (see Section 6.3). These materials are described as **conductors**. When electrons flow through metals, the flow of negative charge forms an electric current. An electric current can also be carried by ions, which can have either positive or negative charges (see Section 8.5).

Table 10.1 shows good conductors, moderate conductors, poor conductors and insulators. The best conductors are metals because their outer shell electrons are free to move. The outer electrons in insulators are held tightly in covalent bonds.

Figure 10.6 Plastics like polythene and PVC are good insulators. They are used to insulate electrical wires and cables.

Insulators are substances that can hold their charge. Electrons cannot flow through them, so they cannot conduct an electric current.

Conductors are substances through which electrons flow easily, so they conduct an electric current.

Conductors			Insulators
Good	**Moderate**	**Poor**	
• Metals, e.g. copper, aluminium, iron	• Carbon (graphite)	• Water	• Plastics, e.g. polythene, PVC
	• Silicon	• Humans	• Rubber
• Alloys, e.g. steel, brass			• Wood
			• Air

Table 10.1 Some important conductors and insulators

 How do we use static electricity?

Static electricity is important in the working of smoke precipitators, photocopiers and paint spray guns.

Smoke precipitators

When coal is burnt in power stations and factories, a lot of smoke is produced. The smoke contains tiny particles of soot and ash. It is important to remove this soot and ash before it gets into the air and causes pollution. In power stations this can be done using an electrostatic smoke precipitator (Figure 10.7).

As the smoke goes up the chimney, it passes through a negatively charged metal grid. The smoke particles pick up electrons from the grid and become negatively charged themselves. The grid now repels these negative smoke particles towards the chimney lining. Here they are attracted by positively charged collecting plates. The smoke particles lose their charge on the collecting plates and then fall and collect (precipitate) at the bottom of the chimney.

6 From the list in the box below, name:
a) one metal;
b) one alloy;
c) two non-metals;
d) two good conductors;
e) one (moderate) semiconductor;
f) two insulators.

> brass   graphite   sulfur
> titanium   wood

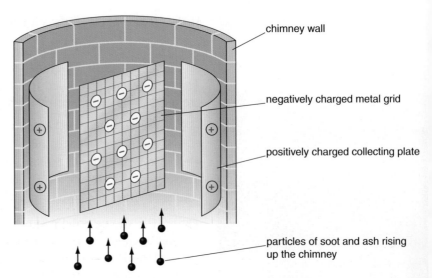

Figure 10.7 An electrostatic smoke precipitator

Photocopiers

Some substances are photoconductors. They conduct electricity in the light, but not in the dark. In a photocopier, there is a roller coated with a thin layer of photoconductor (Figure 10.8).

- At the start of the copying process, the photoconductor is given a positive charge.
- The page being copied is then lit with a strong light. This projects a shadow of the page onto the charged photoconductor.

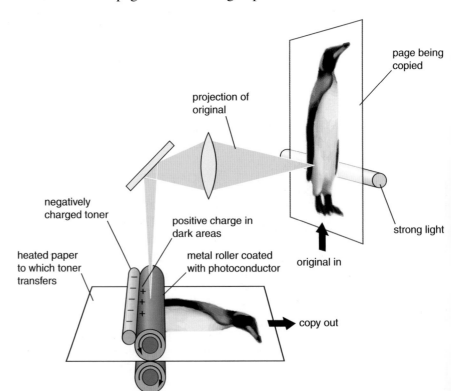

Figure 10.8 The photocopying process

- The bright areas of the photoconductor now lose their charge because it conducts in the light. But the dark areas keep their positive charge. So, places where charge remains on the photoconductor match the dark parts on the page being copied.
- At the same time, the roller moves near black powder called toner which is negatively charged. The toner is attracted to and sticks on the positive parts of the photoconductor.
- A blank sheet of paper is then heated and pressed against the roller.
- This melts the toner which sticks to the paper making a copy of the original page.

Figure 10.9 A workman re-spraying parts of a car using an electrostatic paint spray gun

❼ An electrostatic paint spray gun like the one in Figure 10.9 produces a fine spray of positive droplets.
a) How does the charge on the droplets help to keep the spray fine and evenly spread?
b) The car bodywork is given a negative charge. Why is less paint needed if the car bodywork has a negative charge?
c) Why is the workman wearing protective head gear?

Activity – 'Static' in pipes

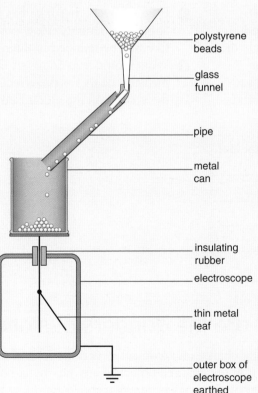

polystyrene beads

glass funnel

pipe

metal can

insulating rubber

electroscope

thin metal leaf

outer box of electroscope earthed

1 Polystyrene beads fall through the funnel and flow down the pipe.

2 Friction between the beads and the pipe produces electrostatic charges on the beads and the pipe.

3 Beads fall into the metal can and their charge transfers to the can and to the T-piece and leaf of the electroscope

4 As the charge on the T-piece and leaf increases, the metal leaf moves to a greater angle with the vertical bar of the T-piece.

Figure 10.10 Investigating the electrostatic charges produced when polystyrene beads flow down a pipe

Industrial liquids and powders are often moved from one place to another through pipes. Enormous quantities of flour and custard powder are moved in pipes. As the liquids and powders flow along a pipe, static electricity is generated. The static electricity is produced by friction as particles in the liquid or powder rub against the pipe. Voltages as high as 1000 volts can be produced. These high voltages can result in sparks and start a fire, as many of the liquids and powders will burn.

Investigation

Ellie and Jake set up the apparatus in Figure 10.10 to study the problem of 'static' in pipes. They used different sizes of polystyrene beads.

❶ The polystyrene beads become negatively charged as they flow down the pipe and the pipe becomes positively charged.
  a) What charge will the can, the T-piece and the metal leaf have when the polystyrene beads start to fill the can?
  b) Why does the leaf move to an angle with the vertical part of the metal T-piece?
❷ Ellie and Jake poured 50 cm³ of small beads down the pipe and then estimated the angle the metal leaf moved out. They repeated their experiment, first with 50 cm³ of smaller beads and after that with 50 cm³ of very small beads. Their results are shown in Table 10.2.

Type of beads used	Estimated angle of thin metal leaf with vertical
Small	15°
Smaller	25°
Very small	45°

Table 10.2

a) Copy and complete the following sentences:
  i) As the deflection of the metal leaf increases, the charge on the electroscope _____.
  ii) As the polystyrene beads decrease in size, the charge on the electroscope _____.
b) Why do you think very small beads cause greater deflection of the metal leaf than small beads?
❸ In flour mills, very large charges build up as the powdery flour passes along the pipes. How can this problem be overcome? (*Hint*: How can you get rid of charges?)
❹ How do you think the charge on the can, T-piece and leaf will change if a longer pipe is used? Explain your answer.
❺ State three variables that Ellie and Jake controlled to make sure their investigation compared the beads fairly.
❻ How could Ellie and Jake's results be made more reliable?
❼ Ellie suspects that Jake has estimated the angle inaccurately. How could human error like this be reduced in their investigation?
❽ What would you do to get more precise measurements for the effect of bead size on the charge on the electroscope?

10.4 ## What are the dangers of static electricity?

Sparks are caused when static electric charges move suddenly and an electric current flows for a very short time.

If the static charge on an object is very large, electrons may jump across the gap from the charged object to any nearby conductor. This movement of electrons is an electric current. In some cases, there may be enough current to form a **spark**. Even a small spark can be dangerous.

> **Earthing** involves connecting a charged body to a metal spike or plate in the ground so that it is discharged safely.

This danger can be overcome by **earthing** the object that may become charged. To earth an object you connect it to a large metal plate in the ground by a conducting wire. If any charge now collects on the object, it just flows harmlessly along the wire to the earth. The object is discharged (loses its charge) and there is no danger of sparks.

Fuel in pipes

When tankers deliver fuel to petrol stations and aircraft, a charge can build up as fuel flows through the delivery pipe. To prevent charge building up, the petrol storage tank and the aircraft are earthed (Figure 10.11).

8 Figure 10.11 shows an aircraft being refuelled.
  a) Explain how electrostatic charge can build up on the fuel pipe and on the aircraft during refuelling.
  b) Why is the build-up of charge on the aircraft dangerous?
  c) In order to prevent charge building up, a copper cable is connected between the aircraft and the tanker. Why does this prevent charge building up? (*Hint*: The fuel pipe is also connected to the tanker.)

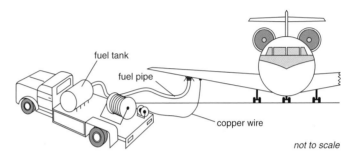

Figure 10.11 An aircraft being refuelled

Aircraft tyres

When an aircraft lands, there is enormous friction between its tyres and the runway. To reduce the build-up of charge, aircraft tyres are made of special rubber that conducts electricity. So, any charge that forms on the tyres flows straight to earth (Figure 10.12).

Figure 10.12 When an aircraft lands there is enormous friction between the tyres and the runway. Sometimes, sparks fly and the tyres begin to smoke.

CHAPTER 10 What is static electricity and how is it used?

Activity – Lightning strikes!

Figure 10.13 shows what happens when lightning strikes the lightning conductor on a church spire.

1 Copy and complete the following explanation using the terms from the box below.

> cloud   convection   copper   earth
> electrons   energy   flash of light
> negative   positive   spire

Large heavy thunderclouds are filled with water vapour and ice crystals moving around in strong _____ currents. As these move around, charge builds up and the bottom of the thundercloud has a large _____ charge. The lightning conductor on the church spire is made of a thick _____ strip down the outside of the building. This is connected from a metal spike at the top of the _____ to a large metal plate in the ground. When the thundercloud passes overhead, the charge on the cloud repels _____ from the top of the lightning conductor. This causes the top of the lightning conductor to become _____. If the charge on the cloud is large enough, electrons jump across the gap from the _____ to the spike. In some cases, so much _____ is lost by the electrons that a _____ is produced. Fortunately, the electrons can flow down the conductor to _____ without damaging the church.

2 Explain why the lightning conductor on the church is:
a) fixed to the ground;
b) made of metal;
c) attached to the highest point on the church.

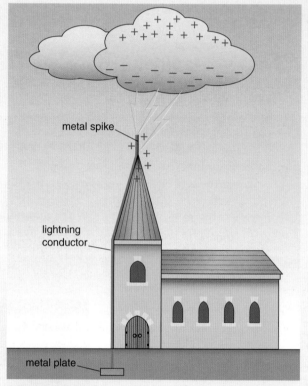

Figure 10.13 Lightning strikes the lightning conductor on a church spire.

Summary

✓ **Static electricity** results when materials have stationary charges.

✓ When certain insulating materials are rubbed against each other, friction causes electrons to be rubbed off one material onto the other.

✓ The material gaining electrons becomes negatively **charged**. The material losing electrons is left with an equal positive charge.

✓ Two bodies (objects) with the same charge **repel** each other and two bodies with different (opposite) charges **attract**.

✓ **Insulators** are substances that can hold their charge. Electrons cannot flow through them, so they cannot conduct an electric current.

✓ **Conductors** are substances through which electrons flow easily, so they conduct an electric current.

✓ An **electric current** is a flow of charge. The charge may be carried by electrons or by ions.

✓ Electrostatic charges are important in the working of smoke precipitators, photocopiers and paint spray guns.

✓ Static electricity can be dangerous. If the charge on an object becomes very large, a **spark** may jump across the gap between the charged object and an earthed conductor nearby.

✓ The dangers of static electricity and sparking can be overcome by **earthing**.

EXAM QUESTIONS

❶ Match the terms A, B, C and D to the statements numbered 1, 2, 3 and 4.
    A A conductor   1 allows electrons to
                                flow.
    B An electric current 2 conducts in the light.
    C An insulator   3 is a flow of charge.
    D A photoconductor 4 holds its charge.
                                          (*4 marks*)

❷ Clingfilm is thin plastic material made of polythene. When clingfilm is peeled off a roll, it becomes charged and tends to stick to itself.
    a) What can you conclude about the charges on different parts of the clingfilm which stick to each other?   (*1 mark*)
    b) Why does the clingflim become charged?
                                          (*1 mark*)
    c) Explain, in terms of electrons, how different parts of the clingfilm become charged.
                                          (*2 marks*)

❸ a) This question is about photocopiers. Copy and complete the following passage using words from the box.

bright	charge	conduct	dark	light
metal	photoconductor	same		

Photocopiers have a _____ roller coated with photoconductor. Before copying starts, the _____ is given a positive charge. The page to be copied is lit with a strong _____ and an image of the page is projected onto the photoconductor. The _____ areas of the photoconductor now lose their _____ because it can _____ in the light, but the _____ areas keep their charge. So, the places where charge remains on the photoconductor are the _____ as the dark parts on the page being copied.
                                          (*8 marks*)
    b) Why does a photocopier need toner?
                                          (*2 marks*)
    c) Why does the toner need to be charged?
                                          (*1 mark*)
    d) Why is the photocopy usually warm when it comes out of the copier?   (*2 marks*)

Chapter 11
What affects the current in an electric circuit?

At the end of this chapter you should:

- ✓ be able to understand and draw circuit diagrams using standard symbols;
- ✓ recognise the current–potential difference graph for a resistor at constant temperature, a filament lamp and a diode;
- ✓ be able to use the equation:
  potential difference = current × resistance;
- ✓ know that the current through a component depends on the resistance of the component;

- ✓ recognise errors in the wiring of a three-pin plug;
- ✓ understand the difference between direct current (d.c.) and alternating current (a.c.);
- ✓ be able to explain how mains electricity can be used safely;
- ✓ understand that an electric current is a flow of charge;
- ✓ know that the rate at which energy is transformed in a device is called the power.

Figure 11.1 The first Blackpool Illuminations, held in 1879, had just eight electric arc lamps. Today's illuminations, having one million lamps connected by more than 320 kilometres of cables and wiring, stretch out over a distance of 10 kilometres. If one light bulb 'blew', would all the lights go out?

Circuits – starting out

Remember that an electric current is a flow of charge (see Section 10.2). For a current to flow through any **component** in a circuit:

- there must be a **potential difference** across the component. This means the circuit must include a cell, a battery or be plugged into the mains supply.
- The circuit must also be complete with no gaps, broken components or switches turned off.

Each component in a circuit has a standard symbol. Rather than drawing a complicated picture, symbols are used to draw circuit diagrams.

Figure 11.3 shows the symbols you need to know, with the names of the components they represent.

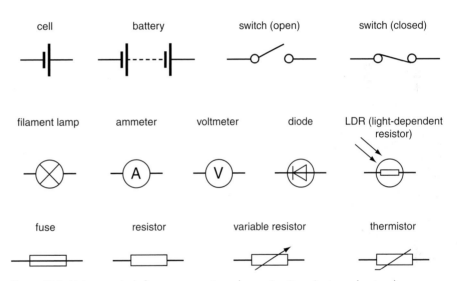

Figure 11.3 Using symbols for components makes a circuit easier to understand.

The current in a circuit is measured with an ammeter connected in **series**.

The potential difference is measured with a voltmeter connected in **parallel** across a component.

Potential difference (or p.d. for short) is measured in volts.

> ❷ Which two of the circuits shown in Figure 11.4 are connected correctly? Give a reason for each of your answers.
>
>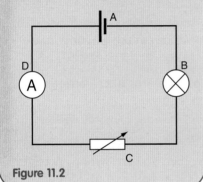
>
> **Figure 11.4**

A **component** is a part of an electric circuit.

Potential difference (or p.d.) is often called voltage. A potential difference causes a current to flow.

> ❶ Copy the circuit shown in Figure 11.2. Label the components A, B, C and D with their correct names.
>
> **Figure 11.2**

In a **series** circuit there is only one path for current to follow.

In a **parallel** circuit each path is independent of the others. There could be a break in one path and the other paths would still have a complete loop for current to flow.

CHAPTER 11 What affects the current in an electric circuit?

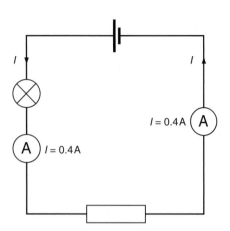

Figure 11.6 The same current flows through components joined in series.

1.5 V   1.5 V   1.5 V

Figure 11.7 The cells are joined correctly. The potential differences add to give 4.5 V.

1.5 V   1.5 V   1.5 V

Figure 11.8 One cell is round the wrong way. The p.d. of this cell cancels out the p.d. of one of the other cells. The total p.d. is only 1.5 V.

Figure 11.9 A 12 V car battery is six 2 V cells joined together.

③ Look at the circuit shown in Figure 11.5. Which switches have to be closed to make these lamps light?
a) P and Q only
b) N only
c) P, Q and N

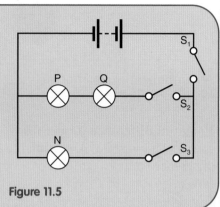

Figure 11.5

How are series circuits different from parallel circuits?

Components joined in series follow each other in one complete loop. The same current flows through each component and wire in the circuit.

The ammeters in Figure 11.6 show the same reading. This is because the current is the same at all points in a series circuit. So, only one ammeter is needed in a series circuit.

A parallel circuit gives more than one pathway for the electric current. Some current will always go down each pathway.

Cells and batteries

If you call one cell on its own a battery, then you are wrong. A battery is a number of cells joined together. A cell or battery provides charges with energy that can be transformed into other types of energy as the charges flow around the circuit.

Potential difference – cells in series

For cells joined in series, the total potential difference is worked out by adding the separate potential differences together. This works only if the cells are joined together correctly, positive (+) to negative (−).

④ Work out the total potential difference of each cell combination shown in Figure 11.10.

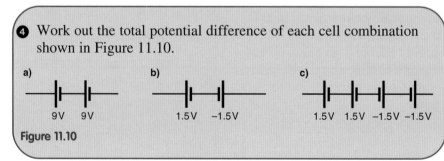

a)

9 V   9 V

b)

1.5 V   −1.5 V

c)

1.5 V   1.5 V   −1.5 V   −1.5 V

Figure 11.10

What does resistance mean?

All components try to stop the flow of an electric current. The more easily a current flows through a component, the less **resistance** the component has. A component with a high resistance lets only a small current flow through it.

The resistance of many components is not fixed. For example, a lamp has a higher resistance when it is hot than when it is cold (more about this in Section 11.3).

Some components change their resistance as temperature and light changes (more about this later).

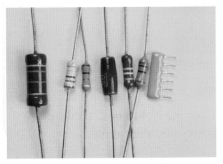

Figure 11.11 These resistors can be used to change the current in a circuit.

> The **resistance** of a component is how hard it tries to stop current flowing through it. Resistance is measured in ohms (Ω).

Adding resistors in series

Adding more lamps to a circuit (Figure 11.12) makes the current go down, which means the resistance of the circuit has gone up.

The total resistance of a series circuit is the individual resistances added together.

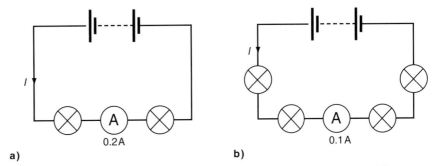

a)   b)

Figure 11.12 Adding components to a series circuit increases the resistance of the circuit.

Example

total resistance = 5 + 10 = 15 ohms (Ω)

❺ Work out the total resistance of the following arrangements.

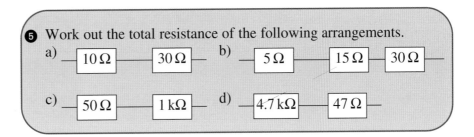

CHAPTER 11 What affects the current in an electric circuit?

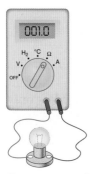

Figure 11.13 The resistance of the lamp, or any other component, can be measured with an ohmmeter. The resistance of this lamp is small because the lamp is cold.

Linking potential difference, current and resistance

The potential difference across a component, the current through a component and the resistance of a component are linked by the equation:

potential difference = current × resistance

This equation is often written using symbols as:

$$V = I \times R$$

If you do use symbols, make sure you use the right ones. Table 11.1 gives the symbols for these three quantities and their units.

Quantity	Symbol	Unit	Symbol
Current	I	ampere	A
Potential difference	V	volt	V
Resistance	R	ohm	Ω

Table 11.1 If symbols are used they must be the correct ones.

Example
A current of 0.5 A flows through a 24 Ω resistor. What is the potential difference across the resistor?

potential difference = current × resistance = 0.5 × 24 = 12 volts

6 Calculate the potential difference across each of the devices given in Table 11.2.

Device	Current through device in amps (A)	Resistance of device in ohms (Ω)
Resistor	0.5	20
Lamp	3	4
Kettle	10	23
Motor	5	83
Iron	4	57.5

Table 11.2

7 Copy and complete the following sentences by choosing the correct words in brackets.
a) The resistance of a filament lamp [goes up / goes down / does not change] as the lamp gets hot.
b) The most likely time for a filament lamp to 'blow' (the filament melts) is at the moment it is switched on. This is because the filament is [cold / hot] so its resistance is [low / high], making the current through the lamp [small / large].

Two special types of resistor

Light-dependent resistor (LDR)

A **light-dependent resistor (LDR)** is a component whose resistance decreases as the brightness of light falling on it increases.

The resistance of a **light-dependent resistor (LDR)** changes as the brightness of light shining on it changes. Table 11.3 and Figure 11.14 show that the resistance goes down as the brightness of the light goes up.

Light level	Resistance in ohms
Dark	1 000 000
Bright	2 000

Table 11.3 Resistance of an LDR

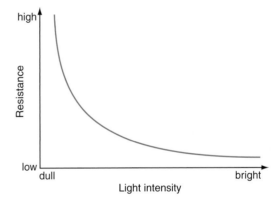

Figure 11.14 The resistance of an LDR changes with the brightness of light.

The LDR can be used as a sensor in light-operated circuits, such as security lighting. The change in resistance of LDRs is used in digital cameras to control the total amount of light that enters the camera.

Thermistor

A **thermistor** is a component whose resistance decreases as the temperature increases.

The resistance of a **thermistor** changes with temperature. As the temperature of the thermistor goes up, the resistance goes down (Figure 11.15).

A thermistor can be used as the sensor in a temperature-operated circuit, such as a fire alarm. Some electronic thermometers use a thermistor to detect changes in temperature.

high
Resistance
low
low
high
Temperature

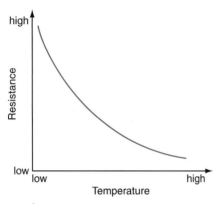

Figure 11.15 The resistance of a thermistor changes with temperature.

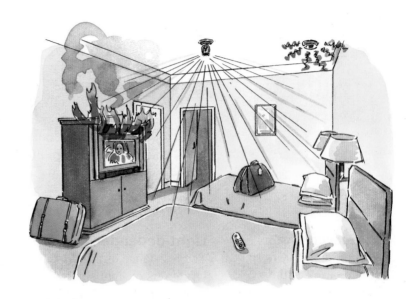

Figure 11.16 The change in the resistance of a thermistor can be used to switch on a sprinkler system and alarm automatically.

8. Copy and complete the following sentences.
   a) Resistance is measured in ______.
   b) A light-dependent resistor (______) has its highest resistance in the ______.
   c) The resistance of a thermistor changes with ______.

9. Figure 11.17 shows three circuit diagrams. Use the information on the diagrams to calculate the potential difference across the resistor, thermistor and light- dependent resistor.

a)
A
0.3A
20Ω
b)
A
0.1A
250Ω
c)
A
12mA
(0.012A)
1000Ω

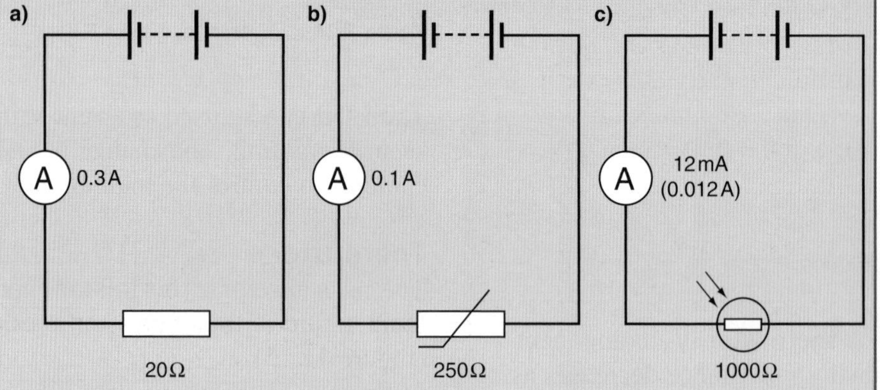

Figure 11.17

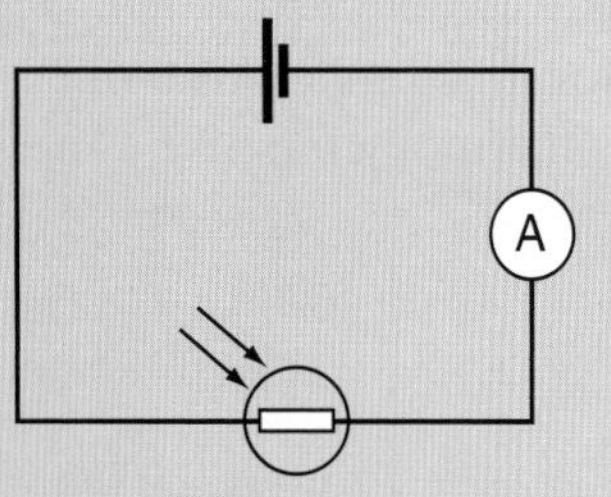

A

Figure 11.18

10. Ramesh is using the ammeter in Figure 11.18 as a simple light intensity meter.
    a) Explain why the reading on the ammeter changes when the light intensity changes.
    b) Sketch a graph to show how the ammeter reading changes with light intensity.

Activity – Misti designs an oven thermometer

Misti has designed the circuit shown in Figure 11.19 to replace the broken thermometer in her oven. Misti uses the thermistor as a temperature sensor. Only the thermistor goes inside the oven; the rest of the circuit stays outside the oven.

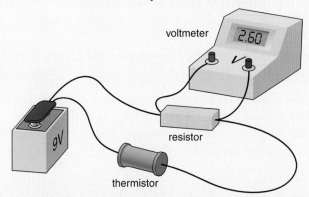

Figure 11.19 Misti's design for an oven thermometer

1. Draw a circuit diagram of Misti's oven thermometer design.
2. Explain why the voltmeter reading changes as the oven temperature changes.

The reading on the voltmeter goes up when the oven temperature goes up. Before she could use her oven thermometer, Misti had to calibrate it. She did this by putting the thermistor in a beaker of water and heating the water. She recorded the different water temperatures and the reading on the voltmeter at those temperatures. Misti then drew the graph shown in Figure 11.20.

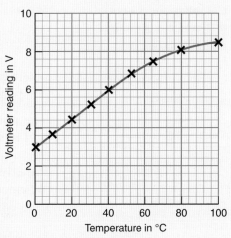

Figure 11.20 Misti's calibration graph

3. When Misti tried her thermometer in her oven and repeated the readings she obtained voltmeter readings that varied between 7.0 V and 8.0 V.
   a) Use the calibration graph to find the temperature of the oven when the voltmeter reading was 7.0 V.
   b) Use the calibration graph to find the temperature of the oven when the voltmeter reading was 8.0 V.
   c) What is the range of temperatures inside the oven?
4. Misti realises there is a problem with her design. It cannot be used to measure high oven temperatures.
   What is the maximum temperature this design can be used to measure?

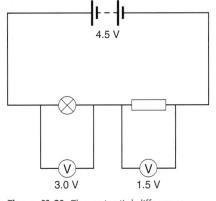

Figure 11.21 The potential difference across a component depends on the resistance of the component.

More about series and parallel circuits

Potential difference – components in series

The current through components joined in series is the same. But the potential difference across the components may be different. The potential differences are the same only if the components have the same resistance.

In Figure 11.21 the voltmeters are giving different readings. The reading across the lamp is higher, so the lamp must have the bigger resistance.

11 a) Calculate the potential difference across the resistor shown in Figure 11.22.
b) Calculate the reading on the voltmeter.

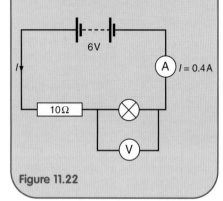

Figure 11.22

Adding the two voltmeter readings gives the total potential difference across the circuit components. In this case:

total potential difference = 3.0 + 1.5 = 4.5 V

This is the same as the potential difference of the battery. So the potential difference of the battery has been shared between the two components.

The potential differences across the components in a series circuit add to give the potential difference of the power supply.

Parallel circuits

When components are joined in parallel, the potential difference across each component is the same.

Joining components in parallel gives the electric current different paths. Some current will go down each path. How much goes through each component depends on the component's resistance. The one with the biggest resistance has the smallest current flowing through it.

In Figure 11.23 half the total current flows through each lamp. So the resistance of the lamps must be the same because the current has split into two equal parts.

In a parallel circuit, the total current flowing through the whole circuit is the sum of the currents flowing through each path.

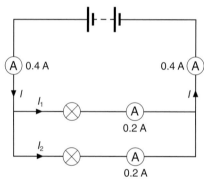

Figure 11.23 The current in a parallel circuit divides between the different paths.

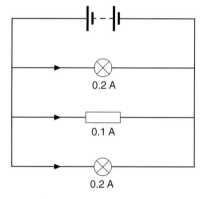

Figure 11.24 Total current = 0.2 + 0.1 + 0.2 = 0.5 A

12 Figure 11.25 shows a resistor joined in series to a lamp. The current through the lamp is 0.3 A. The potential difference across the lamp is 4 V.
a) What is the current through the resistor?
b) Calculate the potential difference across the resistor.

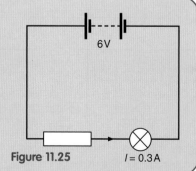

Figure 11.25

Figure 11.26 Overloaded circuits can cause fires.

Appliance	Working current in A
Computer	1
Hairdryer	4
Television	2
Stereo	1
Heater	10

Table 11.4 Different appliances draw a different current from the mains electricity supply.

Overloaded circuits

With an adaptor you can plug a lot of appliances into a single mains socket. The adaptor connects all the appliances in parallel. This means that the current taken from the socket will be the sum of the currents flowing through each appliance.

If the computer, stereo and television are plugged into the adaptor:

$$\text{total current} = 1 + 1 + 2 = 4\,\text{A}$$

This is not a problem. Up to 13 amps can safely flow through the wiring of the mains electricity supply.

But if you plugged the hairdryer, television and heater into the adaptor, this could cause a big problem.

$$\text{total current} = 4 + 2 + 10 = 16\,\text{A}$$

The total current is too large for the connecting wire. The wire could get so hot it could cause a fire.

> ⓭ The total current through an adaptor cable must not go over 13 amps.
> a) Which appliances given in Table 11.4 could be plugged safely into the adaptor along with the heater and television?
> b) Would it be safe to plug the heater, hairdryer and computer into the adaptor? Give a reason for your answer.

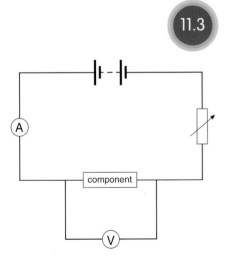

Figure 11.27 A circuit used to investigate the relationship between current and potential difference

11.3 What does a current–potential difference graph show?

The circuit shown in Figure 11.27 can be used to show how the current through a component depends on the potential difference across the component.

Adjusting the variable resistor changes the potential difference across the component and the current through the component.

When the component is a resistor

As long as the temperature of the resistor stays the same, the graph is always a straight line going through the origin (0, 0). In the graph shown in Figure 11.28 overleaf a potential difference of 4 V gives a current of 1 A. But doubling the potential difference to 8 V doubles the current to 2 A. This means that the resistance of this resistor is not changing.

Connecting the resistor the other way round in the circuit does not change its resistance. The graph is still a straight line.

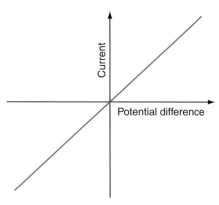

Figure 11.28 Complete current–potential difference graph for a resistor

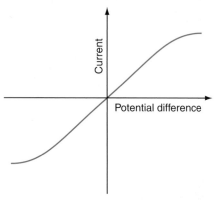

Figure 11.29 Current–potential difference graph for a filament lamp

A **diode** is a device that allows current to flow in one direction only.

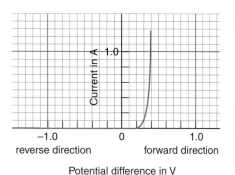

Figure 11.30 Complete current–potential difference graph for a diode

When the component is a filament lamp

A filament lamp uses a very hot wire (filament) to give out light.

Turn up the potential difference across the lamp, and the light gets brighter and hotter. As the filament gets hotter its resistance goes up. So, if the potential difference doubles the current does not double and the graph is not a straight line.

Connecting the lamp the other way round makes no difference to the way the resistance of the lamp changes. The resistance always goes up when the temperature of the filament goes up.

When the component is a diode

A **diode** is different to both a resistor and a filament lamp. The resistance of a diode does depend on which way round it is connected in a circuit.

Diodes let current flow in only one direction (called the forward direction). In the reverse direction diodes have a very high resistance so no current flows.

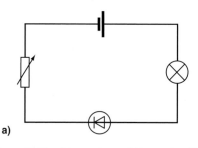
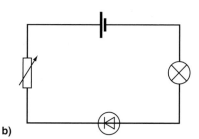

a)   b)

Figure 11.31 a) Lamp is on. **b)** Lamp is off.

⑭ Copy and complete the following sentences:
a) The resistance of a resistor does not _____ provided the _____ does not change.
b) The resistance of a filament lamp _____ as it gets _____ and brighter.
c) The _____ of a diode depends on which way round it is connected into a circuit.

Activity – QTC (Quantum Tunnelling Composite)

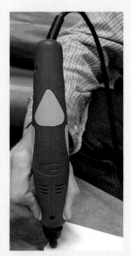

Figure 11.32 The outside casing of this prototype drill contains QTC. Squeezing the drill controls its speed.

Figure 11.33 QTC textile switches can be incorporated into clothing and bags. Tapping the switches controls your mobile phone and MP3 player. They are even used in space suits.

QTC, invented in 1997 by David Lussey, is an amazing new material. It looks just like a piece of black rubber. However, unlike rubber, when it's squashed it changes from an insulator to a conductor.

The range of uses for QTC is huge – from toys to textile switches, robotic sensors to space travel. The list just seems to keep growing.

Josh designed a simple experiment to check out what he had read about QTC. The apparatus he used is shown in Figure 11.34.

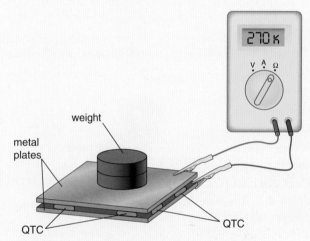

Figure 11.34 Measuring the resistance of QTC with an ohmmeter

Josh sandwiched pieces of QTC between two metal plates. He then used various weights to squeeze the QTC. For each new weight Josh waited 20 seconds before taking the ohmmeter reading. He did this because he had noticed that the reading often changed in the first few seconds. Even after 20 seconds the reading still changed, but more slowly. For each weight Josh wrote down a range of resistance values. These are shown in Figure 11.35 overleaf.

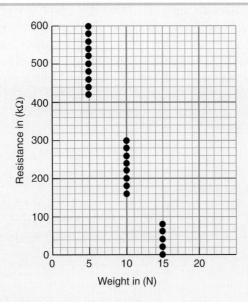

Figure 11.35 For each weight the QTC has a range of resistance.

1 With a weight of 20 N Josh measured the resistance as 10 Ω. Why did Josh not plot this value on his results chart? (*Hint*: Look at the resistance scale.)

2 Josh put an unmarked weight onto the QTC 'sandwich'. The reading on the ohmmeter was about 200kΩ. How many newtons do you think this weight was?

3 Josh noticed that each weight produced a different range of resistance values.
   a) Which weight produced the biggest resistance range?
   b) Do the resistance ranges for different weights overlap?
   c) Can QTC be used to tell one weight from a different one? Give a reason for your answer.

11.4 What is the difference between direct current and alternating current?

> **Direct current (d.c.)** is electric current that flows in the same direction all the time.
>
> A **cathode ray oscilloscope (CRO)** is a device that displays how a potential difference varies over time.

A **direct current (d.c.)** always flows in the same direction around a circuit.

Cells and batteries produce a constant direct current (d.c.).

You can use a **cathode ray oscilloscope (CRO)** to show that the potential difference of a d.c. supply is constant. The display or 'trace' on the CRO screen shows the potential difference in volts across the supply. In Figure 11.36 connecting a cell to the CRO made the line jump up above the middle line. Connecting the cell the other way around would make the line jump down. The bigger the potential difference of the cell, the further the line jumps.

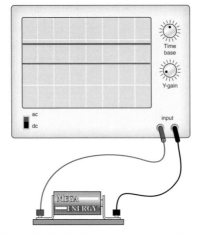

Figure 11.36 The line (trace) on the CRO shows that the cell produces a constant potential difference. The zero value is shown as a red line.

> **Alternating current (a.c.)** is electric current that continually changes its direction.
>
> The **frequency** of an a.c. current is how many times per second the electric current reverses its direction.

Alternating current is like having a cell in a circuit where you keep turning the cell around. First the current goes one way, then it goes back again. But a.c. changes direction faster and more often than you could turn the cell around.

An alternating current (a.c.) is one that is constantly changing its direction. The number of times the current changes direction in one second gives the **frequency** of the supply.

> **15** Copy and complete the following sentences.
>   a) A direct _____ provided by a _____ or a battery always flows in the _____ direction.
>   b) An _____ current is always changing _____.

Comparing CRO traces for two different a.c. supplies

Figure 11.37 shows the CRO traces for two a.c. supplies. The controls on the oscilloscope were the same for both supplies.

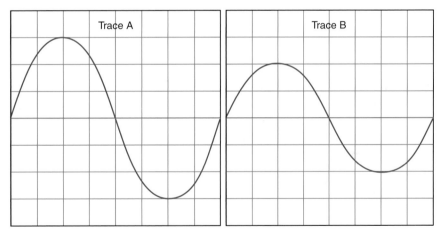

Figure 11.37 The two a.c. supplies have a different potential difference.

Trace A is 1½ times taller than trace B. This means the peak potential difference of supply A is 1½ times bigger than that of supply B.

CHAPTER 11 What affects the current in an electric circuit?

16 Figure 11.38 shows the CRO traces for different electricity supplies. Which of the supplies:
a) has the largest peak potential difference;
b) has the smallest peak potential difference;
c) gives a direct current?

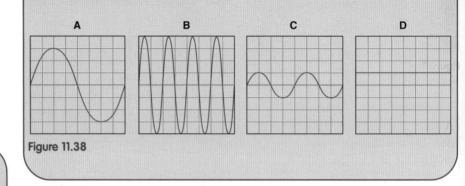

A   B   C   D

Figure 11.38

17 Copy and complete the following sentences.
In the UK mains electricity is an _____ current supply. It has a _____ of 50 _____ (Hz).

The mains electricity supply

In the UK, mains electricity is an a.c. supply with a frequency of 50 Hz. This means the current flows one way, then back again, 50 times in each second.

11.5 How can the mains electricity supply be used safely?

Many electric appliances are designed to work from the mains electricity supply. These appliances are connected to the mains using a cable and three-pin plug. Both the cable and plug are designed to make the appliance safe to use.

The cable

Inside the cables are either two or three copper wires (called the inner cores). Copper is used because it is a good electrical conductor.

A layer of plastic covers each wire and another layer forms the outside of the cable. Plastic is used because it is a good insulator and it bends easily without breaking.

Figure 11.39 Three-core and two-core cables

Figure 11.40 The outside of a three-pin plug and its wall socket

> A **fuse** is a thin wire that is designed to melt and break a circuit.

Figure 11.41 Electricity is useful but also dangerous. Many fires are caused by electrical faults.

A three-pin plug

The outside case of the plug is made of plastic or rubber. Plastic and rubber are good electrical insulators.

Pushing the plug into a socket joins the three brass pins of the plug to the terminals of the socket. Brass is a good electrical conductor.

Inside the plug there is a cable grip and a fuse. The cable grip holds the cable firmly in place. If the cable is pulled the cable grip will stop the copper wires inside the plug being pulled loose.

Fuses

A **fuse** is a thin piece of wire that lets a current up to a certain value flow through it. Above this value the fuse will overheat and melt. We often say that the fuse has 'blown'. For example, a 3 A fuse will melt or 'blow' if a current bigger than 3 A flows through it.

The fuse joins the live pin of the plug to the live wire inside the plug. If a fault causes the fuse to melt, the live wire is disconnected and the circuit is broken.

Most plugs are fitted with a 3 A or 13 A fuse. It is important that the right fuse is used with an appliance. Appliances like table lamps and TVs take small currents (well below 3 A), so they should have plugs with 3 A fuses. Kettles, irons and hairdryers usually take currents bigger than 3 A, so they should have plugs with 13 A fuses.

> **18** An electric coffee maker uses a current of 2 A. Why is the plug of the coffee maker fitted with a 3 A fuse and not a 13 A fuse?.
>
> **19** Which of the following materials are electrical insulators?
> **A** brass
> **B** copper
> **C** plastic
> **D** rubber

Connecting an appliance to a three-pin plug

When you buy an electrical appliance it will already have a plug fitted. But at some time you may need to fit a new plug to an older appliance. When you do this the wires from the appliance are colour coded to help you connect them in the right place in the plug.

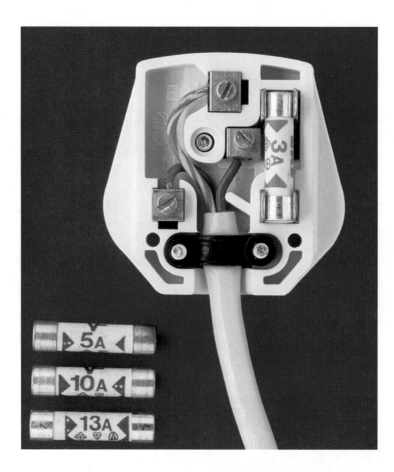

Figure 11.42 A correctly wired three-pin plug:
- the brown wire (live wire) is joined to the fuse, which is joined to the live pin;
- the blue wire (neutral wire) is joined to the neutral pin;
- the green/yellow wire (earth wire) is joined to the earth pin.

20 Copy and complete the following sentences.
  a) Inside a three-pin plug, the _____-covered wire goes to the live pin, the _____-covered wire to the neutral pin and the _____-covered wire to the earth pin.
  b) A _____ joins the live pin of a plug to the live wire in a cable.
  c) A fuse will _____ if the _____ in the circuit is higher than the fuse rating. This will _____ the circuit off.

21 Say why each of the plugs drawn in Figure 11.43 is not safe to use.

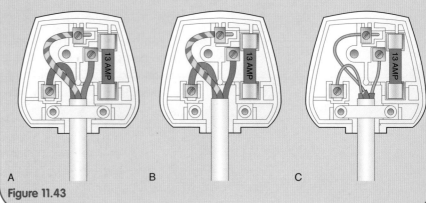

A   B   C
Figure 11.43

A **circuit breaker** is a resettable fuse.

A **residual current circuit breaker** (**RCCB**) is a circuit breaker that disconnects the circuit when it detects current leaking out of the circuit to earth due to a fault.

Figure 11.44 A RCCB plugged into a socket ready for use

22 Copy and complete the following sentence.
A RCCB will switch off an appliance if the _____ in the live wire is different to the current in the _____ wire.

Circuit breakers

The mains supply to a house starts at a consumer unit. Often this is called the 'fuse box'. In the consumer unit are several separate fuses. Each fuse leads to a different circuit supplying electricity to a different part of the house.

Many consumer units now contain **circuit breakers** rather than fuses. The circuit breaker is a fast-acting switch that automatically turns off ('trips') when the current through it goes above a set value. Having mended the fault, all you have to do is press a button to reset the circuit breaker.

A second type of circuit breaker, a **residual current circuit breaker** (**RCCB**), should be used with certain types of appliance, particularly those used outside.

A RCCB works by detecting any difference between the currents in the live and neutral wires of the supply cable. If everything is working properly the two currents are the same. If something happens to make the current in the wires different, the RCCB automatically switches the circuit off.

For extra safety Vince plugs his lawn mower into a RCCB (Figure 11.45). Just as well, because Vince has been careless and cut into the cable insulation. This causes a current to flow through Vince to earth. This means the currents in the live and neutral wires are now different. The RCCB detects this difference and rapidly switches the circuit off saving Vince from a very nasty electric shock.

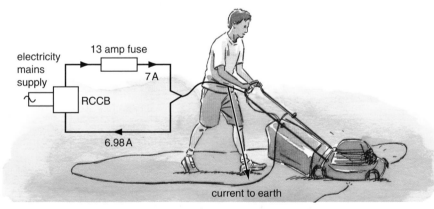

Figure 11.45 Using a RCCB saves Vince from a nasty experience.

23 Give two ways that a circuit breaker is a better safety device than a fuse.

24 Why should electric hedge trimmers always be plugged into a RCCB?

CHAPTER 11 What affects the current in an electric circuit?

Earthing

Any electrical appliance with an outside metal case should be earthed. Figure 11.46 shows an electric toaster. The earth wire from the cable is joined to the metal case of the toaster. A fault could cause the live wire to touch the metal case. If this happens while the toaster is switched on, a large current will flow from the live wire to the earth wire.

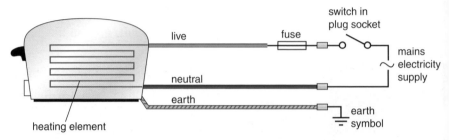

Figure 11.46 The earth wire is an important safety feature of appliances with outer metal parts.

This large current in the circuit causes the fuse to melt, which switches the toaster off.

Without the earth wire the toaster would become live. Anyone who touches the metal case would get an electric shock as the current flows through them to earth.

25 Each picture in Figure 11.47 shows electricity being used dangerously. Explain the danger in each picture.

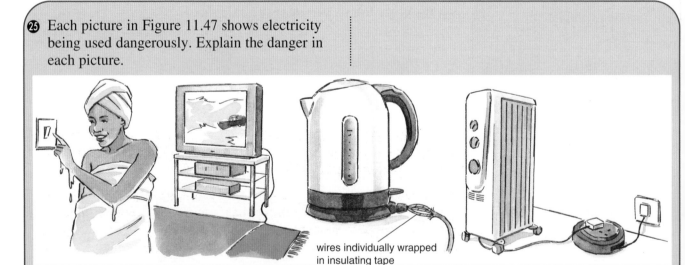

wires individually wrapped in insulating tape

Figure 11.47

26 Zafran leans against his washing machine. Unfortunately the live wire inside the machine has become loose and is touching the metal casing. Explain how the earth wire, which is correctly connected, will protect Zafran from a serious electric shock.

11.6 What links current, charge, energy and power?

Current and charge

An electric current is a flow of charge. In a metal wire, an electric current is a flow of electrons. If current goes up, the rate of flow of charge goes up.

Energy and charge

In any circuit, the battery or mains supply is an energy source that provides energy to charges. Energy is transformed into other sorts of energy as the charges flow around the circuit.

When charge flows through a resistor, some electrical energy is transformed into heat. In an appliance like an electric kettle this is what it is designed to do, but in something like a light bulb the heat energy is wasted.

Power and energy

Sometimes knowing how quickly energy is transferred or transformed is as important or more important than knowing how much energy will be transferred or transformed.

> **Power** is the rate at which a device transforms energy, in J/s or W.

For example, an electric kettle transfers heat energy to the water inside the kettle. But if the transfer takes a long time the water will warm up slowly. To know how quickly the water will warm up you need to know how much energy the kettle will transfer to the water every second. What you need to know is the **power** of the kettle.

$$\text{power} = \frac{\text{energy transformed}}{\text{time}}$$

Units
- Power in watts (W)
- Energy transferred in joules (J)
- Time in second (s)

A 2000 W (2 kW) kettle is a fast-boiling, high-power kettle. It transfers 2000 joules of electrical energy every second. This is a rapid transfer, which is why the kettle boils the water quickly.

Most electrical appliances have an information plate printed on them. This will give the power of the appliance and the potential difference of the power supply that it should be used with. These two quantities are linked to the current that will flow though the appliance by the equation:

$$\begin{array}{ccc} \text{power} & = & \text{current} & \times & \text{potential difference.} \\ \text{(watt, W)} & & \text{(ampere, A)} & & \text{(volt, V)} \end{array}$$

Example
A hairdryer used in the USA draws a current of 10 A from the 110 V mains supply. Calculate the power of the hairdryer.

power = current × potential difference = 10 × 110 = 1100 watts

Activity – Using the information on an information plate

All electrical appliances used at home have an information plate somewhere on the outside. Find the information plates on at least three different types of appliance.

❶ For each appliance write down the power and potential difference from the plate. Don't forget to write down the units.

❷ From the information you wrote down, which appliance uses the highest current? (*Hint*: This will be the one with the highest power.)

Appliances that have a power over 2300 W use a current of over 10 A.

❸ Which appliances in your list use a current of over 10 A?

❹ Suggest the correct fuse rating to use with each appliance in your list.

㉗ Table 11.5 gives the power rating of three different electric heaters. Which heater would warm a room the fastest? Explain the reason for your choice.

Heater	Power rating
A	2000 W
B	1500 W
C	2500 W

Table 11.5

㉘ Table 11.6 shows how long it takes three different electric kettles to boil some water. The starting temperature of the water in each kettle is the same.

Kettle	Mass of water in the kettle	Time to boil the water
X	1.0 kg	4 minutes
Y	500 g	2½ minutes
Z	1.2 kg	4 minutes

Table 11.6

Assuming the kettles are equally efficient, which one has the highest power? Explain the reason for your choice.

㉙ What is the power of a lamp that transforms 2400 J of electrical energy to light and heat in 1 minute?

㉚ Calculate the power rating in watts of:
a) a car starter motor operating from a 12 V supply, taking a 100 A current;
b) a torch bulb operating from a 4.5 V supply, taking a 0.3 A current;
c) a pocket calculator operating from a 3 V supply, taking a 0.0001 A current.

Summary

✓ A **component** is one part of an electric circuit.

✓ **Potential difference** (or p.d.) is often called voltage. A potential difference will cause a current to flow.

✓ The current through a component in a circuit depends on the **resistance** of the component.

✓ The resistance of a **light-dependent resistor (LDR)** goes down as the brightness of the light goes up.

✓ The resistance of a **thermistor** decreases as its temperature increases.

✓ A metal wire at constant temperature has a constant resistance.

✓ The resistance of a filament lamp increases as the temperature of the filament increases.

✓ A **diode** lets current flow in only one direction.

✓ In a **series** circuit there is only one path for current to follow.

✓ For components joined in **series**:
  • the same current flows through each component;
  • the total resistance is the sum of the individual resistances;
  • the potential differences across the components add to give the potential difference of the power supply.

✓ In a **parallel** circuit there are several pathways and each pathway is independent of the others.

✓ For components joined in **parallel**:
  • the potential difference across each component is the same;
  • the total current flowing through the whole circuit is the sum of the currents flowing through the separate pathways.

✓ **Direct current (d.c.)** flows in one direction only but **alternating current (a.c.)** changes direction.

✓ The **frequency** of an a.c. current is how many times per second the electric current reverses its direction. Frequency is measured in hertz.

✓ In the UK mains electricity is a 50 hertz, 230 V a.c. supply.

✓ A **cathode ray oscilloscope (CRO)** is a device that shows how a potential difference varies over time.

✓ A correctly wired three-pin plug contains a **fuse** and an earth wire.

✓ Any appliance with a metal case should be earthed.

✓ A **circuit breaker** is a resettable fuse. A **residual current circuit breaker** (RCCB) disconnects the circuit when it detects current leaking to earth owing to a fault.

✓ **Power** is the rate at which a device transforms energy, in J/s or W.

✓ Important equations that you should be able to use:

potential difference = current × resistance

$$power = \frac{energy\ transferred}{time}$$

power = current × potential difference

❶ Table 11.7 shows the circuit symbols of four electrical components. Copy and complete the table to match each component to one of the functions A, B, C or D.

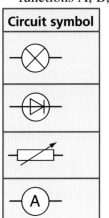

Circuit symbol	Function
	A To control the current flowing in a circuit
	B To measure the current flowing in a circuit
	C To transfer electrical energy to light energy
	D To allow current to flow only one way in a circuit

Table 11.7

(4 marks)

EXAM QUESTIONS

❷ Figure 11.48 shows an electric iron connected to the 230 V mains supply. When the iron is switched on and working normally the current flowing through it is 8 A.

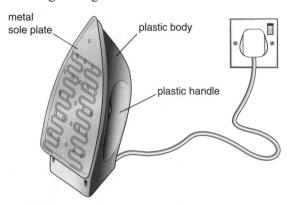

metal sole plate
plastic body
plastic handle

Figure 11.48

a) Use the equation below to calculate the power of the iron. Show your working and give the unit.

  power = potential difference × current

  (3 marks)

b) Which part of the iron is the earth lead from the cable connected to? *(1 mark)*

c) The heating element of the iron is a resistor. Copy out the statement from A, B or C that is correct.

A When an electric current flows through the heating element, heat is transformed into electrical energy.

B When an electric current flows through the heating element, electrical energy is transformed into heat.

C The resistance of the heating element goes down as the element warms up. *(1 mark)*

❸ Tasmin wants to find out how the current through component 'X' varies with potential difference. To do this she sets up the circuit shown in Figure 11.49. Tasmin's one set of results are recorded in Table 11.8.

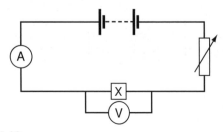

Figure 11.49

Potential difference in V	0.0	3.0	5.0	7.0	9.0	11.0
Current in A	0.0	1.0	1.4	1.7	1.9	2.1

Table 11.8 Tasmin's results

a) i) What did Tasmin do to vary the potential difference across component 'X'? *(1 mark)*

ii) What range of potential difference values did Tasmin use? *(1 mark)*

iii) Suggest why Tasmin should have included some values of potential difference below 3 volts. *(1 mark)*

b) i) Plot a graph of potential difference (horizontal axis) against current (vertical axis). *(3 marks)*

ii) What current flows through component 'X' when the potential difference is 10 V? *(1 mark)*

c) What is component 'X'? Explain the reason for your answer. *(2 marks)*

❹ The ammeters in Figure 11.50 are identical.

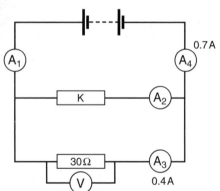

Figure 11.50 Circuit diagram

a) i) What are the readings on the ammeters A_1 and A_2? *(2 marks)*

ii) Is the resistance of K, bigger, smaller or equal to 30 Ω? Give a reason for your answer. *(2 marks)*

b) i) Use the equation:

  potential difference = current × resistance

  to calculate the reading on the voltmeter. *(2 marks)*

ii) What is the potential difference of the power supply? Give a reason for your answer. *(2 marks)*

Chapter 12
What happens during radioactive decay, nuclear fission and nuclear fusion?

At the end of this chapter you should:

✓ understand why the nuclear model of atomic structure replaced the 'plum pudding' model;

✓ know the relative masses and relative charges of protons, neutrons and electrons;

✓ know that atoms have a very small nucleus containing protons and neutrons surrounded by a much larger region of empty space in which there are electrons;

✓ understand how atoms can lose or gain electrons to form ions;

✓ know that alpha, beta and gamma radiations are emitted (given out) when the nuclei of radioactive substances decay;

✓ understand the changes in atomic number and mass number as a result of alpha and beta decay;

✓ know the sources of background radiation;

✓ know that nuclear fission releases large amounts of energy which can be used in nuclear reactors to generate electricity,

✓ understand how the neutrons released by nuclear fission can cause a chain reaction;

✓ know that nuclear fusion involves the joining together of two nuclei with the release of massive amounts of energy.

Figure 12.1 A small nuclear reactor in this submarine provides enough energy for it to remain in the ocean for months without refuelling. The energy comes from the break-up (fission) of the nuclei of uranium atoms. The heat and light emitted from stars also comes from nuclear processes. In this case, the energy comes from the joining together (fusion) of the nuclei of hydrogen atoms.

Where do radioactivity and atomic energy come from?

Radioactive substances such as uranium emit (give out) energy naturally. When radioactivity was first discovered, it was hard to understand where this energy came from.

Marie Curie soon discovered that the strength of the radiation depended only on the amount of uranium in her sample. Nothing she did to the uranium, such as heating it up, affected the rays. This showed that radioactivity depended only on the property of radioactive atoms to break up and emit radiation.

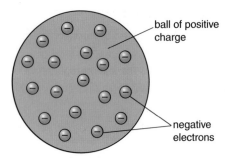

Figure 12.2 Thomson's 'plum pudding' model for the structure of atoms

> In his **'plum pudding' model**, Thomson said that each atom was a positively charged sphere with electrons embedded in it.

What do we know about the structure of atoms?

In 1897, J.J. Thomson discovered tiny negative particles about 2000 times lighter than hydrogen atoms. He called these particles electrons. Thomson obtained electrons when he put very high voltages across terminals made of different metals in different gases. From this he suggested that all substances and all atoms contained electrons (see Section 5.1).

Thomson knew that atoms had no electrical charge overall. This meant that atoms must also contain positive charge to balance the negative charge of the electrons.

In 1904, Thomson put forward a model for the structure of atoms. He said that atoms were tiny balls of positive material with electrons embedded in it, like currants scattered throughout a cake (Figure 12.2). This became known as the **'plum pudding' model** of atomic structure.

Rutherford and his colleagues find the positive nucleus

In 1898, Ernest Rutherford showed that there were two types of radiation emitted by radioactive substances. He called these 'alpha rays' and 'beta rays'. Rutherford and his colleagues didn't know exactly what alpha rays were. But they did know that alpha rays contained particles that were small and positively charged.

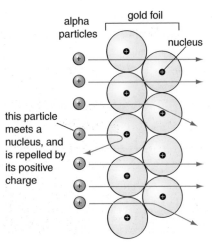

Figure 12.3 Geiger and Marsden's experiment in which alpha particles were 'fired' at very thin gold foil

In 1909, Rutherford suggested an experiment to investigate the structure of atoms using alpha particles as tiny 'bullets' to fire at atoms. Hans Geiger and Ernest Marsden carried out the experiment. They 'fired' narrow beams of positive alpha particles at very thin gold foil only a few atoms thick (Figure 12.3). Geiger and Marsden's results showed that:
- most of the alpha particles went straight through the foil;
- some of the alpha particles were scattered (deflected) by the foil;
- a few alpha particles seemed to rebound from the foil.

Rutherford's prediction

Rutherford predicted how the particles would behave using Thomson's 'plum pudding model' of atomic structure. He thought that:

- some alpha particles would pass straight through the empty space in Thomson's model;
- other alpha particles would be slightly deflected if they were attracted by the negative electrons embedded in Thomson's model.

Rutherford was amazed that a few alpha particles seemed to rebound from the foil. He agreed with Thomson that atoms do have a lot of empty space. This allowed most of the alpha particles to pass straight through the foil.

He concluded that atoms must also have a small positive centre or nucleus. This would explain how some alpha particles are deflected or even rebound from the foil. These alpha particles are repelled as they approach the positive nuclei of gold atoms in the foil.

Rutherford's nuclear model

Rutherford summarised the results of Geiger and Marsden's experiment. He said that:

- atoms have a very small positive nucleus surrounded by a much larger region of empty space;
- in this empty space, electrons orbit the nucleus like planets orbiting the Sun (Figure 12.4).

Rutherford's model of atomic structure was called the **nuclear model**. His nuclear model quickly replaced Thomson's plum pudding model. The nuclear model is still the basic model of atomic structure that we use today.

The work of Thomson, Rutherford and their colleagues means we now know that:

- the positive charge of the nucleus is due to positive particles called protons;
- protons are about 2000 times heavier than electrons;
- electrons have a relative charge of -1 and protons have a relative charge of $+1$;
- atoms have equal numbers of protons and electrons, and therefore no overall electrical charge;
- the nuclei of atoms contain neutrons as well as protons. Neutrons have no charge and their mass is the same as that of protons (Section 5.1).

All atoms are made up from protons, neutrons and electrons. These particles are sometimes called sub-atomic particles. Their relative masses and relative electric charges are summarised in Table 12.1.

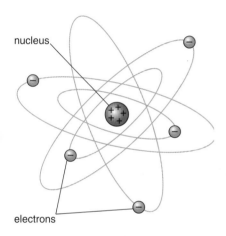

Figure 12.4 Rutherford's nuclear model for the structure of atoms. Rutherford described atoms as miniature solar systems with electrons orbiting the nucleus like planets around the Sun.

> The **nuclear model** of atomic structure was put forward by Rutherford, in 1911. He said that each atom has a very small positively charged nucleus, which is surrounded by electrons.

Particle	Relative mass	Relative charge
Proton	1	+1
Neutron	1	0
Electron	$\frac{1}{2000}$	−1

Table 12.1 The relative masses and relative charges of protons, neutrons and electrons

CHAPTER 12 What happens during radioactive decay, nuclear fission and nuclear fusion?

 12.2

Atoms of different elements

The **atomic number** is the number of protons in an atom.

The **mass number** is the total number of protons plus neutrons in an atom.

Isotopes are atoms of an element with the same atomic number, but different mass numbers.

Atoms of different elements have different numbers of protons. Hydrogen atoms are the only atoms with one proton. Helium atoms are the only atoms with two protons. Lithium atoms are the only atoms with three protons and so on. This means that the number of protons in an atom tells you which element it is. Scientists call this number the **atomic number**. So, hydrogen has an atomic number of 1, helium has an atomic number of 2, and so on.

The atomic number of an atom can tell you which element it is, but it cannot tell you its mass. The mass of an atom depends on the total number of protons and neutrons in its nucleus. Scientists call this number the **mass number** of an atom.

Hydrogen atoms (with one proton and no neutrons) have a mass number of 1. Lithium atoms (with three protons and four neutrons) have a mass number of 7 and copper atoms (with 29 protons and 34 neutrons) have a mass number of 63.

All the atoms of one element have the same number of protons, but they don't all have the same number of neutrons. These atoms of the same element with different numbers of neutrons and therefore different mass numbers are called **isotopes** (see also Section 5.2).

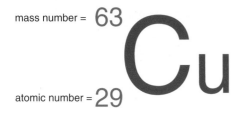

Figure 12.5 We can write the symbol $^{63}_{29}Cu$ to show the mass number and atomic number for a copper nucleus. The mass number is written at the top left of the symbol and the atomic number is written at the bottom left.

From atoms to ions

When atoms are hit by gamma rays and fast-moving beta particles (electrons), they sometimes form ions. Gamma rays and beta particles have enough energy to knock electrons out of atoms forming positive ions (Figure 12.6). Because of this, gamma rays and beta particles are known as ionising radiations.

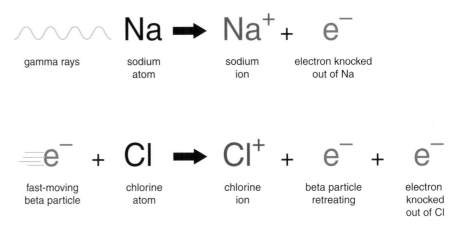

Figure 12.6 The formation of ions when sodium and chlorine atoms are hit by ionising radiations

① a) Why did most of the alpha particles pass straight through the foil in Geiger and Marsden's experiment?
   b) Why did Rutherford conclude that atoms must have a positive nucleus?
   c) Why did Rutherford conclude that the nucleus must be very small compared with the size of the atom?

② Copy and complete the following sentences:

Uranium has two isotopes. Each isotope has 92 protons and _____ electrons and therefore an _____ number of 92. But one of these isotopes has 143 neutrons and the other has 146 neutrons. Their mass numbers are therefore _____ and _____. They are sometimes called uranium-235 and _____.

③ Copy and complete Table 12.2 using words from the box below.

| atomic | chemical | neutrons |
| | physical | protons |

Isotopes have the same:	Isotopes have **different:**
• number of _____ • number of electrons • _____ number • _____ properties	• numbers of _____ • _____ properties

Table 12.2

④ How many protons, neutrons and electrons are there in:
   a) $^{19}_{9}F$ and $^{19}_{9}F^-$;   b) $^{27}_{13}Al$ and $^{27}_{13}Al^{3+}$?

12.3 What causes background radiation?

Nuclear radiation is all around us. This is because there are small concentrations of naturally occurring radioactive elements in many materials. There is also nuclear radiation from the Sun and from medical tests such as X-rays. This **background radiation** gives everyone a small dose of nuclear radiation.

> **Background radiation** is the nuclear radiation that is present all around us. It comes mainly from natural sources.

Fortunately, the level of background radiation is normally low. It is not a health risk for most people. But, people who work with radioactive materials, such as radiographers and radiotherapists, must take special precautions to reduce their exposure to nuclear radiations.

Figure 12.7 shows the main sources of background radiation for people living in the UK.

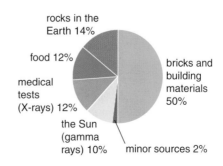

Figure 12.7 The main sources of background radiation in the UK

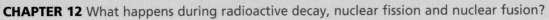

- Various rocks in the Earth and particularly granite contain small percentages of radioactive uranium and thorium. As these elements decay, they emit radioactive radon gas. This gas can accumulate to dangerous levels in mines and houses above granite rocks.
- Bricks and other building materials also give off radiations, because they are produced from rocks and clay.
- Our food contains traces of radioactive materials.
- The Sun and other stars emit gamma radiation. Some of this radiation reaches the Earth.
- X-rays used for tests by doctors and dentists are ionising radiations.

What happens during radioactive decay?

Radioactive materials emit radiation all the time. During **radioactive decay**, the unstable nuclei of radioactive atoms break up. The break-up is random. When the nuclei break up, they emit **alpha particles**, **beta particles** and **gamma rays**. But what happens in terms of protons, neutrons and electrons during radioactive decay?

Alpha decay

Radioactive decay is the random emission of radiation as alpha particles, beta particles and gamma rays from the unstable nuclei of radioactive atoms.

Alpha particles are helium nuclei, $^{4}_{2}He^{2+}$.

Beta particles are electrons with almost zero mass and a charge of -1, so they are written as $^{0}_{-1}e$.

Gamma rays are very penetrating electromagnetic rays.

Unstable isotopes, such as radium-226, uranium-238 and plutonium-238, decay (break up) by losing an alpha particle. This is called alpha decay. The nuclei of these isotopes are just too heavy – they contain lots of protons and neutrons. The nuclei become more stable by losing mass in the form of an alpha particle. An alpha particle contains just two protons and two neutrons.

So, when an atom of $^{226}_{88}Ra$ loses an alpha particle, it loses two protons and two neutrons from its nucleus. The atom left behind has a mass number of 222 (four less than $^{226}_{88}Ra$) because it has lost two protons + two neutrons. Its atomic number is 86 (two less than $^{226}_{88}Ra$) because it has lost two protons.

All atoms of atomic number 86 are those of radon, Rn. So we can summarise the alpha decay of radium-226 in a nuclear equation as:

$$^{226}_{88}Ra \rightarrow \, ^{222}_{86}Rn + \, ^{4}_{2}He$$

Beta decay

Other radioactive isotopes decay by losing a beta particle (electron, $^{0}_{-1}e$). During beta decay, a neutron in the nucleus splits up into a proton and an electron. The proton stays in the nucleus, but the electron is ejected (pushed out) as a beta particle. So, the mass number of the remaining nucleus stays the same because the total number of protons + neutrons has not changed. But, its atomic number increases by one because it has one more proton (Table 12.3).

For example, when carbon-14 ($^{14}_{6}C$) loses a beta particle ($^{0}_{-1}e$), the product nucleus has an atomic number one more than $^{14}_{6}C$. This is $^{14}_{7}N$. The nuclear equation for the process is:

$$^{14}_{6}C \rightarrow ^{14}_{7}N + ^{0}_{-1}e$$

The products formed after radioactive decay are sometimes called decay products.

	Alpha decay	Beta decay
Isotopes involved	Atomic number greater than 83	Atomic number less than 83
Particle lost	$^{4}_{2}He^{2+}$	$^{0}_{-1}e$
Change in mass number	−4	0
Change in atomic number	−2	+1

Table 12.3 Comparing alpha decay and beta decay. In both cases, the atomic number changes so one element is converted to another element.

Remember that:
- Nuclear equations only show changes in the nuclei of radioactive atoms. They do not involve electrons in the shells of the atom.
- The electrons ejected in beta decay come from the nucleus and not from the shells of the atoms concerned.
- The total mass and total charge of the decay products are the same as those of the initial nucleus.

5 Uranium-238 ($^{238}_{92}U$) decays by losing an alpha particle to form thorium (Th).
   a) What is the mass number of the thorium produced?
   b) What is the atomic number of the thorium?
   c) Write a nuclear equation for the decay process.

6 a) What are the values of A, B, C and D in the beta decay equation below?

$$^{43}_{A}K \rightarrow ^{B}_{C}Ca + ^{D}_{-1}e$$

   b) Write a nuclear equation for the beta decay of $^{24}_{11}Na$ to magnesium.

7 Explain the following terms:
   a) radioactivity;
   b) nuclear reaction;
   c) alpha decay.

12.5 Nuclear fission and atomic energy

Chemical reactions and nuclear reactions

Chemical reactions involve changes in the electrons in the outer parts of atoms (Section 5.6). During chemical reactions, electrons are either:
- transferred from one atom to another or
- shared between two atoms.

On the other hand, nuclear reactions involve changes to nuclei in the centre of atoms. During nuclear reactions, one element is converted to another element by:
- radioactive decay;
- nuclear fission or
- nuclear fusion.

You will study nuclear fission and nuclear fusion in this and the next sections.

Figure 12.8 During the Middle Ages, alchemists dreamed of changing 'base' metals like lead into gold. Their dreams were never realised. However, since 1940, scientists have produced more than 20 new elements. All of these elements come after uranium in the Periodic Table. They are all radioactive and most of them decay very rapidly.

Activity – From Dalton to the atom smashers

Figure 12.9 John Dalton was born in Cumbria in 1766. For most of his life he taught science and mathematics in Manchester. John Dalton put forward his atomic theory in 1807.

Read the passage below and then answer the questions

Dalton's ideas about atoms are still helpful to scientists. But modern knowledge about elements and atomic structure has shown that some of his ideas were wrong. Dalton said:

- all matter is made up of tiny particles, called atoms;
- atoms cannot be made;
- atoms cannot be broken apart;
- all the atoms of one element are exactly alike;
- atoms of one element are different from those of all other elements.

In the 1920s, Rutherford and his colleagues turned sodium into magnesium and aluminium into silicon. Then, in 1940, chemists in the USA managed to make (synthesise) new elements. They did this by bombarding heavy elements like uranium with neutrons. For, example, neptunium-239 and plutonium-239 were obtained by bombarding uranium-238 with neutrons.

❶ We now know that matter is composed of smaller particles than atoms. What are these smaller particles called?

❷ Atoms of new elements were first synthesised (made) by chemists in the 1940s.
  a) Name two of the elements synthesised by chemists.
  b) Where do these synthesised elements appear in the Periodic Table?
  c) Why do you think that neutrons were better 'bullets' than protons and alpha particles for synthesising new elements? (*Hint*: Think about the type of charge on protons and alpha particles.)

❸ a) What type of element breaks apart naturally?
  b) What happens when these elements break apart?

❹ a) What name is given to atoms of the same element which are not exactly alike?
  b) How do these atoms differ?

❺ How do atoms of one particular element always differ in atomic structure from those of all other elements?

❻ In 1938, German scientists bombarded uranium-235 with neutrons. The process released enormous amounts of energy and split the uranium atoms in two. The process was called fission. Fission means 'splitting'. State one of the consequences of atomic fission and 'splitting the atom'.

Nuclear fission

Nuclear fission is the splitting of an atomic nucleus. This releases large amounts of energy.

In 1938, Otto Hahn, a German scientist, discovered **nuclear fission** by chance. Hahn and his colleagues were trying to make a new element by bombarding uranium with neutrons. Instead, the neutrons caused the uranium nuclei to break up violently forming two smaller nuclei. More neutrons were also released plus vast quantities of energy (Figure 12.11).

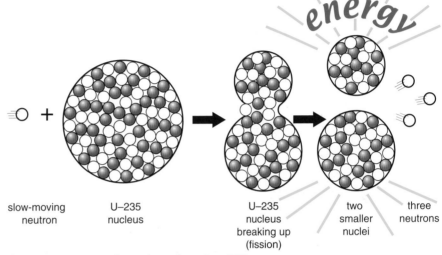

slow-moving neutron   U–235 nucleus   U–235 nucleus breaking up (fission)   two smaller nuclei   three neutrons

Figure 12.11 Fission of a nucleus of uranium-235

Figure 12.10 Lise Meitner worked with Otto Hahn in Germany for several years. Lise was Jewish and had to flee from Germany in 1938. Hahn was the first to split the atom, but Lise Meitner explained the process and called it nuclear fission.

Nuclear fission differs from radioactive decay in two ways.
- Nuclear fission does not happen spontaneously like radioactive decay. It happens only when unstable nuclei like uranium-235 absorb neutrons.
- Nuclear fission involves the break-up of one large nucleus into two fragments of roughly the same size. During radioactive decay, the products are one large fragment and one very small fragment (either an alpha particle or a beta particle).

Natural uranium contains two isotopes, $^{235}_{92}U$ and $^{238}_{92}U$. Only 0.7% is uranium-235. The rest is all uranium-238. Experiments show that only uranium-235 takes part in nuclear fission. This led scientists to an important conclusion. If natural uranium is enriched with more uranium-235, the neutrons released during fission can go on to split more uranium nuclei. And this could start a **chain reaction**.

A chain reaction occurs when the neutrons released by splitting one nucleus go on to split more nuclei. The reaction needs no further input.

In an atomic bomb, the fission of enriched U-235 atoms releases three neutrons. These three neutrons each collide with other U-235 atoms, releasing nine neutrons; these nine release 27, then 81, and so on. Each time, more and more energy is produced. This results in an uncontrolled reaction giving out vast amounts of energy and radiation.

In a nuclear reactor, a lower concentration of U-235 is used to produce a controlled chain reaction. In this case, only one of the three neutrons released at each fission goes on to cause another fission. This produces a steady chain reaction and a steady release of energy.

CHAPTER 12 What happens during radioactive decay, nuclear fission and nuclear fusion?

Activity – How do nuclear reactors work?

Figure 12.12 shows a simplified diagram of a gas-cooled nuclear reactor. At the centre of the reactor, rods of 'enriched' uranium are stacked inside a large block of graphite. Neutrons released by the fission of uranium-235 are slowed down by collision with carbon atoms in the graphite. A slow-moving neutron splits a nucleus more easily.

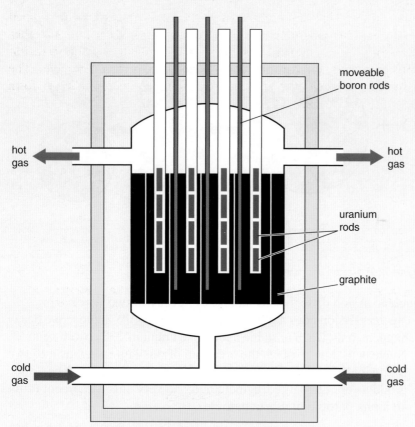

Figure 12.12 A simplified diagram of a gas-cooled nuclear reactor

The energy released by nuclear fission in the uranium rods heats up the reactor. The temperature of the reactor is controlled by moveable rods of boron. The boron rods absorb neutrons. A controlled chain reaction can be obtained by carefully adjusting these neutron-absorbing rods. The heat produced is taken away by carbon dioxide which circulates through the reactor. The heat is used to turn water into steam. The steam drives a turbine to generate electricity.

Reactors have also been developed that use plutonium-239 as the fuel in place of uranium-235. Plutonium-239 can use fast neutrons, unlike uranium-235, which works better with slow neutrons. This means that a plutonium reactor does not need a graphite block to slow down neutrons. These reactors are called fast reactors. The first atomic power station to use a fast reactor for generating electricity was built at Dounreay in Scotland.

1. Why are the uranium rods sunk in a graphite block?
2. How do the boron rods control the temperature of the reactor?
3. What should a technician do if the reactor core suddenly gets too hot?
4. Why is the reactor surrounded by thick concrete?
5. How is the energy from nuclear fission converted into electricity?
6. Which two fissionable isotopes are used in nuclear reactors?
7. Why is the symbol for a neutron $_0^1$n?
8. Draw a labelled diagram to show:
   a) how a controlled, steady chain reaction can occur in a nuclear reactor;
   b) how an uncontrolled, explosive chain reaction can occur in an atomic bomb.

12.6 Nuclear fusion

The energy released by our Sun and other stars comes from **nuclear fusion**. Fusion means 'joining together'. During nuclear fusion, two nuclei are joined together to form just one larger nucleus and energy is released.

> **Nuclear fusion** is the joining together of two atomic nuclei, resulting in the release of large amounts of energy.

Temperatures get to about 15 000 000 K (fifteen million Kelvin) at the centre of the Sun. At these temperatures, all the electrons are stripped off atoms. The remaining nuclei collide at high speed with each other and with protons and neutrons. Some of the collisions result in fusion. If fusion occurs, the particles stick together to form larger nuclei. The main fusion processes in stars involve hydrogen nuclei fusing to form helium (Figure 12.13).

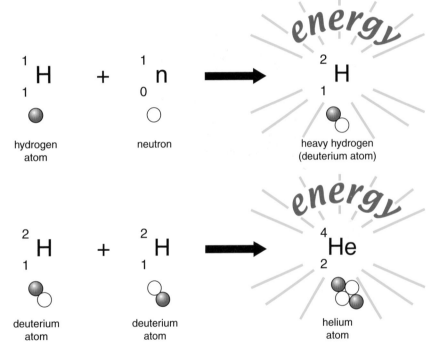

Figure 12.13 The fusion processes which produce helium from hydrogen inside a star

Summary

✓ Experiments by Rutherford and his colleagues led to the idea that atoms have a small positive nucleus containing protons and neutrons. The nucleus is surrounded by a much larger region of empty space in which there are electrons.

✓ This idea became known as the **nuclear model** of atomic structure, which rapidly replaced the **'plum pudding' model** suggested by Thomson.

✓ All the atoms of a particular element have the same number of protons. The number of protons in an atom is known as the **atomic number**.

✓ The total number of protons + neutrons in an atom is known as the **mass number**.

✓ **Isotopes** are atoms of an element with the same atomic number, but different mass numbers.

✓ The main sources of **background radiation** in the UK are rocks in the Earth, bricks, building materials, our food, the Sun and medical tests.

✓ During alpha decay, the nucleus loses an **alpha particle**. The mass number of the nucleus decreases by 4 and its atomic number decreases by 2.

✓ During beta decay, the nucleus emits a **beta particle** (an electron). The mass number of the nucleus remains unchanged, but the atomic number increases by 1.

✓ **Gamma rays** are a form of radiation emitted during radioactive decay. They have a very short wavelength.

✓ During **nuclear fission**, a nucleus first absorbs a neutron. The nucleus then splits into two smaller nuclei releasing two or three neutrons and large amounts of energy. The neutrons released in the process can start a **chain reaction**.

✓ Two fissionable elements commonly used in nuclear reactors are uranium-235 and plutonium-239.

✓ During **nuclear fusion**, two nuclei join together forming one larger nucleus and releasing vast amounts of energy.

EXAM QUESTIONS

❶ Copy and complete the following sentences.

In a nuclear reactor, the fuel rods are made of 'enriched' _____. For _____ to occur, the uranium-235 atoms must first absorb a _____. The process releases energy in a controlled _____ reaction and can be used to generate _____. Some reactors use _____ as the fissionable material in place of uranium-235. *(6 marks)*

❷ What do 24, 12, Mg and 2+ mean in the symbol $^{24}_{12}\text{Mg}^{2+}$? *(4 marks)*

❸ Match the processes labelled A, B, C and D to the statements numbered 1, 2, 3 and 4 below:

A alpha decay   1 nuclei join together
B beta decay   2 nucleus absorbs a neutron
C nuclear fission   3 nucleus loses an electron
D nuclear fusion   4 nucleus loses two protons   *(4 marks)*

❹ a) What is nuclear fission? Say what happens and what is produced. *(5 marks)*
 b) State one way in which nuclear fission is similar to radioactive decay. *(1 mark)*
 c) State one way in which nuclear fission is different to radioactive decay. *(1 mark)*
 d) What numbers or symbols replace the letters A–D in the following nuclear equation?

$$^{A}_{92}\text{U} \rightarrow\ ^{234}_{B}\text{Th} +\ ^{C}_{2}\text{D}\qquad \textit{(4 marks)}$$

❺ Many people are concerned about our use of nuclear energy. Their worries can be summed up in three words: 'cost, disposal and security'.
 a) Suggest two major costs involved in providing electricity from nuclear energy. *(2 marks)*
 b) Explain why people are concerned about disposal. *(2 marks)*
 c) What are people's concerns about security? *(1 mark)*
 d) Suggest two benefits or advantages of using nuclear energy to generate electricity. *(2 marks)*

Data sheet

1. Reactivity series of metals

Potassium   most reactive
Sodium
Calcium
Magnesium
Aluminium
Carbon
Zinc
Iron
Tin
Lead
Hydrogen
Copper
Silver
Gold
Platinum   least reactive

(elements in italics, though non–metals, have been included for comparison)

2. Formulae of some common ions

Positive ions		Negative ions	
Name	Formula	Name	Formula
Hydrogen	H^+	Chloride	Cl^-
Sodium	Na^+	Bromide	Br^-
Silver	Ag^+	Fluoride	F^-
Potassium	K^+	Iodide	I^-
Lithium	Li^+	Hydroxide	OH^-
Ammonium	NH_4^+	Nitrate	NO_3^-
Barium	Ba^{2+}	Oxide	O^{2-}
Calcium	Ca^{2+}	Sulfide	S^{2-}
Copper(II)	Cu^{2+}	Sulfate	SO_4^{2-}
Magnesium	Mg^{2+}	Carbonate	CO_3^{2-}
Zinc	Zn^{2+}		
Lead	Pb^{2+}		
Iron(II)	Fe^{2+}		
Iron(III)	Fe^{3+}		
Aluminium	Al^{3+}		

Periodic Table

Key

1	
relative atomic mass	**H** (atomic symbol)
	hydrogen (atomic name)
	1 (proton number)

1	2											3	4	5	6	7	0
																	4 **He** helium 2
7 **Li** lithium 3	9 **Be** beryllium 4											11 **B** boron 5	12 **C** carbon 6	14 **N** nitrogen 7	16 **O** oxygen 8	19 **F** fluorine 9	20 **Ne** neon 10
23 **Na** sodium 11	24 **Mg** magnesium 12											27 **Al** aluminium 13	28 **Si** silicon 14	31 **P** phosphorus 15	32 **S** sulfur 16	35.5 **Cl** chlorine 17	40 **Ar** argon 18
39 **K** potassium 19	40 **Ca** calcium 20	45 **Sc** scandium 21	48 **Ti** titanium 22	51 **V** vanadium 23	52 **Cr** chromium 24	55 **Mn** manganese 25	56 **Fe** iron 26	59 **Co** cobalt 27	59 **Ni** nickel 28	63.5 **Cu** copper 29	64 **Zn** zinc 30	70 **Ga** gallium 31	73 **Ge** germanium 32	75 **As** arsenic 33	79 **Se** selenium 34	80 **Br** bromine 35	84 **Kr** krypton 36
85 **Rb** rubidium 37	88 **Sr** strontium 38	89 **Y** yttrium 39	91 **Zr** zirconium 40	93 **Nb** niobium 41	96 **Mo** molybdenum 42	**Tc** technetium 43	101 **Ru** ruthenium 44	103 **Rh** rhodium 45	106 **Pd** palladium 46	108 **Ag** silver 47	112 **Cd** cadmium 48	115 **In** indium 49	119 **Sn** tin 50	122 **Sb** antimony 51	128 **Te** tellurium 52	127 **I** iodine 53	131 **Xe** xenon 54
133 **Cs** caesium 55	137 **Ba** barium 56	139 **La** lanthanum 57	178 **Hf** hafnium 72	181 **Ta** tantalum 73	184 **W** tungsten 74	186 **Re** rhenium 75	190 **Os** osmium 76	192 **Ir** iridium 77	195 **Pt** platinum 78	197 **Au** gold 79	201 **Hg** mercury 80	204 **Tl** thallium 81	207 **Pb** lead 82	209 **Bi** bismuth 83	[209] **Po** polonium 84	[210] **At** astatine 85	[222] **Rn** radon 86
[223] **Fr** francium 87	[226] **Ra** radium 88	[227] **Ac*** actinium 89	[261] **Rf** rutherfordium 104	[262] **Db** dubnium 105	[266] **Sg** seaborgium 106	[264] **Bh** bohrium 107	[277] **Hs** hassium 108	[268] **Mt** meitnerium 109	[271] **Ds** darmstadtium 110	[272] **Rg** roentgenium 111							

Elements with atomic numbers 112–116 have been reported but not fully authenticated

*The Lanthanides (atomic numbers 58–71) and the Actinides (atomic numbers 90–103) have been omitted.

Cu and **Cl** have not been rounded to the nearest whole number.

Index

a.c. *see* alternating current
acceleration 158, 160–1, 164–5, 167–9
acids 143–5, 147
activation energy 38, 124
aerobic respiration 41
   see also respiration
air resistance 168–9, 175
alkali metals 86–7
alkalis 143–5
alleles 66–8
alpha decay 224, 225
alpha particles 74, 220–1, 224
alternating current (a.c.) 209–10
amino acids 21, 37, 47
   in proteins 4, 40, 41
ammeters 197, 198
ammonia 136–7, 146
amylase 36, 42, 44, 46
animal cells 2–3, 6, 60
appliances, electrical 205, 210–14, 215–16
asexual reproduction 65
atom economy 119, 137
atomic energy 220, 227–8, 229
atomic numbers 76, 78, 85, 222
atomic power stations 228
atoms 96, 99, 116
   close-packed 98, 100
   mass of 74, 76–9
   structure of 73–5, 84, 220–2
attraction 110, 188

background radiation 223–4
bacteria 29, 31, 45, 56, 65
balanced forces 163
Banting, Fredrick 55–6
batteries 198, 204, 208, 215
Best, Charles 55–6
beta decay 224–5
beta particles 222, 224
bile 43–4
biological detergents 35, 48–9
biomass 25–6
biotechnology 27, 36, 45
bladder 54, 57
'blending theory' 66
blood 42
   ions in 53
   temperature of 54
   waste products in 56–7

water content of 8, 53–4
blood sugar 53, 55
body temperature 4, 26, 41, 53, 54
Bohr, Niels 84
bone marrow 59–60
braking distance 170–1
braking force 170–1
Brown, Robert 2
BSE 28
by-products 119–20, 137
   see also waste products

carbohydrase 46, 48
carbon 30, 106–7, 150
carbon cycle 30–1
carbon dioxide
   in atmosphere 15, 31
   in carbon cycle 30–1
   from respiration 56
   in photosynthesis 14–15, 16–17, 19, 22–4
carnivores 25, 26, 30
carriers 68
car safety 156, 171, 179–81
catalysts 36, 108, 125, 128–30, 137
cathode ray oscilloscope (CRO) 208, 209
cell division 2, 57–60
cell membrane 3, 4, 7, 42, 67
cells
   chemical reactions in 4, 6, 36, 40–1, 56
   functions of 2–3
   movement of substances in 4, 6–9
   sex 59, 62, 63–5, 69
   specialised 2, 8, 42, 59–60, 62
   stem 59–62
   structure of 2–5
   water in 4, 5, 8, 53
cells (electrical) 198, 208
cellulase 29, 36
cellulose 5, 29, 41
cell wall 3, 5, 29, 41
Chadwick, James 74
chain reactions 227–8
charge 187–8, 191–3, 197, 215
   on ions 75, 111
   relative 75, 221
chemical bonds 37, 88–92, 98, 113
chemical energy 21, 26, 172, 173, 174
chemical properties 78, 86–7, 120
chemical reactions 116–19, 124–5, 225

and catalysts 128–30
   in cells 4, 6, 36, 40–1, 56
   energy changes in 131–4
   rate of 121–3, 125
chlorophyll 5, 14, 21
chloroplasts 3, 5, 14, 19, 41
chromosomes 57–9, 63–5
circuit breakers 213
circuit diagrams 197
circuits
   overloaded 205
   parallel 197–8, 204
   series 197–8, 199, 203–4
close packing 98, 100
clothes 48, 108, 109, 207
collision model 124–5, 127
collisions 124–5, 182
combining power 105, 111
combustion 41, 131
components 197, 199, 205–6
   in parallel 204
   in series 198, 203
compounds 80–1, 89–90, 102, 148
concentrations 6–9, 53, 125, 131
conductors 98, 101, 110, 189, 210–11
   photoconductors 190–1
consumer unit 213
continuous-flow system 46
cooking 115, 121–2, 128
copper 77, 98, 152–3, 210
covalent bonds 88, 91–2, 102–3, 105, 106
CRO *see* cathode ray oscilloscope
crumple zones 179–80
crystallisation 142
crystals 96–7
Curie, Marie 220
current 189, 192, 215
   alternating (a.c.) 209–10
   in components 197, 200, 205
   direct 208
   in parallel circuits 198, 204
   in series circuit 198, 199, 203–4
current–potential difference graph 205–6
cystic fibrosis 67, 68–9
cytoplasm 3, 4, 26, 41

Dalton, John 226
'dark chain' 31
d.c. *see* direct current

decay
   organic 29
   radioactive 224–5, 227
deceleration 159, 164
decomposers 30–1
dehydration 8, 53–4
denaturation 38, 41
deoxyribonucleic acid *see* DNA
dependent variables 123, 180
detergents 35, 48–9
diabetes 55–6
differentiation 59–60
diffusion 6–7, 8, 15, 42, 56
digestion 29, 31, 36, 42
   digestive enzymes 42–4
   digestive system 42–4
diodes 206
direct current (d.c.) 208
direction 157, 175
diseases 28, 55–6, 62, 67–9
displacement reaction 147
distance–time graphs 159–60
DNA (deoxyribonucleic acid) 58, 62
   DNA fingerprinting 58
dominant alleles 66, 67, 68
'dot-cross' diagrams 89–92

earthing 193, 213–14
ecosystems 26, 28, 31
effective collisions 124, 127
efficiency of energy transfer 26
egg cells 59, 62, 63–5, 69
elastic potential energy 174
electrical appliances 205, 210–14, 215–16
electrical cables 98, 210
electrical charge *see* charge
electrical energy 215
electric current *see* current
electricity
   generating 228
   insulators 189, 207, 210, 211
   non-conductors 104, 110
   static 187–93
   see also mains electricity
electrodes 148–9
electrolysis 148–53
   uses of 152–3
electrolyte 148
electronic theory of chemical bonding 88
electrons 73–5, 84–7, 220–1

in electrolysis 148–50
movement of 98, 100, 189, 215
sharing 88, 91–2, 106
and static electricity 187–8, 192
transfer of 88–90, 110
electron shells 84–7
electron structures 84–7, 89–92
electrostatic forces 187–8
elements 78, 80, 148, 222
embryos 59–60, 62, 63
embryo screening 69
endothermic reactions 132, 134, 137
energy
   activation 38, 124
   atomic 220, 227–8, 229
   in bodies 4
   in cells 41
   chemical 21, 26, 172, 173, 174
   in chemical reactions 124–5, 131–4
   in ecosystem 31
   efficiency 36, 46, 48–9
   elastic potential 174
   electrical 215
   in food chain 25–7
   from food 4, 25
   from respiration 41
   kinetic 38, 172, 173, 174
   light 5, 14, 18, 30, 133
   pyramids of 26
   reducing use of 119, 137
   transferring 26, 172–3, 175
   transforming 173, 174, 198
   and work 172–3
energy levels (electrons) 84–7
environmental issues 49, 120, 137
   see also pollution; waste products
enzymes 36–9
   in bodies 42–4, 53, 57
   in cells 4, 40–1
   in decay process 29, 31
   in detergents 35, 48–9
   in industry 45–7
   in photosynthesis 14, 19, 41
equilibrium 135
exothermic reactions 131–2, 133, 134, 137
experimentation 55–6

fair tests 17, 180
fermenter 45
fertilisation 63–4

fertilisers 28, 136, 142, 146
Fischer, Emil 40
fission 219, 227–8
food 36, 47, 224
   as energy source 4, 25
   production 23–4, 26–8
   see also cooking; food industry
food chains 25–7, 30
food industry 36, 45, 46–7
'food miles' 28
food webs 41
foot and mouth disease 28
forces 162–5, 172–3, 175
   balanced 163
   between particles 100–1, 102, 104, 106, 107
   electrostatic 187–8
   frictional 164, 173
   unbalanced 164, 177
formulae 103, 105, 111
fossil fuels 31, 189
frequency 209
friction 171, 176, 187, 192, 193
frictional forces 164, 173
fructose 46
fuel costs 48, 118
fungi 29, 31, 45
fuses 211, 214
fusion 219, 229

Galileo 167
gall bladder 43–4
gametes 63–4, 65
gamma rays 222, 224
Geiger, Hans 72, 220, 221
genes 4, 58, 63, 65, 66
   defective 67, 69
genetic diagram 64
genetic modification 45, 46, 56
giant covalent structures 99, 106–7, 112, 113
giant ionic lattices 110
giant ionic structures 99, 110–11, 113
giant metallic structures 99, 100, 112, 113
giant molecules 91, 106
giant structures 100
glands 42
glucose 41, 46
   in blood 55
   in plants 14, 19, 20–1, 30
GM *see* genetic modification
graphs 123, 125, 159–60, 205–6

gravity 166, 167, 168–9
greenhouse crops 23–4, 27
greenhouse gases 49
growth 4, 21, 25, 31, 59

Haber, Fritz 136–7
Haber process 136–7
Hahn, Otto 227
halogens 87
health issues 46, 109, 120, 223
    see also diseases; safety
heat 101, 173, 175, 215
herbivores 25, 26, 27, 30
homeostasis 53
hormones 55
Human Fertilisation and Embryology Authority
        (HFEA) 69
Huntingdon's disease 67, 68
hydrochloric acid 43–4
hydrogen ions 143–4
hydroxide ions 143–4, 147

independent variables 123, 180
indicators (pH) 145–6
industrial chemistry 81, 118, 119–20, 129, 136–7
inheritance 66–7
inherited diseases 67–9
insecticides 28
insulators 189, 207, 210, 211
insulin 4, 55–6
in vitro fertilisation (IVF) 69
ionic bonds 88–90, 110
ionic compounds 86–7, 89–90, 110–11, 141,
        145
ionising radiations 222, 224
ions 75, 96, 99, 189, 222
    in bodies 53
    in electrolysis 148–51
    in solution 141–2, 145, 148, 150–1
    see also ionic compounds
irreversible reactions 117
isotopes 77–8, 222, 224–5
IVF see in vitro fertilisation

kidneys 8, 53–4, 57
kinetic energy 38, 172, 173, 175

lattices 97, 100, 106, 110
LDR see light-dependent resistors
'light chain' 30

light-dependent resistors (LDR) 201
light energy 5, 14, 18, 30, 133
light intensity 16, 18, 19, 22, 23
lightning 186, 194
limiting factors 16–19, 22, 23
lipase 42, 43, 48
liver 43–4, 55, 57
'lock and key' model 37, 40
lungs 56, 67

macromolecules 99, 106–7
    see also giant covalent structures
mains electricity 205, 210
    safety 205, 210–14
Marsden, Ernest 220, 221
mass 165, 166, 175
    of atoms 74, 76–9
mass number 76, 78, 222
mass spectrometer 77, 78
medical research 61–2
Mendel, Gregor 66
metals 88, 100–2, 147, 150, 189
    alkali 86–7
    and electrolysis 149, 152–3
microorganisms 29, 30, 45, 87
mitochondria 3, 4, 41
mitosis 59, 60, 63
models 37
    of atoms 84, 100, 220–1
    collision 124–5, 127
    of diffusion 6
    of light intensity 18
    'lock and key' 37, 40
    of solutions 131
    of structures 106, 107, 112
molecules 91, 96, 99, 104
moles 77, 80
momentum 175–7
    conservation of 182
    and safety 177–9
movement 4, 26, 41
muscles 26, 41, 47, 53, 55

nanomaterials 95, 108–9
nerve cells 62
nerve impulses 26, 54
neutralisation 132, 144, 145–6
neutral solutions 145–6
neutrons 73–5, 221, 227–8
nitrates 21, 41, 136

noble gases 85
non-conductors 104, 110
non-metals 86, 88, 102, 110
nuclear equations 224, 225
nuclear fission 219, 227–8
nuclear fusion 219, 229
nuclear model 221
nuclear reactions 225, 227–9
nuclear reactors 219, 227–8
nucleus (atom) 74, 77, 221
nucleus (cell) 2, 3, 4, 57–8
nutrient cycling 29, 31

optimum pH 38
optimum temperature 19, 38–9
osmosis 8–9, 15, 53
over-hydration 8, 53–4
oxygen 7, 14, 16, 143, 150

pancreas 4, 42, 43–4, 55–6
parallel circuits 197–8, 204
Parkinson's disease 62
partially permeable membrane 7
particles 96–7, 99, 113
    forces between 100–2, 104, 106, 107
    nanoparticles 108
    sub-atomic 73–5, 221
p.d. see potential difference
Periodic Table 76, 85–7
permanent vacuole 3, 5
pH 38, 43, 45, 145–6
photoconductors 190–1
photocopiers 190–1
photosynthesis 5, 30
    and enzymes 14, 19, 41
    limiting factors 16–19, 22, 23
    products of 14, 20
    rate of 16–19, 22–4
    raw materials 14–15
physical properties 78
plant cells 2–3, 5, 6, 14, 60
plants 20–1, 25, 41, 136
    in carbon cycle 30–1
    inheritance in 66–7
    reproduction 65
    see also photosynthesis
'plum pudding' model 220–1
plutonium 228
pollution 49, 116, 142, 189
    see also waste products

potential difference (p.d.) 197, 198, 200, 203–4, 205, 208–9
precipitation reaction 142
primary consumers 25, 26
primary producers 25
products, of reactions 81, 116, 117–18
protease 36, 42, 43–4, 47, 48
proteins 4, 36–7, 57, 66–7, 136
    digestion of 36, 43–4, 57
protein synthesis 40–1
protons 73–5, 76, 187, 221–2
pyramids of biomass 25
pyramids of energy 26

Quantum Tunnelling Composite (QTC) 207

radiation 220, 223–4
radioactive decay 224–5, 227
range 181
rate 16, 122
    of diffusion 7
    of enzyme reactions 37–9
    of photosynthesis 16–19, 22–4
    of reactions 36, 118, 121–3, 125, 129
RCCB see residual current circuit breaker
reactants 81, 116, 118
reactions
    chemical see chemical reactions
    nuclear 225, 227–9
reaction times 170–1
reactivity series 147, 151
recessive alleles 66, 67, 68
reflex responses 54
relative atomic mass 77–9, 80–1
relative charges 75, 221
relative formula mass 80–1
relative mass 74–5, 77, 78, 221
reproduction 65
residual current circuit breaker (RCCB) 213
resistance 199–202, 203–4
resistors 201–2, 205, 215
respiration 4, 21, 36, 41, 56
resultant forces 163–4
reversible reactions 117, 118, 135
ribosomes 3, 4
Rutherford, Ernest 72, 84, 220–1, 226

safety
    car 156, 171, 179–81
    electrical 205, 210–14

equipment 177–9
salivary glands 42, 44
salts 142, 144, 145–8
Schleiden, Matthias 2
Schwann, Theodor 2
seat belts 179
secondary consumers 26
series circuits 197–8, 199, 203–4
sex cells 59, 62, 63–5, 69
sex chromosomes 63–4, 65
sexual reproduction 65
simple molecular structures 99, 102–5, 113
simple molecular substances 102–5
simple molecules 91–2, 102
skin 2, 54, 59
'slip' 101
slope (of graph) 123, 159–60
small intestine 42, 43
smoke precipitators 189–90
sodium chloride 89, 140, 153
soluble salts 146, 147
solutions 8–9, 131, 141–2, 145–6
    electrolysis of 150–1
solvents 141
sparks 192–3
specialised cells 2, 8, 42, 59–60, 62
spectator ions 142, 143–4, 145
speed 157, 159–60
sperm cells 63–5, 69
starch 14, 19, 20, 36, 42
stars 219, 224, 229
state symbols 116
static electricity 187–92
    dangers of 192–3
    uses of 189–91
stem cells 59–62
stomach 42, 43–4
stomata 13, 15, 16
stopping distance 170–1
structures 96–7, 99
sub-atomic particles 73–5, 221
substances
    properties of 98–9
    structures of 96–7
substrates 36, 38
Sun 108, 223, 224, 229
surface area 108, 125
sustainability 119, 137
sweating 53

temperature 201
    body 4, 26, 41, 53, 54
    and enzymes 37–9, 45
    and photosynthesis 16, 19, 22
    of reactions 125
    and resistance 206
temperature receptors 54
terminal velocity 169
thermal decomposition 132
thermistors 201–2
thermoregulatory centre 54
thinking distance 170–1
Thomson, J.J. 72, 220, 221
three-pin plugs 210, 211–12
trophic levels 25, 26

unbalanced forces 164, 177
uranium 227, 228
urine 26, 54, 57

vacuole 3, 5
velocity 157–8, 160, 169, 175
velocity–time graphs 160–1
Virchow, Rudolph 2
voltmeters 197, 203

washing powder, biological 35, 48–9
waste products 116
    in bodies 56–7
    organic 29
    reducing 46, 118, 119, 137
    treatment of 142
water
    in bodies 8, 53–4
    in cells 4, 5, 8, 53
    and electrolysis 150–1, 152
    in photosynthesis 14, 15
    in plants 20
    saving 48, 49
    as solvent 141
weight 166, 169
work 172–3, 175

X chromosomes 64, 65
X-rays 96–7, 100, 106, 223, 224

Y chromosomes 64, 65

zygotes 63